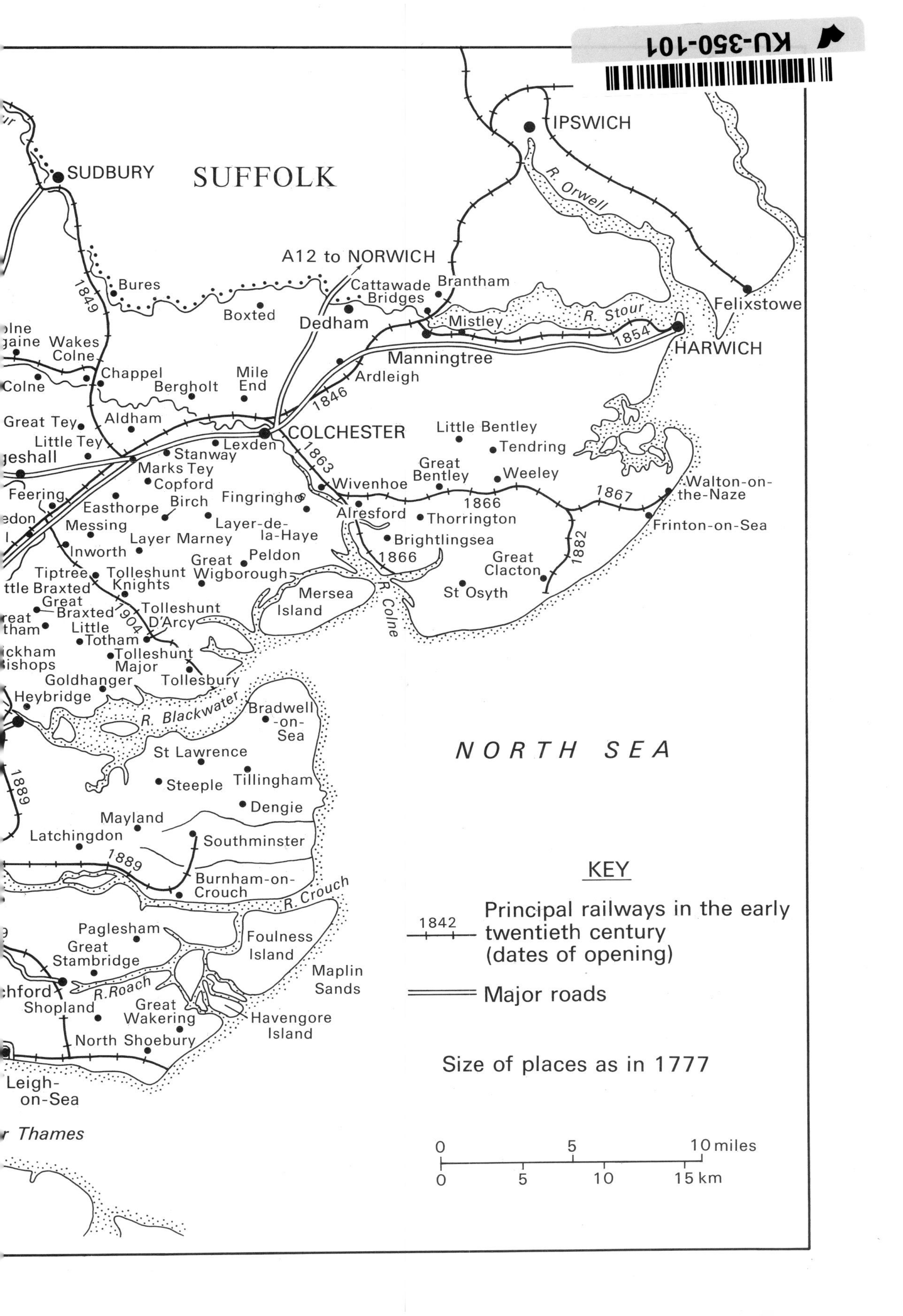
SUFFOLK
SUDBURY
IPSWICH
R. Orwell
A12 to NORWICH
Bures
Cattawade
Bridges
Brantham
Boxted
Dedham
Mistley
R. Stour
1854
Felixstowe
HARWICH
1849
Wakes
Colne
Chappel
Bergholt
Mile
End
Manningtree
Ardleigh
1846
Great Tey
Aldham
Little Tey
COLCHESTER
Lexden
Stanway
1863
Little Bentley
Tendring
Marks Tey
Copford
Great
Bentley
Weeley
Feering
Birch
Fingringhoe
Wivenhoe
1866
1867
Walton-on-
the-Naze
Easthorpe
Alresford
Thorrington
Frinton-on-Sea
Messing
Layer-de-
la-Haye
Layer Marney
Brightlingsea
Inworth
1866
1882
Great
Wigborough
Peldon
Great
Clacton
Tiptree
Tolleshunt
Knights
Mersea
Island
R. Colne
St Osyth
Great
Braxted
1904
Tolleshunt
D'Arcy
Little
Totham
Tolleshunt
Major
Goldhanger
Tollesbury
Heybridge
R. Blackwater
Bradwell
-on-
Sea
NORTH SEA
St Lawrence
Steeple
Tillingham
1889
Dengie
Mayland
Latchingdon
Southminster
1889
Burnham-on-
Crouch
R. Crouch
KEY
1842
Principal railways in the early twentieth century (dates of opening)
Major roads
Paglesham
Foulness
Island
Great
Stambridge
Maplin
Sands
R. Roach
Shopland
Great
Wakering
Havengore
Island
North Shoebury
Size of places as in 1777
Leigh-
on-Sea
0
5
10 miles
0
5
10
15 km

SEEDTIME

The History of ESSEX SEEDS

SEEDTIME

The History of ESSEX SEEDS

Elinor M. C. Roper

Phillimore

1989

Published by
PHILLIMORE & CO. LTD.
Shopwyke Hall, Chichester, Sussex

ISBN 0 85033 682 1

Printed and bound in Great Britain by
RICHARD CLAY LTD.,
Bungay, Suffolk

To the farmers and seedsmen of Essex
amongst whom I have enjoyed so much of my life;
with respect and affection

Contents

List of Illustrations

Acknowledgements

Even before 1914 our seedgrowing had begun to show signs of decline. By 1977, the acreage of seeds had fallen so dramatically that, at a committee of Essex seedsmen, it was agreed that before all was forgotten its history should be recorded. I was asked to undertake this task and started to collect material in September 1978.

To name everyone who has contributed to the contents of this book would be cumbersome. I thank and am very indebted to them all. Had they not bothered to answer my innumerable questions, to search their desks, cupboards, libraries, archives, scrapbooks and photograph albums and later to check their individual sections for accuracy making sure that nothing had been written that might cause hurt, this book could not have been written.

My very sincere thanks to Sir Nigel Strutt for consenting to write the foreword. Any words of thanks to the Perry Foundation cannot be other than entirely inadequate. For their most generous help my gratitude is great.

It gives me pleasure to acknowledge the ready assistance received from the National Seed Development Organisation, the Official Seed Testing Station and the Seed Production Branch. Also from the Pea Growers' Research Organisation; from Professor J. K. A. Bleasdale of the National Vegetable Research Organisation; and from Gordon Hillman of the Institute of Archaeology (London University) who so enthusiastically gave of his knowledge and experience.

I received help from the Essex Record Office; the reference library in Chelmsford; the Botanical and Palaeontology departments of the British Museum of Natural History; the library of Writtle Agricultural College; and last, but certainly not least, the branch of the Essex County Library at Witham. It would be quite wrong to single out for praise any merchant, firm or works. Their considerable contributions may be seen in the text and their courtesy and helpfulness, in the face of one request after another, have never waivered.

My very sincere thanks to Mr. D. T. D. Clarke, of the Colchester and Essex Museum, for patiently correcting Chapter One. Also to Dr. John Harvey whose very generous response to my cries for enlightenment on matters medieval was both immensely helpful and cheering; Miss Edith H. Whetham, who drew my attention to the 1901 Report on Agricultural Seeds, can never have suspected the number of fruitful and interesting alleys to which this would lead; and without considerable editing by Dr. S. J. Ellerton, parts of Chapter Eleven could so easily have been riddled with inaccuracies.

My gratitude to those who worked closely with me is inestimable: Muriel Eakins, who disentangled the original hastily scribbled notes; my cousin, Grace A. Clarke, for her unflagging encouragement, much typing and re-typing of the innumerable alterations and especially for her vigilant and competent correction of spelling, punctuation and grammar (any mistakes that have crept in since she last saw the text are entirely my fault). B. A. Bonner has cheerfully made copies of the many loaned photographs and has also allowed the inclusion of some from his own collection. The lucky discovery of Alan Dench of Colchester introduced professionalism to our photographic material; his skill when confronted with faded, grubby and creased prints is remarkable. Special thanks must be awarded to Rodney Fry for drawing such a splendid map; to Auriol Griffith-Jones for so fortuitously stepping in to compile the index and to Kim Prior for her neat and carefully-produced line drawings.

There are some who have done valiant work behind the scenes. It is they who have borne my times of elation, dejection and, on occasions, fury. Without their ready and very differing support this book might never have reached a publisher. The list is alphabetical, each one will know their role – Noel Blyth, Margaret Collin, Jill Goodwin, Hilda Grieve, J. R. Keyworth, A. E. Maddison, L. A. W. Prior, L. P. Sampson and Olive Wheaton. Finally, my thanks to Phillimore & Co. Ltd. for publishing this book. It has been a total joy to experience their courtesy and their competence.

Illustration Acknowledgements

The author wishes to express grateful thanks to the following people who have either loaned photographs or given permission for illustrations to be reproduced in this book: R. Aitkin, D.S.O., no. 94; E. H. Ashby, no. 49; Fred Birkin, no. 77; B. A. Bonner, nos. 1, 9, 56, 57, 59, 60, 68, 78, 79 & 95; the Late Lt.-Col. C. A. Brooks, nos. 84 & 85; Carter's Seeds Ltd., nos. 63 & 65; W. A. Church (Bures) Ltd., nos. 54, 70, 100, 101, 102 & 104; Eric Creek, no. 58; Kenneth Cutts, no. 45; the late Eric Deal, no. 34; Major Charles Fenwick, no. 105; R. A. Fry, no. 103; T. A. Glover, nos. 61 & 62; Hasler's of Dunmow, no. 82; Gordon Hillman, no. 81; Hurst's, nos. 48 & 50; E. W. King's collection (reproduced by courtesy of K. R. Phillips), nos. 35, 36, 37, 40, 41, 74 & 75; J. K. King's (reproduced by courtesy of Francis H. Nicholls), nos. 10-23, 25-31, 33, 67 & 72; E. Marriage & Sons Ltd., nos. 86, 87, 88, 89 & 90; Peter Martin, no. 83; the late R. A. S. Rutkin, no. 8; B. S. Saunders, no. 38; Nathaniel Sherwood, nos. 46 & 47; Brian Taber's collection, no. 43; Dorothy Taber's collection, nos. 42 & 53; John Tarlton, nos. 51 & 52.

All the line drawings were produced by Kim Prior and the map was drawn by Rodney Fry (please note that the dates for the opening of the railway lines on this map are taken from A. C. Edwards' *A History of Essex*). The author is grateful to these people for their painstaking work. The seed reproduced on the half title page is the fruit of *Polygonum nodosum* Pers. found in late-glacial muds at Hockham Mere, Norfolk, and at Clacton-on-Sea, Essex.

Glossary

Bines	The long stems of plants such a runner beans and nasturtiums — particularly when they are drying off.
Bolting	The production of seed-heads by a biennial plant in its first year.
Braird	Germination, growth to first leaf.
Bunt or Stinking Smut	Fungal disease (*tilletia caries*) of some cereals and grasses. It attacks the seedling plants and, at flowering, settles in the ovary and fills the developing grain with black, fishy-smelling spores. At thrashing time, these grains burst open and release the spores all over the sound grain. If the seed is not suitably treated afterwards the whole cycle starts again when it is sown.
Bushel	An imperial bushel of wheat is 60lbs.
Caboche	Middle English for cabbage, derived from Latin *caput*, meaning head: cabbage — brassica that had a head. O.E. word for cabbage was 'kale', which has equivalents in all Celtic languages. Celts probably brought *B. oleracea* to England; Anglo-Saxons acquired a taste for it.[1]
Cavings	The separated chaff and small trash from thrashed seeds.
Coomb	A coomb = 4 bushels; 2 coombs = 1 quarter.
Cultivar	A different variety but without the gene arrangement having been fixed and so the capriciousness has not been bred out.
Customarii	Both upper and lower class *villeins* were called customarii.
Deb	To plant in a prepared hole. In other areas 'dib' or 'dibble'; in Essex almost always 'deb' or 'debbed'.
Eglantine	The sweet briar and some other species of rose having branches with sharp prickles.
Faggot	A bundle of sticks or twigs bound together as fuel, or to be used as a plant support.
Florist	Originally a producer of flowering plants and seeds rather than a seller of cut flowers.
Fulling	The scouring and beating of cloth to shrink it to a closer texture.
Fustian	A coarse twill cotton fabric.
Gishurst Compound	A mixture of flowers of sulphur and soap.
'Hard' Seed	A seed with a seedcoat which is impervious to water or oxygen, both of which are required for germination, or to carbon dioxide that may accumulate within the seed and retard or even prevent germination; sometimes overcome by scratching or scarifying the seed, or by brief immersion in concentrated sulphuric acid followed by thorough washing.
Herber	Translation of medieval Latin word *herbarium* meaning close garden with lawn, flower garden, or garden of medicinal herbs.
Herbereur	Probably implies a specialist in pleasure gardens.[2]
Hoy	A large one-decked boat having a rounded bottom and commonly rigged as a sloop.

Photoperiod	Length of light on a given day.
Polyploidy	The polyploid condition; having more than two sets of chromosomes.
Ringel	In this context, a metal ring attached to the end of a leather strap used to tighten the strap round the bale of hay or straw. May also mean a metal ring through which parts of a horse's harness pass.
Ryed	Sifted. The action of 'reeing' or 'rying'; hence rying sieve.
Steckling Bed	Bed of small plants (usually beet) in which they are grown prior to being planted out in the second year.
Skirret	Edible water parsnip. A native of China and Japan.
Sium Siscarum	To prepare: clean, parboil, fry in best oil or butter, eat hot.
Slips	Twigs torn from the parent plant, ideally with a 'heel' attached from which it may root.
Stetch	In this context, a strip of ploughed land between two waterfurrows; usually ploughed to fit the width of the drill to be used. Therefore it varies in width.
Synonyms	Set up by Council of N.I.A.B. It was an N.I.A.B. 'thing' and was not official but by general agreement until, in 1979, the National List of Varieties Regulations came into force.
Teart	Land which when grazed by cattle gives rise to a copper deficiency in their diet.
Thrave	In Essex, composed of eight sheaves. Six sheaves are abutted in line, in pairs and then the two ends closed with the remaining two sheaves — in Essex known as 'trave'.
Waxe pound	As in waxing and waning — a generous pound.
Withy	A flexible twig, usually of willow. In this context, used in place of string.

Foreword

by Sir Nigel Strutt, T.D., D.L., F.R.A.S.E.

Elinor Roper was for many years the Ministry of Agriculture's advisory and technical officer in east-central Essex. She has been greatly respected and loved by the farmers she served with outstanding devotion. In her retirement she has chosen to write the history of Essex seed business. This may be considered a narrow and provincial subject in the context of world food production. So it is, but it has been so far unrecorded. Miss Roper has researched with great diligence and has produced an important record of an extremely interesting enterprise. In the process she has found it necessary to enter into the wider spheres of rural social history, and here she is an engaging scribe. She makes the scene live even if it is 400 years ago. One can weave with Miss Roper in Braxted-juxta-Coggeshall in 1783 and smuggle with Miss Roper in Tolleshunt D'Arcy in 1822. Nothing is too small to escape her interest, and the book is great fun to read. It is of historical importance and a strong candidate for inclusion in many libraries. It is also fascinating for all those who are proud of and value the history of Eastern Counties farming. This small area on the western littoral of the North Sea has had an outstanding history of agricultural enterprise second to none for nigh on 500 years; Miss Roper explains the enormous influence of water transport, without which this could not have been achieved. Essex was anything but monocultural. The reader of this book cannot fail to be intrigued by the response of farmer to the various challenges which occurred over the centuries. Miss Roper's book will take its place among many others which record rural life in England. Its style sustains the reader's interest and enjoyment throughout. I am very pleased to have been asked to write this Foreword warmly commending it.

Nigel Strutt.

List of Abbreviations

A.S.M.E.R.	Amalgamated Seed Merchants Ltd.
A.S.T.A.	Agricultural Seed Trade Association.
B.A.S.A.M.	British Association of Seed and Agricultural Merchants. Established 1972 from the amalgamation of the National Association of Corn and Agricultural Merchants and the Seed Trade Association. Now absorbed into U.K.A.S.T.A., B.A.S.A.M. represents its members' interests to the Government and other official bodies with the grain, seed, feed and agricultural distribution industries.
E.P.S.T.A.	Essex Provincial Seed Trade Association.
E.W.A.E.C.	Essex War Agricultural Executive Committee.
F.I.S.	Federazione Internationale Sementi (International Seed Federation).
G.R.I.	Grassland Research Institute.
G.C.R.I.	Glasshouse Crops Research Institute.
N.A.C.A.M.	National Association of Corn and Agricultural Merchants.
N.I.A.B.	National Institute of Agricultural Botany.
N.S.D.O.	National Seed Development Organisation.
N.S.P.S.	National Sweet Pea Society.
N.V.R.O.	National Vegetable Research Organisation.
O.S.T.S.	Official Seed Testing Station.
U.K.A.S.T.A.	The United Kingdom Agricultural Supply Trade Association. Formed in 1977 by the merger of B.A.S.A.M. and C.A.F.M.A. (The Compound Animal Food Manufacturers' Association), and continues the role of B.A.S.A.M. with the interests of animal feed producers.

Introduction

To Set the Scene

Hurrying along the A12 or meandering down an Essex lane at some time you may have felt compelled to slow down, or even to stop, to gaze in wonder at the golden brilliance of a crop of oil seed rape. If it were a sunny day there would be the bonus of the soporific sound of bees about their business. Perhaps you have wondered, too, what could possibly be happening in another field striped with crops of many colours, with something like a native

1. 'With something like a native kraal at one end.'

kraal at one end. These are the crops which provide seeds for farmers, market gardeners, garden centres, herbalists and the pharmaceutical trade, flavourings for gin, the finest machine oils, and to fill the thousands of pictorial packets for private gardeners and allotment holders.

This book is about the history and merchanting of these seeds — why, to where and when this trade came to Essex and developed to a stage when the county became the premier seed-growing area of the country. It is not intended as a textbook or as a grower's guide, as both technical and good cultural information are readily available from other sources. It is only where a crop or method of cultivation has become obsolete, or is of particular interest, that detailed information has been given. Aspects of allied trades have also been explored and, where they add interest or clarification, are included in the text.

The aim has been to provide a book for all kinds of reader on a subject which hitherto has been virtually untouched, and which is both entertaining and factually correct. The first two chapters pass rapidly through the ages, pinpointing fragments of relevant information which have come to light and lead on to the acceleration of development in the 18th century and onwards.

Chapter One

Pre-Glacial to 1485

The duration of life on earth of any species of flowering plant is about twelve million years.

S. P. Mercer: *Farm and Garden Seeds*

In the pre-glacial era (in this context meaning before the last four glaciations of this country), before even the most primitive type of man appeared in Essex, plants were here producing and distributing their seeds. Some of these seeds have been found at Nazeing and Clacton, and examples may be seen in the British Museum of Natural History in London.

Millions of years passed before parts of the animal kingdom developed arms and legs

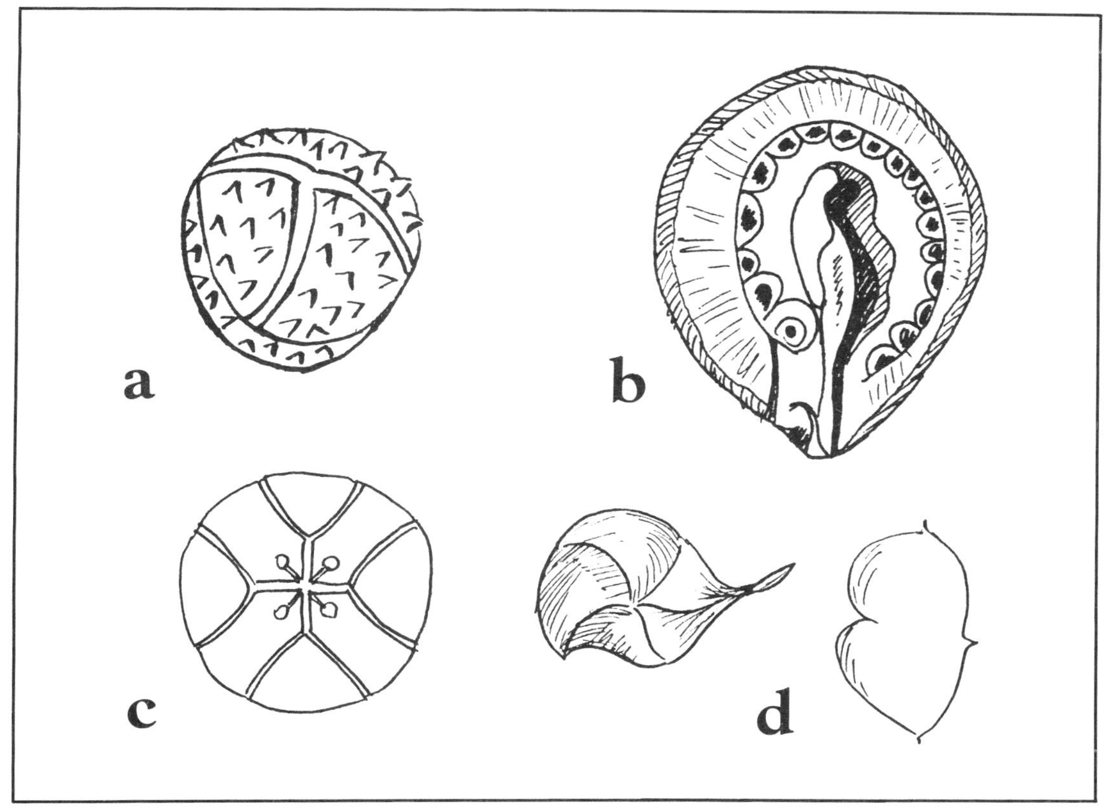

2. Pre-glacial seeds: (a) Megaspore of Isoetes Echinospora Durien from Nazeing; (b) Menisperameites Abutoides; (c) Cornaceae; (d) London Clay Flora.

and, having gained the ability to move from one environment to another, lost the ability to grow a replacement for an irreparably damaged limb and could not reproduce from a cutting. Once man had evolved, his mobility and particular type of brain enabled him to influence the production and distribution of plants and their seeds virtually at will.

After experiencing the last Ice Age, Britain, although still joined to mainland Europe, was left with one of the smallest number of indigenous plants in the temperate world.[1] This was because as arctic conditions crept forward, and plants suffering the effects attempted to move away towards the equator, their escape was prevented by the Atlantic Ocean, the frozen ridges of the Alps and the Pyrenees and by the Mediterranean sea.

Broadly speaking this dearth of plant species continued until in the age of the first Elizabeth, increasing numbers of ships began to leave Britain for the East, and for the Americas where the north-south arrangement of mountain ranges had not prevented the natural retreat or subsequent re-establishment of the flora. Species which had been absent for centuries were then, by the agency of man, transported back to this country together with the genetic mixtures and mutations consequent upon the retreat.

The first human Essex settlers about whom there is definite information, are considered to have arrived around the year 400,000 B.C.[2] They were Palaeolithic 'Flake Culture' people whose diet apparently included seeds and berries containing seeds.

Neolithic people may have settled here by the year 3,000 B.C.[3] Once a settlement had come into being the women, who were left at home while the men went hunting, busied themselves making and tending the fields which have been found near their dwellings. Here, seeds could have been sown and a few plants of fruits and herbs transplanted from further afield. Not only would this have saved time when a meal had to be prepared but gathering would have been safer from attack by wild beasts and the plants, being less crowded, would have grown bigger. Agriculture had begun.

The land-bridge which once joined this country to the rest of Europe was probably severed some time after 7,000 B.C. The subsequent water barrier between us has often been advanced as a reason for this country's supposed backwardness in horticulture, as compared with the rest of Europe. I do not subscribe to this view and suggest that, bearing in mind the probable state of the 'track' roads in those days, it was often more pleasant, and perhaps quicker, to travel by water whenever possible. These early travellers probably untied their boats much as, today, we get out our cars. Certainly until after the Second World War, when cars became a commonplace possession, parts of coastal Essex had little communication with places inland, but a journey to 'over the other side' was not so remarkable. This indicates that in former times water was frequently an aid rather than a hindrance to communication.

Between 2000 and 1800 B.C., Bronze Age skills are likely to have reached, or to have developed, in Essex. When this happened artisans, who neither dug nor hunted for a living, provided metal goods which they were able to exchange for food. If Essex farmers had not done so before, they must by then have been producing food surplus to their own requirements, to exchange with an industrial population whose goods they desired. As a consequence more seeds will have been needed. Two storage pits full of peas (*Pisum sativum*) have been found at a Middle Bronze Age site at North Shoebury, Essex (subsequent re-examination of the pottery has placed these peas in the Early Iron Age)[4] and there were beans (*Vicia faba var. minor*) at a late Bronze Age site at Frog Hall, Fingringhoe, Essex.[5]

When somebody first noticed a plant growing better than its fellows, and saved its seeds for the next year's crops, even if better growth was often due to the proximity of a dung pat, rather than its genetic make-up, this will not always have been so. Luck will sometimes have been with the observer and an improved strain of seed will have been found. The long search for a way to produce new and better seed may then be said to have started.

Essex moved into the Iron Age from approximately 800 B.C. and from this time onwards agriculture in the county began to make real progress. Wheat, barley, oats, beans (*Vicia faba*), field peas, flax and vetches were all in production. Heavy goods such as salt, pottery, bronze, iron and tin were being transported about the country and it may not be too far-reached to suggest that seeds which could be grown well in the dry climate of Essex, were already being taken to other parts to be grown for food as distinct from seed.

Broadly from 800 to 600 B.C. there was a flourishing export and import trade with the Continent,[6] including for example, a limited trade in luxury goods such as swords, shields, cauldrons, horse trappings, metal dress pins and even a few magnificent torques. That such imports were copied and modified with enthusiasm and native skill clearly indicates that by this date there existed in Britain a stratified society, served by competent craftsmen rather than the woad-tattooed savages that some people still associate with this period.

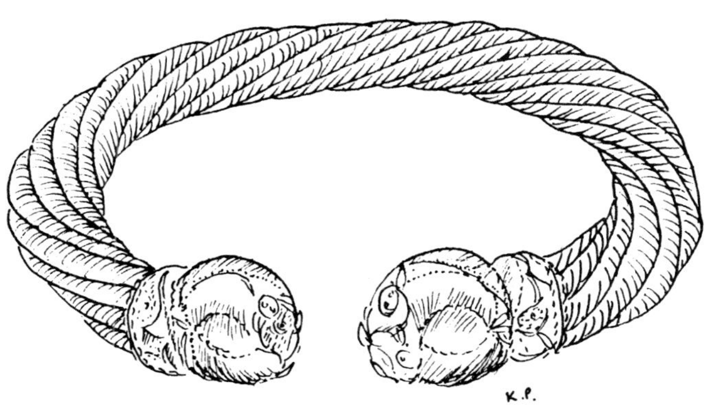

3. 'Even a few magnificent torques.' This Iron Age example (1st century B.C.) is from Snettisham in Norfolk. Diameter 19.5cm.

It could even be that some improved strains of food plants had already been achieved, for as Sir George M. Taylor points out:

> In 1833 the French horticulturist M. Vilmorin took the wild carrot in hand in an endeavour to improve it . . . In four generations he succeeded in producing roots from the wild plants which must have been similar to those used in ancient times — for the carrot, in a very primitive form, has been cultivated for many centuries . . . and from which modern types have been evolved. The roots, to begin with, were mostly white, but the colour character appeared in the third generation, and was stabilised and made permanent by Vilmorin. The roots were inclined to be fibrous, but that undesirable trait was soon bred out.[7]

Bearing in mind that Vilmorin was experimenting some 10 years before Mendel had discovered his genetic laws, we can believe in the possibility that some man or woman, before the year 600 B.C., may at least have reached the stage of improvement at which Vilmorin had arrived in his fourth year. Certainly by the early 12th century orange-rooted carrots existed, because there is a coloured picture of a carrot plant with a well-developed root of an orange colour in the Herbal of the Abbey of Bury St Edmunds, *c*.1120.[8] Again there are references to carrots with 'red roots' on sale in a Paris market in 1400 and, in England *c*.1450, that 'carrots growing in gardens are red'.[9]

From very early there is mention of a cereal trade, some of which may have been seed corn. About a century before the Romans first came to Britain (55 B.C.) some of the Belgae, a tribe from north-east Europe, invaded and occupied south-eastern England. They spread rapidly and finally, under King Cunobelin, established their capital at Colchester in Essex. Having come from a region of flourishing agriculture, and probably bringing their seeds and ploughs (the *caruca*) with them, on our kinder soils they raised cattle and grew corn well enough to have a sizeable surplus for export.[10] (Documents held in the Essex Record Office refer to the carucate as a measure of land. It was originally the amount of land that a yoke of oxen could plough in a season. The *caruca* was the heavy continental plough and was an improvement on the lighter and earlier *aratrum*, in that it had better draft and ability to cut the soil both vertically and horizontally.)

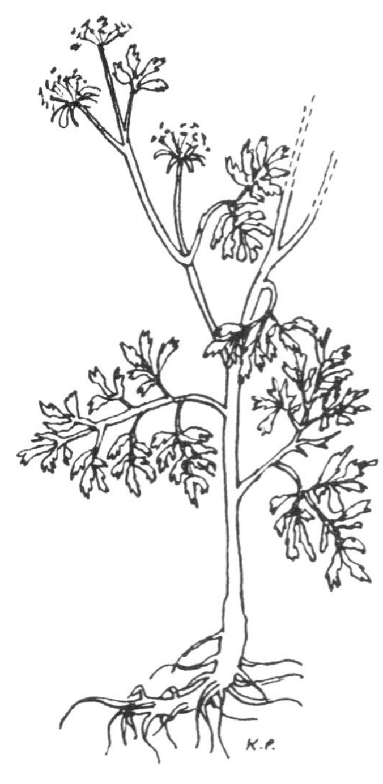

4. An early type of yellow carrot.

Certainly at the time of the second Roman invasion in A.D. 43 the British were growing a considerable amount of corn, for within a few days of arrival, the invading army was able to obtain enough to support four legions of soldiers and 1,700 cavalry for a fortnight.[11] The Roman occupation must have boosted this corn production and created a demand for more seed, for by A.D. 359-60[12] Zosirus, Julian and Ammianus Marcellinus were recording the export of corn from Britain for use of Roman troops in the Rhineland.

Which seeds the Romans introduced into this country is open to debate. So far as vegetables are concerned the fact that they grew a wide range in their own country does not necessarily mean that they introduced them all to Britain. Most could already have been here, for Tacitus, writing in the first century, claimed the climate of Britain was suitable for the cultivation of all vegetables except the olive and the vine, and during previous generations there had been continuous contact with Europe and beyond.

We know that the wealthiest Roman villa owners tried to establish Italianate gardens of enclosed courts and covered walks with shrubs and, indeed, vines. They may have tried to grow vegetables to which they were accustomed in their homeland for family consumption. No doubt the troops and the native population ate whatever was available in the locality. Certainly, in those Roman records which relate to this country, the only commonly mentioned vegetables are beans (*Vicia faba*), radishes and cabbage. Recent archaeological research has also revealed a considerable number of peas (*Pisum sativum*) in the Roman soil levels of London.[13]

The way Roman London, with its population of up to 25,000, was supplied with food shows the need for a rudimentary seed trade but I have found no mention of any such until centuries later. Yet one cannot believe that the market gardeners and farmers, whose holdings were in and adjacent to the towns, would always have grown their own seed. Perhaps the whole matter was too obvious to merit a painstaking record. Certainly by A.D. 350 the time looked ripe for the appearance of a formal trade if growing dissension within the Roman Empire had not caused the withdrawal of its army from Britain. The result was chaos. With the removal of any overall authority and direction, trade at home came more or less to a standstill. Many towns were depopulated and abandoned, and the quite considerable overseas trade ground to a halt.

The disturbed centuries between the Roman and Norman occupations were a period of successive waves of Saxon and Norse invasion for plunder, for land settlement (such a settlement, which has been excavated and re-built at West Stow, West Suffolk, is now open to visitors), and the establishment of rival kingdoms with war between them. It is not a period in which one would expect much advance in either seed growing or merchanting. Despite this, towards the end of the Dark Ages (broadly from A.D. 500 to 1000) there are clear indications of a build-up of commerce and a culture which included an appreciation of amenity as well as utilitarian horticulture. Interestingly, both were of Saxon and not Roman origin.

For instance, even if trade had collapsed when the Romans went home, the Port of London seems to have gathered itself together again by A.D. 730 when the Venerable Bede described the city as 'the mart of many nations by land and sea'. By A.D. 754 commerce was sufficient for there to be a regular tariff on goods entering this port; in A.D. 875 Thorolf of Norway sent to England for wheat,[14] and by A.D. 987 our Danish settlers with their far-flung trade connections were helping us to build up foreign trade with Europe (Scandinavia, Italy) and the Orient.

From very early times man has attempted to improve his medical skills and to find out more about the use of plants towards this end. The flow of such information to Britain is said to have come first from Greece and then from the Islamic world and there must have been an allied trade in medicinal seeds.

When the medical torch had been taken up by the monks in Christian monasteries which had been established in this country from A.D. 597, books about herbs were brought here from monastic foundations abroad and copies were painstakingly reproduced by hand. Then came the marauding Vikings who had no knowledge of, or respect for, a Christian God. To these people, books about medicine and poisons represented 'magic' and of this they had a mortal fear, and so burnt every volume that they were able to lay their hands upon. As a consequence, Boniface, the eighth-century 'Apostle of the Saxons', received many letters from England asking him for new books, particularly on medicine, and at the same time complaining of the difficulties of obtaining both drugs and herb plants mentioned in the books which were available to his correspondents.[15]

That some Herbals were available and even being compiled during King Alfred's reign (A.D. 871-901) is evidenced by the existence of *The Leach Bok of Bald*. It is now housed in the British Museum and is believed to be the oldest Herbal in England. In it, amongst others, there are prescriptions sent by Helias, the Patriarch of Jerusalem, to King Alfred. As a final example of scholarship in these 500 years there is the remarkable vocabulary which the grammarian Aelfric compiled in A.D. 995. In this he lists over two hundred herbs and trees, only nine of which are today considered as unlikely to have been grown in one or other of the more important monastic gardens in this country.[16] Seeds from them will undoubtedly have been gathered and exchanged.

About this same time Charlemagne, Roman Emperor and King of the Franks, was receiving both botanical and medical information from Caliph Harun al Raschid, at Baghdad. It may even be that he too was finding the importation of herbs both expensive and uncertain of delivery, because when he instituted what may be called the first 'Health Service' in Europe, he evidently decided to grow his own herb supplies. In A.D. 802 an edict[17] was issued which gave a list of herbs to be grown in towns throughout his realm, that all might share their benefits and a plentiful, cheap and locally available supply be ensured. This list of 75 plants begins with the Madonna Lily and it is of interest that, to this day, Molly and Joan Golding of Tolleshunts Farm, Tolleshunt D'Arcy, Essex, still pot up these petals to be used to heal cuts and pricks from thorns. (*To make lily petal salve*: Put layers of lily petals in a shallow container together with brandy and a covering of olive oil to prevent mould, tie down firmly and when required, peel off some of them and place them on the wound.)

When they were not raiding or trading, both Saxons and Danes are reputed to have been good farmers. Indeed, many of their seafaring expeditions were for the purpose of obtaining more land or the wherewithal to buy some. It is therefore not unreasonable to propound that once they had won themselves a suitable acreage in this country, many were willing to settle peacefully and to get on with their farm work. This was certainly happening during the two centuries prior to 1066 and seeds would have had to be produced.

Apart from their field crops, these settlers cultivated kitchen gardens. They were called 'wort-gardens' or 'leac-tuns', and here they grew successive sowings of at least four members of the cabbage family. Admittedly these were the 'coleworts' (non-heading varieties) which nevertheless were not finished once the tops were cut off, but continued to shoot and to produce greenstuff for a period of several weeks. No doubt some were also sown or were of a variety to come either late or early in the season. Rochford Manor in Essex not only had a Great Garden but also a 'wortgardyn' next to the outer precinct.[18]

For many centuries the onion family held pride of place amongst vegetables — even today what would we do without it? For their 'leac-tuns' (the word onion was not used until after the Norman Conquest) the Saxons would have required seeds, sets or plants of onions (probably more a Welsh than a large round-bulbed type), leeks, chives and shallots.

There is a great deal of confusion as to the general state of development, or even degeneration, in root crops during the Middle Ages and until more information comes to light it is impossible to make a clear statement. During this period what we now think of as root crops are somewhat infrequently mentioned. The general impression is that carrots and parsnips may have reached a fair stage of development by Saxon times; that this was to some extent maintained until a period of degeneration set in; and that recovery was not obvious until the reign of Henry VII or VIII.

It is thought that it was the leaves and not the roots of beet and turnips that were cooked and eaten.[19] Still today we relish a dish of young turnip tops and those folk who know what is good will take the trouble to search for the young leaves of the wild sea beet (*Beta maritima*) and will not throw away those wrung from their beetroot. Both are infinitely superior to our much coarser-flavoured spinach.

Only a little imagination is needed to understand why plants of high flavour and smell were so much prized for cooking. With no refrigerators, much less a deep freeze, what must the last joint from a kill have been like! Even salted, dried and smoked meat would have needed more than a little help by the end of the batch to give it flavour. There must be something to be learnt from the fact that today there is a revival of herb usage. Not now so much to mask flavours as to give some to our deep frozen meat, fish and poultry, and to tone down the cloyingly synthetic taste of many tinned meats and vegetables. Dorothy Hartley[20] describes how the Saxons always flavoured their meat dishes with the plants which were eaten by the animal. Thus for mountain mutton, wild thyme predominated, with a suspicion of wild garlic, some wild marjoram and mint. Saltmarsh mutton was better accompanied by samphire and laver, whilst that from Leicestershire pastures needed the tart barberry or red currant jelly. This is a nice idea which might be followed today if only we knew where our 'lamb' had been reared.

It was not only their food which needed to smell sweeter, for remember, there were no deodorants or any dry cleaning service until very recent times. One cannot but commend the efforts, seemingly to do something to meet this need, which were made by Edward I whose household accounts for 1281 show a monthly purchase of no less than eight and a half pounds of fennel seed for his wardrobe, whereas Edward IV favoured 'lytil bages of fustian stuffed with ireos and anneys'.[21]

The beginnings of a feudal relationship between master and man already existed before 1066. The difference after that date, when Norman baron replaced Saxon thegn as Lord of the Manor, was that many who were freemen then lost their free status and became merged into the labouring peasant class of the unfree villeins. This meant that they were obliged to till and sometimes to provide the seed for their master's land as well as their own; were tied to the land upon which they were born; could not marry or give their daughters in marriage; or sell ox or horse born on their holding without the permission of their lord. Still lower in the social scale were the serfs and they could be actually bought and sold like slaves. It is unlikely that either of these classes of the population would have indulged in any but the minimum of private gardening or seed growing. Indeed, many workers were fed, albeit often sparsely, from the gardens and kitchens of the palaces, estates and monasteries to which they were attached.

To appreciate something of how the manorial system worked and to show how corn was being regularly transported about the country, both to the local mill and for sale further afield, excerpts from the introduction to Canon J. L. Fisher's manuscript are given in Appendix A.

From the early 12th century, until Henry VIII dissolved the monasteries, the Church and religious orders gained political influence and amassed much property included in which was a large acreage of agricultural land. For instance, in Essex at the time of the Conquest, the Manor of Cressing belonged to the Saxon King Harold.[22] After the Conquest it passed to a Norman, Count Eustace of Boulogne and from him to his daughter Maud, the wife of King Stephen. In 1136 this queen 'granted the whole Manor of Cressynge with the advowson of the Church of the same Manor, to the Virgin Mary and the Brothers of the Knighthood of Solomon's Temple at Jerusalem'. So it was that the name Cressing Temple arose and persists to this day. Many centuries later it was to become the home of Frank Cullen, a noted seedsman in Essex, who spent much of his money keeping the two great tithe barns superbly repaired and still in use.

Nearby, at some time after 1140, the Cistercians built Coggeshall Abbey together with a mill and a large barn. This Abbey is sometimes credited with having started the seed industry in this district. Despite considerable research, including consulting the Cistercian Order, I have found no evidence to support this theory.

At least three major mistakes have been perpetrated regarding the development of gardens and woodland during the medieval period in Britain. The first affirms that there was no such thing as considered tree planting until the Renaissance; the second that, throughout the Middle Ages, British gardens consisted solely of utilitarian herb patches with no space devoted to the enjoyment of flowers or trees for their beauty, or on recreation; and the third that, for some centuries, Britain remained behind the rest of north-west Europe in both the skill of its gardeners and the creation of notable gardens. An examination of the accounts for works carried out at abbeys, royal palaces and nobles' estates has revealed that all three dicta are mistaken. The examples given below show this to be true. (Those who wish to understand more of this matter are recommended to read *Medieval Gardens* (1981) by John H. Harvey upon which much herein, relating to this period, has been based.)

From the 13th century onwards there is considerable evidence for an organised trade in seeds, plants and turf for lawns, for garden seats and for the repair and renewal of jousting grounds. It is also apparent that gardening was by then a recognised profession in which there was a hierarchy that stretched from pupils and apprentices to under-gardeners, and through head-gardeners to professional men who charged a fee and were hired to carry out particularly skilled work. The bulk of these gardeners were natives of Britain who made up for any lack of scientific knowledge by an instinctive practical expertise. In fact, it may be stated that it is to these men that we owe the peculiarly haunting charm of the traditional English garden. Theirs was no slavish copying of fashion or uncritical acceptance of the Islamic gardening pattern then creeping in from south of the Pyrenees. It was a considered adoption of what pleased them, that could be adapted to our landscape, as well as be grown with success in our climate.

That seeds were travelling both in some quantity and for considerable distances about the country is shown by a suit brought before the Fair Court of St Ives in 1300. Apparently, when John Spicer of Godmanchester and Peter Chapman of St Ives met in Huntingdon in January 1296, they entered into a partnership to sell seeds in various parts of Scotland. Spicer was to do the work and Chapman to finance the enterprise. Evidently Spicer loaded leek seed, which cost £3, onto pack-horses and proceeded to Scotland. He returned in April from a second journey, and in February 1297 set out on a third trip with three horses again loaded with leek seed. A profit was made but the case was brought because the partners could not agree a division.

By some time around 1092 the garden of Romsey Abbey was clearly good enough to be used as an excuse for a visit by William 'Rufus' and his courtiers; ostensibly to look at the beautiful flowering plants but really to have a look at the heiress of the Saxon line, the little 12-year-old Edith of Scotland who was then boarding in the convent school. This child ultimately became the wife of Henry I and one wonders if it was she who encouraged him to make the enclosed garden in his park at Havering in Essex, a place still known as Havering-atte-Bower. Certainly it is from this king's time that the story of British royal gardens begins and during this reign, and those of the Angevin kings who followed, comes the turning point in British gardening which is so frequently misplaced into the Tudor period. A contributory factor to this advance must have been that Henry III, Edward I and Edward III all married girls who had been brought up in families who possessed gardens of renown, and so probably considered them a necessity of life.

The expenditure for the making and upkeep of these parks often amounted to thousands of pounds for there was woodland and parkland containing long avenues of trees; 'flowery meads' which were probably water meadows from which hay containing many flowering herbs was obtained — somewhat like that made in Switzerland today; jousting grounds; 'woort' gardens; orchards; possibly a vineyard; great lawns with large gardens and more private and smaller gardens, of a quarter of an acre or less, known as 'herbers' and usually situated near to the family apartments. (The word 'herber' should not necessarily be taken to mean a place for the growing of useful herbs. In this context it refers to a small intimate flower garden often in association with grass, trellis and seats.) All had to be maintained and refurbished as need arose and for it all seeds were saved, bought and sold, as at Wykeham's School, Winchester, where in 1394 a supply of 'westmale' cloth was bought to make bags for the collection and storage of their garden seeds.

Abbots were enthusiastic planters of tree seeds such as oak, ash and nuts, as well as sets or plants of elm, willow or poplar. For example, at Alton Priors, a manor belonging to St Swithun's, Winchester, at least 12 acres of woodland were planted in 1260-61. To do this, 19 quarters of nuts were purchased at £1 5s. 4d. and eight and a half quarters of acorns at 8s. 0d. In 1304, Godfrey of Crowland, the abbot of Peterborough, planted a wood to the east of Cranmore in Lincolnshire, and in the next year, another by the manor house of Northolm in Northamptonshire. At some time near to 1350[23] Mayster Jon Gardener wrote, in verse, the original text of his informative book called *The Feate of Gardening*. He is believed to have been in charge of one of the royal gardens, probably at Windsor or perhaps one of those in London. The text is based entirely on his own experience and has no recourse to either classical or any other previous writers. The need for, and acceptance of, such a book surely emphasises yet again the importance that horticulture had by then assumed in Britain. It is noteworthy that Gardener says nothing on the growing of any new varieties of vegetables that were just beginning to find their way into the more notable gardens. Possibly he was not yet inclined to pass on any cultural expertise that he may have gained in this respect; after all, one needs to keep ahead of one's apprentices.

John H. Harvey gives several examples of quantities and prices of seeds bought each year for the kitchen gardens of royal and episcopal households, and these indicate not only the size of the gardens but also the principal seeds and plants grown for culinary use. Onions, leeks, beans and colewort were bought for the Bishop of Winchester's garden in Southwark in 1211. By 1322 a much wider range of seeds was bought for the Archbishop of Canterbury's garden at Lambeth. Both gardens were about two acres in extent, but the latter included hyssop, 'spynbach', lettuce, 'caboche', skirret, cucumber, borage and clary. The appearance of 'caboche' and a very early mention of the root skirret suggests that the new varieties of vegetables were already beginning to be grown for the richer gourmets.

There were also sales of small quantities of hempseed (sold by the bushel). The cultivation of this crop is not thought to have been extensive until the 15th century, when it was used to make tough hard-wearing cloth for clothing as well as for ships' sails and ropes. Other seed purchases noted by Harvey included broad beans, flax, mustard, teazel and vetch.

From the 13th century onwards families living in towns, who had hitherto relied upon the cultivation of a plot of land for much of their food, were becoming more and more separated from the soil and there was an opportunity for someone to fill this gap. Both within and around the City of London there were farmers and smallholders who started to grow for this trade, and it is clear that the gardeners attached to large gardens, noble estates, and the monastic establishments also disposed of their surpluses to this market.

At first sales were direct, by crying in the streets or from carts or stalls set up in convenient places, so that by 1345 those selling near the gate of St Paul's churchyard were so numerous and noisy that traffic was hindered 'both on foot and on Horseback' and 'the scurrility, clamour and nuisance' was such that complaints were made by the local inhabitants on the grounds that it disturbed their worship. The Mayor and Aldermen then ordered the stall-holders to move to an open space by the 'garden wall of the Friars Preachers at Baynard's Castle'.[24] Later came the officially-recognised produce markets and sales through shops. Today, many crops go direct to the canner or freezer before distribution to shops, multiple stores and hypermarkets.

The Vegetable Mystery

Some people think that for a time vegetables virtually disappeared. It all depends upon the reliability of the Reverend William Harrison's report of an event which, admittedly, is reputed to have taken place well before his time. This gentleman, who lived from 1534 to 1593, was born and educated in London, Oxford and Cambridge. He was a topographer and chronologist, and was also chaplain to Lord Cobham, and rector of Radwinter between 1559 and 1593. Between 1571 and 1581 he was also rector of Wimbish and after 1586, concurrently until his death, Dean of Windsor.

Radwinter and Wimbish are both small rural parishes in north-west Essex. They are the kind of place where memories, particularly of disasters, would have been long, for such stories were repeated over and over again for the benefit of younger generations. Furthermore, Harrison was no absentee parson; in fact it is said that he 'seems to have been diligent in his parish',[25] and, be it noted, unlike many of his neighbours, his name does not appear in the list of 'unpreaching ministers' in Essex, drawn up by the Puritans in 1585.

Because he had the reputation of having been a sympathetic, humorous and intelligent man, who mixed well with all classes of society, we can assume that he will have heard all the tales of past days and will have been capable of sifting the evidence. Therefore, when in 1577 he published his *Description of England*, in which the following much argued-over passage occurs:

> Such herbs, fruits and roots also, as grow yearelie out of the ground, of seed, haue been verie plentifull in this land in the time of the first Edward (1272-1307) and after his daies; but in process of time they grew also to be neglected, so that by Henrie the seuenth, and beginning of Henrie the eighth (1509-1547) there was little or no use of them in England, but they remained either unknowne or supposed as food more meet for hogs and sauage beasts to feed vpon, then mankind.

One is encouraged to believe in the veracity of his statement and more especially because it could make seed production sense.

What I believe Harrison is clearly implying is that any improvement of seeds which had occurred before the Norman Conquest was maintained until the deterioration in our climate, which unnoticed when it started in 1303, by mid-century had so worsened that it was having an obvious effect on plant growth and seeds (Appendix B). It should also be remembered that apart from the various wars, the depleted harvests and ensuing years of famine would have reduced the people's resistance to disease. Consequently, when the Black Death (*Pasteurella pestis*) reached England in 1348 it spread and between 1361 and 1403 greatly reduced the population.[26] Furthermore, for generations to come this pestilence, in one form or another, continued to exact its toll.

Because of these unfavourable happenings it is likely that through lack of care there was a considerable deterioration in the amount and quality of this country's seed stocks. Harrison actually says that 'they grew also to be neglected' and after all, in many places, there must have been very few able-bodied people left to do even the barest of cultivation.[27] At Exeter it is recorded[28] that the Black Death 'arrested the building of the Cathedral nave, paralysed our woollen trade and all commercial enterprise and suspended agricultural pursuits'.

The harvest of 1371 was so poor that the resulting famine was still being talked about in the 16th century,[29] and it is possible that any seed stocks that were left further deteriorated or were lost altogether.

Sometimes it is not appreciated that, particularly in these early days, and even to a lesser extent today, the effect of unseasonable weather extends not only over the initial harvest but to those of several succeeding years. In short, too much rain at the wrong time of year is always worrying, and to these early cultivators was a major disaster. Today, we are helped by extensive under-drainage and by big and powerful machines which are capable of cultivating and harvesting large acreages in a short time, thus enabling the work to be done quickly in any dry spell. Even the older members of our society now find it difficult to remember the extent to which farming was once affected by inclement weather. Not that the effect has been entirely eliminated today, but then they had no sprays to burn off lush wet foliage and so give seeds some chance to ripen. They had nothing to combat such pests as slugs and snails, nor any means of drying seeds artificially. Nowadays when all else fails we have helicopters to spray seed corn onto the sodden fields and later on to apply much-needed nitrogen to the crop, and also to spray, with all its hazards, against many weeds, pests and diseases. Nor was it just rain which caused so much havoc. Frost, snow or wind out of season can be equally devastating. No wonder we are still always discussing the weather!

In 1383[30] there was another poor harvest and this time there was not even enough sun to ripen the fruit. Inevitably, and especially on the heavier soils, this would again have been followed by years of reduced harvest yields and deterioration of seed stocks. Yet another period of disastrous weather occurred in 1437-9, and so Harrison was probably right in stating that vegetable cultivation did more or less cease. Surely at best it must have been considerably hampered and therefore reduced until newly-developed, or 'cleaned-up' old varieties of seeds had once again been produced in sufficient quantities for them to be generally available.

By the time that this happened Essex, if only by reason of its geographic position, was fortunately placed to make use of any new ideas and knowledge coming either from London or by way of its coastal and overseas trade. This factor, together with its ready access to the capital city by both road and water, enabled this county to take full advantage of every opportunity in the marketing and production of grains, seeds and greengrocery that arose for many years to come.

Chapter Two

Seed Interests Spread (1485-1750)

> There is a perplexing paradox in the fact that Britain has one of the poorest natural flora of the temperate world, yet certainly the richest range of imported plants growing in her gardens. Our countryside is botanically very simple; our gardens the most complex on earth.
>
> Hugh Johnson[1]

During his reign the frugal and wily Henry VII at last established civil peace. The nobility, who were no longer allowed fortified castles or large forces of armed retainers, turned from the pursuit of war to political intrigue; to an interest in the new horizons opening up through voyages of discovery; and to the renaissance of knowledge and scholarship now flowing in from Europe.

The 16th century was a period when shipyard order books were filling. Those first attracted onto the ships were fortune hunters and adventurers, to be followed by the traders, who were still later joined by botanists, and plant and seed collectors. During the Tudor period a remarkable change took place in many of this country's gardens. We had to be in fashion, and instead of adapting to suit our climate and very individual landscape, we adopted a style of grandiose formality which at times bordered on the grotesque. Like all historical developments this change did not happen everywhere in the country, or always at the same date, and the simpler and more charming style was retained in gardens attached to many a dwelling for at least another century.

In this century to take an interest in gardening was not only usual for a gentleman — it was the fashion. Gardeners were sent abroad, to see the developments in Europe, and further afield to collect interesting plants. At first, thought was seldom given to a plant's beauty, its use or even its suitability for our climate — it was enough that it was new.

At this time tulips, anemones and the Crown Imperial fritillary were coming in from Turkey, sometimes by diplomatic bag. (It is to be hoped that no Crown Imperial was ever sent actually in 'the bag' as these bulbs impart a skunk-like smell. There is a suitcase in my family which once transported one from Holland and it has never been fit to use again!)

Towards the middle of the century it was not only the grand-scale gardens which provided opportunities for trade and employment. The smaller estates of rich yeomen and prosperous merchants were also being developed as simpler and sometimes more charming imitations of those of their superiors. In the 1540s, for instance, Sabine Saunders was to marry John Johnson, a merchant living at Glapthorn Manor, Northamptonshire.[2] Before going there to live she was planning her garden, and as her brother-in-law lived in London, where the seed merchants were, she asked him to obtain a supply of good seeds for her. 'Seeds for my sister's new gardens' were duly obtained and sent to Glapthorn for the spring sowing. In the seed trade, satisfied customers tend to remain loyal to those with whom they have done business, and so it was with Mrs. Johnson, for consignments continued to be sent to her each spring from the city.

The Huguenot Influence

From the point of view of this country's horticultural seed growing and trading this, though by no means the beginning, was certainly the time when these activities began to enlarge.

5. Crown Imperial Lily. 'These bulbs impart a skunk-like smell.'

Flemish, Walloon and French Protestants started to seek refuge in England from the 1540s, and particularly after the horrific massacre of St Bartholomew's night in 1572. Some of these came to Harwich and families bearing their names are still to be found spread over Essex. There are Marriages and Pertwees in Colchester, Docwras in Kelvedon, and Birkins in Tiptree and Coggeshall. Again, there is Ralph Gould, of Hurst's (see pp.113-114), the world-renowned plant breeder who can claim Flemish blood from the silk-weaving family of Overett through his grandmother.

The gardeners amongst these refugees are important, not only for the new and improved seeds and plants that they are reputed to have brought with them, but also because the records emphasise once more how few culinary vegetables were as yet in general use in this country. It also appears that the London gardeners recognised their worth and were not hostile,[3] when, in order to be nearer for trading in the London markets, they moved to market garden land on the north and south banks of the Thames.

Although, in England, little good fruit and few vegetables, as we understand the words today, had hitherto been grown, other countries, whose climate had allowed a greater range, had not been slow to recognise a growing market and there was already a considerable import trade in fruit, salad crops and vegetables. These were, until the end of the 16th century, very expensive and only found on the tables of the rich. For instance, it is said that an improved type of lettuce was first imported for Catherine of Aragon[4] and soon suitable seed must have been introduced because payment to a gardener for lettuce, delivered from York Place to Hampton Court Palace, figures in accounts of 1531, and one lemon bought for a civic feast given to Henry VIII and Anne Boleyn cost six silver pennies.[5]

Sandwich, at one time an important Cinque Port, had become almost deserted by the second half of the 16th century. Here some Flemings settled. Writing 300 years later, Samuel Smiles says in *The Huguenots*:

> The cabbages, carrots and celery produced by the foreigners met with so ready a sale, and were in so much demand in London itself, that a body of gardeners shortly afterwards removed from Sandwich and settled at Wandsworth, Battersea and Bermondsey where many of the rich garden grounds, first planted by the Flemings, still continue to be the most productive in the neighbourhood of the metropolis.

They remained so until built upon in the 19th and 20th centuries and to this day several people in this trade bear Huguenot names. Samuel Hartlib, writing in *The Compleat Husbandman* (1659) says:

> About fifty years ago this art of gardening began to creep into England, into Sandwich and Surrey, Fulham and other places. Some old men in Surrey, where it flourisheth very much at present, report that they knew the first gardeners that came into those parts to plant cabbages, colleflowers and to sow turneps and carrots and parsnips, and raith-rape peas, all of which at that time were great rarities, we having few or none in England but what come from Holland and Flanders. These gardeners, with much ado, procured a plot of good ground and gave no less than eight pounds per acre; yet the gentleman was not content, fearing they would spoil his ground because they did use to dig it. So ignorant were they of gardening in those days.

It is noteworthy that these Sandwich gardeners also established quite a reputation as seedsmen; for instance, in Battersea for cabbage seed and in Deptford for onion seed.

Our gardens, like our people, owe much to the hybrid vigour produced by introductions and adaptations from other lands. By the end of the reign of Elizabeth I almost every traveller, from diplomat and priest to ship's surgeon and merchant trader, received requests or instructions to bring or send home seeds, slips or plants, particularly anything rare or exotic.

In 1597, John Gerard, of *Herball* fame, records that there were two sorts of turnip and possibly also a red one, which he had not yet seen. The best he ever tasted came from Hackney, 'a village near London', sometime around 1618. He also mentions the cauliflower but it does not appear to have been in common use. Around this time also our wild radish was being replaced by a round sort (*Raphanus sativus*) from Central Asia and a long-rooted kind (*R. longipinnatus*) from China; some melons were coming in from Armenia and, by 1699, cabbage seed from Russia. Busoni,[6] the Venetian ambassador's chaplain, was impressed with English cabbages having seen some weighing 35 pounds a pair, and had heard of a single one weighing 28 pounds.

The rise in status of gardeners

Two professions, both under the descriptions of 'gardener', were now rising in number and importance. First, the gardeners attached to Royal Parks, estates, manor houses and properties of lesser degree; secondly, those whom we should now term market gardeners, producing a still limited but increasing variety of fruit, vegetables, herbs, and seeds for sale from their patches of ground within, or just without, the city boundary.

By the early 16th century some monastic lands and gardens had already been leased to established market gardeners. In the monasteries produce had always been grown for the community and their numerous guests, and surplus produce had been sold. The hard manual work, such as digging, had often been done by lay labour (under the supervision of a knowledgable monk). At the Dissolution of the Monasteries (1536-9), some of these lay labourers may have found themselves out of work and perhaps tried to pass themselves off as skilled gardeners together with other unskilled opportunists who, no doubt, set up on their own to supply the expanding market. At any event, the established gardening fraternity were soon complaining of the amount of poor quality produce being sold; of gardeners who were charlatans; and that they would lose their good name.

Their Company of Free Gardeners, which had existed as a fraternity since 1345, was not well enough organised to exert much influence and so a petition, asking for an organisation which would have more authority and control, was sent to the Lord Mayor. In it the gardeners assured the Lord Mayor that:

> . . . they can hurte no Companie in London, for theire life is altogether in the ffieldes or Gardens. And so desirous of Libertie and Ayer [air], that they will not be tied to a shop, nor, are they capable of anie other trade.

And to strengthen their case the Lord Mayor was reminded that it was they who removed 'the dung and noysommes of the citie' and

> . . . imploye thousands of poore people, ould men, woemen and children, in sellinge of their Commodities, in weedings, in gatheringe of stones etc.; which would other wise be verie burdonsome to the cittie and suburbs thereof.

At length, on 18 September 1605, the fraternity of 1345 was incorporated into a guild by Letters Patent as 'The Masters, Wardens, Assistants and Commonalty of the Company of Gardeners of London'. Its Charter was for:

> the trade, craft or mystery of gardening, planting, setting, sowing, cutting, arboring, rocking, mounting, covering, fencing, and removing plants, herbs, seeds, fruits, trees, stocks, sets, and of contriving the conveyances to the same belonging.

One of the stated reasons for the setting up of the Company was to 'inspect the Worth of others, who tended to practise without knowledge, or should offer to invade their Customs'. Furthermore, the Master and Wardens now had full power to seize goods, and if they were not of high enough quality, to destroy them. Nevertheless, the wrangling was still going on as late as 1726.[7]

Meantime, established gardeners attached to large estates were becoming men of increasing consequence; consulted by their employers and their employer's friends; corresponding and mixing with the eminent botanists and gardeners of Europe; being sent abroad to learn new skills; commissioned to travel and bring home specified plants and any others which took their eye; and at some time around 1350 one had even written a most creditable book.

1485-1750 — Gardening books and seed lore

In 1500 even the city of London was as yet but a small town where neighbours still knew one another well enough to exchange plants and seeds over the garden fence. Knowledge of gardening still generally came by word of mouth, by laborious trial and error or by copying someone you happened to know who had found out how to do it. Today, with the plethora of printed matter, daily supplying us with more and more information on almost any subject, it is easy to forget how very localised any new piece of knowledge could remain in those early days.

Until William Caxton introduced his printing press (1476) and translated some 20 good and useful books for dissemination amongst his countrymen 'in our English language', every document had been painstakingly copied by hand and was usually in one or another foreign language.

It was not long before quite a number of books on gardening began to appear although, in the earlier volumes, information on seeds is often rather bizarre. For instance, to ensure that seedlings are strong we are told to sprinkle the seeds with wine before sowing, always to sow when the moon is waxing and, astonishingly, by Thomas Hyll, in the second half of the 16th century:[8]

> That many savours and tastes may be felte in one herb: take first of the lettuce two or three seeds, of the endive so many, of the smallage the lyke, of the Basil, the Leek and the Parsley. Put altogether into a hole and there will spring up a plant having so many savours or tastes.

But perhaps we should not laugh for, as late as my childhood, knowledge of plant breeding was so sparsely understood that a charming old gentleman, when asked why he was burying tobacco at the root of a rose tree, explained that he wanted to produce a blue rose, and noticing one day a blueness in the smoke from his pipe, the idea had come to him that perhaps tobacco contained something that would help him towards his ambition!

Thomas Hyll, too, in *The Gardeners' Labyrinth* (1586) when recommending garden enclosures to discourage 'Thieves or Robbers, fowls and beast' wrote:

> Stew up with honey, a mixture of the ripe seeds of eglantine, briar berries, brambles, white thorn, gooseberries and barberries. The same mixture lay diligently into old and untwisted Ship or Welropes, or other long worne ropes, that the seeds bestowed or couched within the soft haires of them may be preserved and defended from the cold unto the beginning of spring.

The seed-filled rope was planted in two furrows about three feet apart and eighteen inches deep. Within a few years the bushes resulting from this planting would 'grow to a most strong defence of the Garden . . . that, with diligence cut, waxeth so thick and strong that hardly any person can enter into the ground, saving by the Garden doors'. Surely this was a precursor of the modern seed-tape.

The greengrocery trade in Flanders is said to have reached a high level by the 14th century, and by 1603 there were complaints in print of foreign competition, and against those who sold inferior seed.

One of the complainants, Richard Gardiner, was a linen draper and churchman of Shrewsbury. He sold both vegetables and seeds from his land and drew up a small produce and seed list giving the prices of each item, together with a do-it-yourself booklet entitled *Profitable instructions for the Manuring, Sowing and Planting of Kitchen Gardens*, a copy of which, published in 1603, is even believed to be a second edition. His 'seed catalogue' quotes turnip at 12 pence the pound, beans at two pence the quart and 'my price for those principall carret seedes is after the rate of two shillings the waxe Pound, without deceipt'.

During this period England was notorious for the frequency of its famines, and Richard Gardiner thought that if more carrots were grown this would relieve the starvation. He also deplored the fact that these roots were being imported from Holland at great expense, when everyone could be growing their own or purchasing from gardeners in this country and for far less money.

The saving and marketing of selected seed stocks had become a recognisable trade by the 16th century.[9] For some time most seedsmen had their headquarters in London and, as still happens today, either grew on their own land, or had seeds grown for them by approved farmers and nurserymen.

At first sales were from their own premises, often but a small barn or weatherproof shed, from stalls in street markets, and at fairs. Quite soon small seed shops began to appear, sometimes in association with a corn chandler or an apothecary and so it was that many of our now famous seed houses began.

By the middle of the 16th century, the range and quantity of seed demanded had considerably widened. Thomas Tusser, who once farmed in Essex, lists 42 herbs for kitchen use, and another 22 for salads and sauces. Under 'Herbs and Roots, to boil or butter' he gives beans, carrots, cabbages, parsnips, rape, turnips, peas, pumpkins, radishes, gourds and 'citrons' as well as over twenty fruits and nuts which together with such things as briar hedges were sometimes grown from seeds.

Horticulturally it was an exciting era. Nurserymen and gardeners competed with each other to obtain seeds of the newly-imported trees and evergreen shrubs which were becoming so popular. Seeds and seedlings from France were greatly improving our top-fruit orchards and, by at least Henry VIII's reign, there may have begun to be a demand for cut flowers in vases as suggested by no less than three such in the Holbein painting of Sir Thomas More and his family in 1528. One of those who set out to meet the growing demand was a Mr. Child, whose frequently quoted story bears repetition because it is probably typical of what was happening at this time and also has a possible connection with an Essex firm.

1560-1666 — a 16th-century Seedsman: Mr. Child of Pudding Lane

By 1560, Mr. Child was established as a seed merchant in London, with premises amongst the huddle of wood, lath and plaster buildings in a narrow alley near Billingsgate market and Queenhithe Dock. The alley was known variously as Pudding, Rother or Red Rose Lane.

To quote John Stow's *Survey of London* (1598) the name Pudding arose from

> the butchers of Eastcheap have their scalding house for hogs there, and their puddings, with other filth of beasts, are voided down that way to their dung boats in the Thames.

Was the alternative of Red Rose Lane a Lancastrian or a horticultural connection, or, indeed, could it signify a 'red light' district? Certainly, by Stow's time (*c.*1525-1605), it was a place of commerce mainly for basket makers, turners and butchers, but he does also report the existence of several gardens in the vicinity.

One can speculate on what Child was selling — perhaps seeds of the new plant *Nicotiana tabacum* first imported by Sir John Hawkins[10] in 1565, for there was, despite Royal condemnation, a growing demand to test its narcotic properties when smoked or taken as snuff.

Probably Child's main trade would have been in garden seeds, his vegetables will have included seeds and sets of the onion tribe, plants and seeds of various coleworts, and 'caboche', asparagus and perhaps early Hastyngez peas or the Rouncivall marrowfat pea, and some seeds of purple, yellow, white and red carrots. There would have been a demand for an increasing number of flower seeds such as wallflower, violet, stock, sweet william, columbine, campion, cowslip, hollyhock, marigold, pansies, pinks, snapdragons, forget-me-not and probably snowdrop (the double ones were the most favoured) and daffodil bulbs, with perhaps even a few of the new and expensive tulip bulbs then coming into vogue. The rose was already the most popular flower in England and he would surely have had a collection.

Evidently Mr. Child's business flourished for there was still a descendant of the founder in the seed business up to the time of London's Great Fire. We do not know if he was still in Pudding Lane. If he was he must have been burnt out on that September night. By 1665 the properties in the lane were tottering, their roofs almost touching and the way so narrow that a cart had difficulty in getting through.

However, it is known that it was an hour or so before the fire from Farynor the baker's spread to the next house and if Mr. Child was in the lane and sufficiently alive to the impending danger, he must have been able to save at least some of his precious seeds. We are unlikely ever to find out what actually occurred. He might have moved his business to beyond the built-up area before it all happened. Certainly, the remarkable thing about the aftermath of the fire was the speed with which the London merchants rebuilt their establishments.[11] Perhaps, although so far historically unproven, we may be permitted to believe that Child the seedsman did likewise. In any event the name of Child appears in 1810 amalgamating with another seed firm, J. & J. Field, to become Field and Child. It is thought that J. & J. Field's ancestors started their seed business about the same date (1560) as Mr. Child of Pudding Lane. We know of the firm as J. & J. Field in 1771, and that it had previously gone under the name of J. Field. There is no proof that the 1810 Child was descended from Child 1560. Equally, there is no proof that he was not.

In any case, through their amalgamation with Cooper Taber of Witham, Essex, whose connections include the Field business, the firm of Hurst, Gunson, Cooper, Taber Ltd., Witham, Essex, can justly claim at least one link with the seed trade before 1771. This family tree will be discussed further in Chapter 5 because it is typical of the amalgamations and takeovers that have occurred amongst seed houses from the 16th century onwards.

1485-1750 — Gathering momentum

The discovery of new lands fortunately happened when this country was enjoying a period of relative peace and aided by the printing press, was increasingly well-informed. Had this happy coincidence not occurred, it is doubtful whether our gardens or our seed trade would have developed as quickly or extensively as they did. As it was we were able to take advantage of the new knowledge flowing in from outside. At the same time we were in possession of sufficient ships, together with men of the right calibre to man them, and we were financed by a nobility consisting largely of prosperous merchants, often willing to impoverish themselves rather than be out-done by their neighbours in one gardening fashion after another. Even today the speed with which new plants were introduced and gardening skills extended during this era is remarkable and has possibly never been surpassed.

Plants and seeds were moving from country to country in all directions. From the mid-17th century the comings and goings between North America and England are particularly noticeable. In fact, it was now that what was to develop into our very large seed export trade began, first to North America and later to South America and Canada.

The *Mayflower* left Plymouth in 1620. We know that seeds were part of her cargo and we can imagine the women carefully filling little spaces in their luggage with those that the particularly favoured for cooking, for medicine or to remind them of home. Once they had settled, requests were sent back to England by any ship that was making the journey although, in time, certain ships became known for their particular care of passengers or goods, as did grain barges round our Essex coast in later years. The settlers sent for stockings, food, glass, nails, books, sheepskins, gunpowder and a further supply of seeds. As Ann Leighton puts it:[12]

> The little ships labored back and forth across the Atlantic, making crossing after crossing,

so that today, the authorities on plants of New England are uncertain as to whether this plant or that is truly indigenous.

In the summer of 1631 the sailing ship *Lyon*, under the captaincy of 'kind Mr. Pierce', brought for John Winthrop (Jr.) in Massachusetts, a collection of seeds the bill for which survives.[13] It is from

> Robert Hill gr [?grocer or greengrocer] dwelling at the three Angells in lumber streete — 26th July 1631

and is chiefly for herb seeds with a few vegetables, namely parsnip, beet, cabbage, carrot, cauliflower, leek, onion, pumpkin, radish and artichoke. Altogether there were 59 items at a total cost of £1 6s., the most expensive being two ounces of cauliflower seed at 2s. 6d. an ounce.

In the 17th and 18th centuries this interest in horticulture gathered momentum in all its aspects, from the hydraulics of fountains, grottoes and lakes; through the geometry of parterre, knots and mazes; the surveying and building construction of vistas, mounts, garden banqueting rooms, and glasshouses; to the engineering of heated glasshouses; transcending differences of class, religion, education, politics and national loyalties.

From the mid-17th century onwards there was anxiety that more trees were being cut down for firewood, glass factories, and iron foundries than were being planted. John Evelyn, the famous diarist, produced what is, perhaps, the first book on forest conservation when he wrote *Sylva* in 1664. By 1722, when Thomas Fairchild (1667-1729) wrote *The City Gardener*, one of the difficulties he mentioned was the smoke-polluted atmosphere. This has a familiar ring!

The common interest

As time went on, beginning perhaps towards the end of the 16th century, it was not sufficient for a seedsman or a head gardener to select and save seeds from his better plants. In order to maintain his reputation, new and more interesting or useful varieties had to be produced.

This was not so easy, for little was yet known about plant breeding. Any new introduction depended on its having been found and sent safely from another country, or on a lucky mutation, or even a disease, such as the virus which produced striped tulips. Some introductions, like the pomegranate, rarely came to perfection in our climate; others such as the runner bean are still being planted each year in our fields and kitchen gardens. Gradually all kinds of people, both humble and great, were drawn together by this common interest.

There was Peter Collinson (1694-1768), a London-born Quaker, haberdasher and linen draper in Gracechurch Street; John Bartram (1699-1777), an American Quaker of Derbyshire stock — apparently a somewhat rough-hewn character — who farmed with his wife and large family in Pennsylvania; and the third member of this rather odd alliance,[14] the young Robert James, eighth Lord Petre (1713-42) a staunch Roman Catholic living at Ingatestone Hall, Essex.

Peter Collinson was certainly one of the men of his day to be approached for advice upon plants, seeds and the means of obtaining them. His correspondence was prodigious and to all parts of the globe. His friends ranged from the Duke of Richmond to John Clarke, a butcher in Barnes, who

> conceived an opinion that he could raise cedars of Lebanon from cones of the great tree at Hendon Place . . . [and] succeeded so perfectly that within a few years he was supplying the nurserymen and many noblemen.

This enthusiast also went on to raise magnolias and other exotics with equal success and became one of Collinson's trusted suppliers. Thus, when Charles Lennox, Duke of Richmond, asked Collinson to get him some cedar trees for his estate at Goodwood we find in Collinson's accounts, an entry for 8 June 1761, that John Clarke had been paid £79 6s. for 1,000 five-year-old cedar trees planted by the Duke during the previous March and April. These accounts also include seeds from St Petersburg and, through St Petersburg by the caravan route, from Jesuit priests in China.

The first extensive planting of trees grown from seed sent from North America was at Thorndon Hall, Essex, by the eighth Lord Petre — some 44,000 trees.[15] These seeds had been collected and sent by John Bartram.

It is worth noting that the indigenous British trees are almost all deciduous. With the introduction of evergreens, the whole winter scene could be changed and, in due course, the practical use of evergreen shrubs as shelter belts and as cover for game birds came to be appreciated.

Plant and seed collectors

The very real dangers to, and courage required by, collectors of plants and seeds should be appreciated, for only those with a consuming interest (or sufficient monetary encouragement) would have undertaken even one journey and many collectors made several.

One of the first recorded and surely the most engaging of the collectors was John Tradescant (the elder). It seems he would join any ship, whatever the purpose of its sailing, so long as it was visiting places where there were plants or seeds in which he was interested.

We read of him in 1618 as naturalist on a mission to Russia, the only success of which appears to have been his load of plants and a notebook which was virtually the first flora of that country. In 1620 he was making dangerous landings on the Algerian coast as a gentleman adventurer, professedly to worry pirates. He returned however with a coveted apricot and a report that the corn flag of Constantinople (*Gladiolus byzantium*) grew by the acre in Barbary. Again in 1625, while he was gardener to the Duke of Buckingham, he joined an unfortunate expedition to liberate La Rochelle from which he returned with a reputation as an engineer rather than a botanist! Perhaps this collector extraordinary is most often remembered by a little plant to which Linnaeus gave the name *Tradescantia virginiana*. In Essex he was responsible for the planning and construction of the garden with an avenue of lime trees, at New Hall, near Boreham.

At the time of his death his son John was collecting in Virginia for their museum of plants in Lambeth. When this museum was catalogued and *Museum Tradescantia* published in 1656, plants were listed from New England, Virginia, Barbados, Constantinople, Persia, North Africa and China. Surely this offers clear proof of the energy and extensive connections of such men, as well as their practical skill as gardeners.

Henry Compton was Bishop of London, which diocese then included Essex, from 1676-1713. He used his position and patronage of ecclesiastical appointments abroad to make sure that those who were sent out as missionaries had the necessary knowledge for intelligent plant and seed collecting. There is a story of one such, Mark Catesby, who unwittingly spent the night with a rattlesnake between the sheets![16]

Between 1712 and 1726 John Lawson was collecting in Carolina and Virginia. On one of his trips he was captured by hostile Tuscarora Indians[17] who, according to a witness, 'struck him full of fine small splinters of torchwood like hog's bristles and set them gradually afire'.

John Bartram's son Billie was lucky to survive an attack by alligators in the Everglades; and when the Royal Horticultural Society sent David Douglas to the Pacific coast of America in 1882 he endured 10 years of privation and danger, finally being forced to eat two of his horses to escape starvation. On his several journeys to the west coast of America, often travelling alone or with Indians over thousands of trackless miles, he very sensibly concentrated upon the collection of seeds rather than plants. He died in Hawaii, aged 35 years, by misadventure, suicide, or, more likely, murder. The job was far from being a sinecure.

Packaging

Collectors were learning more about how to pack specimens for their journeys along caravan routes and across oceans. It was no easy matter to provide for contingencies which, as well as the length of the journey, might include salt water spray, wide changes in temperature, depredation by rats, mice and cockroaches and also the attitude of the transporters. Ships' crews were liable to pitch plants overboard at the least sign of rough weather and to drink the alcohol in which specimens were preserved, conveniently losing the specimen overboard, and there was always the hazard of privateers. Surprisingly, these latter sometimes looked after and arranged delivery of these specimens to a suitable person!

A record of plant packaging instructions occurs in the 1670s when the diarist John Evelyn asked his friend, Samuel Pepys, who was by this time Secretary of the Admiralty, to try to get him some North American specimens. Evelyn's instructions were that

> Seedes are best preserv'd in papers, . . . nuttes in barrils in dry sand . . . [and] trees in barrils, their roots wrapped about moss.

Further, he understood that if the roots were rubbed over with honey this substance, having a styptic quality, would hinder the loss of moisture from 'their perspiring'. Similarly, since orange trees suffered so badly from salt spray, it was recommended that only pips be sent.

Among the seed-growers of today there is occasionally found one who, simply by feeling and looking at a completely unfamiliar seed, seems to know by instinct just what cultural treatment it will require. Such a one was Lord Petre's gardener, James Gordon, who by 1741 had set up as a nurseryman at Mile End, and also had a shop in Fenchurch Street. I am indebted to the Honourable G. R. Strutt of Terling in Essex, for sending me the following stories which illustrate this point:

> There is a rare tree (one survivor only I think) in Mauritius, whose seeds until recently defied all attempts at germination. Some bright person then reflected that the missing facility might be passage through the crop of a dodo. He therefore constructed an artificial dodo, resembling a coffee grinder, and has, I believe, had success after passing the seeds through a bashing in it.

Another agent sometimes needed for germination is fire. Certain plants in Australia have adapted themselves to produce seeds with an unusually thick, hard coat. This enables the young plant within the seeds to remain alive for a considerable time while waiting for conditions for germination to be favourable:

> In a bush fire of moderate intensity the hard seed-coat is split. The forestry experts believed the occasional accidental fires should be prevented or extinguished as soon as possible. To their surprise, the woodland deteriorated when this was done. It turned out that by limiting accidental fires to, say, one in twenty years, the accumulated sticks leaves, etc. burned too fiercely and totally destroyed the seeds. If, however, the fires were allowed to occur frequently, their intensity was enough to split the seeds for germination without totally destroying them. So their good intentions in preventing fires were mistaken, nature having already dealt with the problem.

Today, seedsmen have a scarifying machine which rubs down hard seed-coats. It is particularly useful for clover which, in a very dry season, will develop a high proportion of hard-coated seeds. this is not only a nuisance because it may produce a 'thin plant' in the first year, but, even more troublesome, some of the seeds are likely to germinate and contaminate other crops over a following period of years. Inspectors of seed crops have to be particularly on the look-out for such rogue plants if they are of a different variety from the crop being grown.

Trained collectors

The early botanists, plant and seed collectors were often as interested in making a dried and pressed collection of their finds as in sending home live material. Furthermore, they were not always practically competent gardeners and so the number of live specimens which arrived at their destination was disappointingly small and, even on safe arrival, frequently died for lack of suggestions as to how they should be treated.

Later, towards the end of the 18th century, the approach became more professional with the sending out of young gardeners, often Scotsmen, who had received proper training and were more competent to select plants for our climate and use, as well as to send with them suggestions as to how they might be successfully grown.

John Ellis, a London merchant, who lived opposite Christopher Gray's Nursery, in King's Road, Chelsea, became interested in the practical problems of plant and seed introduction. In 1759 he tried coating acorns with clay or gum arabic and, alternatively, embedding them in wax. After many years of careful experiment he concluded that to travel and arrive in a viable condition seeds must first be fully ripe and dry, and that if such acorns were completely covered in wax and stored in a cool part of the ship they would 'keep sound for a twelvemonth'.

In 1770 he published *Directions for bringing over seeds and plants from the East Indies and other distant countries in a state of vegetation.* All sorts of containers were used for packaging seeds ranging from ordinary paper to earthenware pots, bottles and even snuff boxes of tortoiseshell and silver. If possible these were to be suspended from the cabin rafters to get the benefit of circulating air.

When, in 1780, Dr. John Coakley Lettsom wrote an account of Dr. John Fothergill's garden at Upton, Essex,[18] he stated that seeds could be embedded in yellow beeswax or placed in paper or cotton saturated with beeswax. Seeds, particularly those coming from abroad, could also be mixed in dry sand and packed firmly corked in glass bottles which were then stored in boxes, surrounded with common salt. They could also be placed in a box between alternate layers of moss to allow them to germinate. Dr. Lettsom recommended that seeds that had germinated by the time the ship reached St Helena should be sown in boxes of soil mixed with small pieces of glass to prevent rats or mice from burrowing into the soil. Anything looking sickly was sometimes left in a plant-hospital in St Helena until it was well enough to be sent on.

By 1799 small plant cabins or portable greenhouses became a familiar sight on the poops of ships. In 1806, a gardener on a ship bound for China wrote home to Sir Joseph Banks complaining that

> the first mate does not approve of having a garden on the poop at all. He says it rocks the ship all to pieces. The captain agrees in the same story and when the beams creak in the cuddy they all turn to me and d—-the flower pots'.[19]

Ray Desmond tells us of 'The French author of *Le Managier de Paris, 1893* who believed that the best way to despatch rosemary was to wrap its branches in waxed cloth which was then sewn and smeared with honey and powdered with wheaten flour'.

In the closing years of the 18th century, plants were beginning to come in from collectors in South Africa, and by 1939-49 when Frank Ludlow and George Sheriff were collecting in the Himalayas, Tibet and Bhutan, 'they were able to transport plants and seeds home by air — a far cry from the early days of seeds embedded in beeswax, or gum arabic for their eight-and-a-half months' sailing from the other side of the world to England'.

By 1750 much connected with plants and seeds had happened. In 1650 the precursor of the Royal Society suggested the benefit arising from the addition of clover to pastureland. As Arthur Brown tells us,[20] by 1700 turnips were being fed to sheep in Essex and by 1724, at Little Bentley, a farmer was growing crops of both turnips and clover. In fact, seed crops were becoming increasingly popular, coriander and caraway being 'one of the staple pieces of husbandry in Coggeshall and Kelvedon'. The Department of Botany (1669) was established at Oxford, as were the gardens at Chelsea (1673) and Kew (1750). Thomas Fairchild's 'mule', a cross between a carnation and a sweet william, is preserved in the Ashmolean Museum. (Fairchild was the first nurseryman known to have experimented with hybridisation.) Melons were being grown and sold in England in quite large quantities. In Colchester, there was still a good sale for a medicinal sweetmeat made from Eryngium (Sea Holly), and the forebears of Cant's, the rose growers of Colchester, were, by 1724, already established as nurserymen and gardeners.

6. White Clover.

From the mid-17th to the early 18th century, John Ray, of Black Notley, was receiving plants and seeds from the plant collectors. John Ray (1628-1705) was the son of an Essex blacksmith who, after a local schooling, went on to study Classics at Cambridge University. Latin became the language in which it was most natural for him to write and amongst those with whom he corresponded were the Jesuit pharmacist, George Joseph Kamel, who sent him plants from the Philippines, and the Anglican missionary, John Bannister, then in Virginia. Some believe that it is Ray and not Linnaeus who should be given credit for our botanical classification. Certainly, William Derham, D.D., F.R.S., who wrote a life story of Ray (incorporated into the book *Memorials of John Ray*, edited by Edwin Lankester for publication by the John Ray Society, London), would have agreed with whoever it was who is said to have proclaimed publicly that:

> The Swede, Carl Linnaeus, is often referred to as the Father of Modern Botany. By this token, then, I would suggest that the Grandfather should be the Englishman, John Ray, for it was from the work of Ray that Linnaeus formed the basis for his classification of flora and fauna.

On the death of John Ray it is recorded by William Derham that his monument in Black Notley churchyard was 'erected at the expense, in part at least, of Bishop Compton' and to this day his memory is preserved in the genus of plants which was dedicated to him, namely Raiania and its species.

During the 1730s the large seed firms were already getting out of London and establishing themselves in more rural areas. However, the old herb garden still lingered on as it was when John Aubrey (1626-97) wrote of Sir John Danvers, at Chelsea House:

> He was wont, in fair mornings in the Summer, to brush his Beaver-Hatt on the Hysop and Thyme, which did perfume it with its naturall Spirit; and would last a morning or longer.

1750-1985 — A Very Busy Period

> I have in it communicated such Notions as I have gathered, either from the reading of Severall Authors, or by conferring sometimes with Scholars, and sometimes with Country People; to which I have added some observations of mine owne, never before published. Most of which I am confident are true, and if there be any that are not so, yet they are pleasant.
>
> Preface of William Cole's *The Art of Simpling* (1659)

In the following chapters the history of the firm, district, family, crop or organisation is told from the point at which it became involved with the seed trade. Some were innovators, others held longer to the old ways and so, as the history of each is explored, the reader may become confused as to the period in which a new idea was introduced. Before the appendices, on pp.256-61, is a chronology of those historical events which have had a marked effect upon the Essex seed trade from *c.*1750 to 1985. It may help to give point to the happenings in each account.

Chapter Three

Some 18th-century Seedsmen

The 18th-century Seed World

Although there are earlier signs, it is from the mid-18th century, and running concurrently with the continuing advances in gardening practice, that an increasing interest in agriculture burst upon British society. The upsurge of change was directed towards a general improvement in farming methods. It covered such fields as the improvement of crops; better methods of livestock husbandry; advances in farm mechanisation; and fundamentally most important

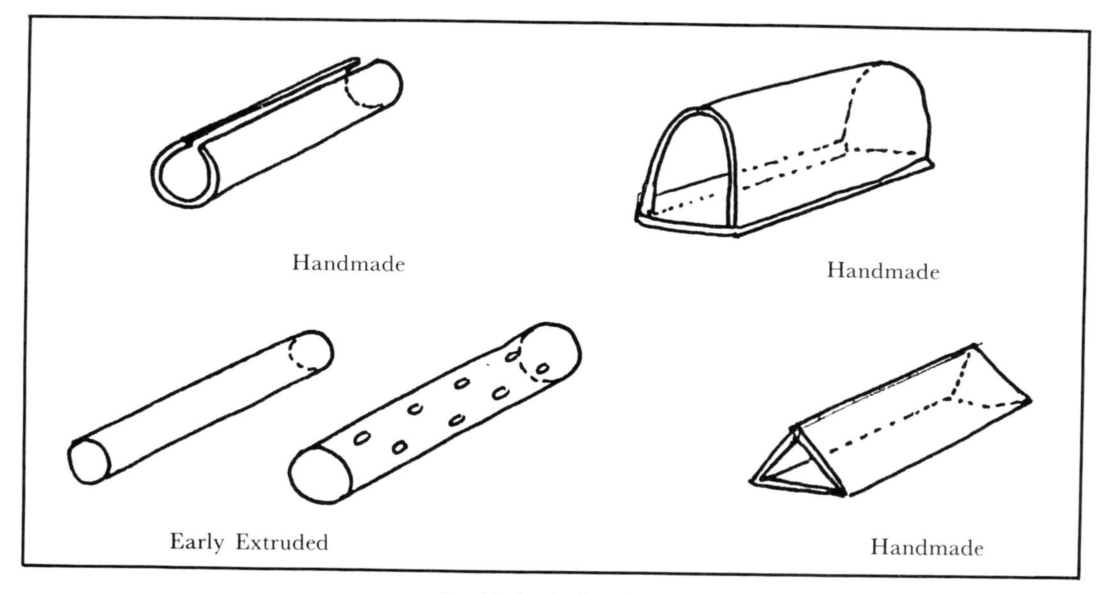

7. Early drain pipes.

of all, for no crop can give of its best without it, a search for a better understanding of what constitutes proper field drainage and how this may be achieved. The result was that, by 1764, the Society for the Encouragement of Arts, Manufactures and Commerce (today's Royal Society of Arts) was astonished to find that agriculture (an interest in which had not been foreseen) overshadowed all its other activities.

Just as gardening had come into vogue so agriculture, and all that this word embraces, became a proper interest for a gentleman, whether of town or country background. Farming in the 18th century was fashionable and many of the improvements made owed as much to considerations of prestige as to financial gain. Nevertheless, those from outside farming who purchased agricultural land (such as Charles, 2nd Viscount Townshend (Turnip Townshend) who was originally a politician, and John Mechi of Tiptree, a successful

London cutler), often brought with them extra capital and better business methods, together with minds freshly receptive to the subject. They were eager to experiment and sometimes, because they observed from a different angle, achieved a real breakthrough, so that by 1760, Arthur Brown states,[1] 'an altogether keener atmosphere prevailed', by 1770-1815 Essex agriculture by contemporary standards reached a high peak of improvement and profitability', and by 1840 'Essex farmers were generally ahead of those in most English counties and the new techniques of the progressive minority of 1800 had become the general practice of the majority'.

Two events that were to influence the volume of our seed production were the enclosure of land and a fundamental change of attitude towards the feeding, and particularly the winter feeding, of farm livestock.

Much has been written against Enclosure, most of which (except that the practice was forced upon the countryside too quickly and sometimes with great injustice) is ill-considered and too-fiercely partisan. Certainly, so long as the open fields remained there was little chance or incentive for agricultural methods to improve.

Surprisingly, it is but a short time ago that many men and all beasts, particularly cattle, were very largely forced to survive the winter by living off what fat they had been able to lay onto their bodies during the months of plant growth and harvest. Previously many beasts were slaughtered to be salted down to provide human food. After harvest the medieval animals were allowed to roam the strips of unenclosed cultivated land, heaths and commons to eat up whatever was available; possibly the cattle first to take off tall herbage, closely followed by the sheep which favour the shorter plants, pigs to root, and finally poultry to scratch and peck up anything that was left. After that both man and beast hoped that the winter would not be too long. Indeed, in some parts of the country, turning animals out to pasture in the spring was known as 'the lifting' because many a beast had no strength to stand and had to be carried from shed to pasture.

Once fields were enclosed their crops had some protection from foraging animals, and could be sown with more hope of producing a reasonable yield. Then, as fodder roots and ley-grass became popular, the problem of providing food with which to overwinter these animals was very largely solved. The difference that this increased supply of food made to their well-being is clearly shown by the fact that, in 1710, the weight of cattle sold at Smithfield market was less than half that of ordinary cattle in 1795.[2]

John Harvey[3] writes that there were at least 30 large firms of nurserymen and a dozen seedsmen in and around London from the time of George III (1760-1820). After 1730, he suggests that surviving bills of the great estates indicate a switch of patronage from the London seed firms to those setting up in their own locality.

By 1736 a revolution had taken place in the flora and cultivation of our gardens. At about the same time tree, shrub and flower seeds were coming from America to Europe. So that after 1800 'London in spite of a late start, had long overtaken Paris as the centre of the plant trade'.[4]

In Essex, vegetable and herb seeds were being grown on a field scale by the 17th century and were firmly established as agricultural crops by the mid-18th century, and some of these seeds were for export. Arthur Young, in his *Annals of Agriculture* (1770), mentions 'city men' coming down to inspect seed crops which farmers had contracted to grow for their firms.

Many seed firms chose Essex when searching for suitable sites for their trial grounds and for land upon which to grow their seeds, or to contract for them to be grown. Their choice was probably influenced by the fact that in 1800 this county was not favoured as a commuter belt or residential area, and so land was available at reasonable prices for a much longer time than in, for instance, Middlesex or Surrey. Also, the county had easy access by water to the London markets and this allowed heavy goods, such as seeds, to be moved even when the roads were impassable. In addition, Essex has advantages such as a variety of the right kinds of soil; it is neither too hilly, nor too flat; the approximate 20-inch rainfall usually occurs in the winter months when seed crops are not ripening; and it is the second sunniest area in Britain, with drying winds in spring and summer. Almost four hundred miles of extraordinarily indented coastline allow salt water to creep up the many river inlets, thus moderating the risk of frost. The unique character of this county's very hybrid inhabitants must also have affected their choice. Here were lively people with enterprise and some vision, ready to apply themselves to the many facets of growing seed crops and sturdy enough to withstand the disappointments that these crops so often bring. They were able to adapt, to 'kilter up' and, if need be, even to invent, the many tools required for the trade.

Therefore, soon after 1750 and right through the 1800s and beyond, Essex market gardeners and nurserymen enlarged their businesses. Several of them founded seed firms and some of these, still under the same names, remain with us today. With local seed firms came local contracts and a strong bond of trust, understanding and loyalty between grower and merchant, each depending for his living on the prosperity of the other and, if for no other reason, helping each other out in times of adversity. Many a seedsman has financed his grower's next crop after a disastrous harvest. Similarly, in years of glut, growers have been known to take half-price or to allow to postponement of part of the payment.

Between 1770 and 1790, some three thousand miles of canal were constructed in this country (see Chronology p.256). Bearing in mind that there were no railways and that most roads were undrained and had no smooth, hard surface, one can appreciate that these inland waterways linked, as they were, with rivers and passing through the heart of many towns, greatly facilitated the movement of both heavy and fragile goods, including seeds and pot plants.

Throughout this century and beyond, in Essex almost every working-class family, however mean or overcrowded its living accommodation, had an adjoining garden or small plot of land which was owned or rented somewhere in the vicinity. This ground can almost be said to have provided an annex to the dwelling house, a place to which both husbands and children (when not employed) could retreat after work or school. This left room for the housewife to carry out her tasks, grandparents to sit by the hearth watching cook-pots and babies between naps, space for a loom, spinning wheel or Tambour lace frame to be in use, and the sick or dying to lie, more or less peacefully, on couch or bed.

In the garden or field there was almost invariably a lock-up shed or a shelter of some kind. Here, in wet weather, children could take refuge to play, while the men mended, made and sometimes invented equipment for field and home, or ryed their seeds. For some, this plot not only supplied food for the family with occasionally a small quantity to sell or barter, but was also a place of recreation in which to indulge an absorbing interest such as the production of better quality seeds or a more economic pig.

With the demise of the cloth trade, between 1780 and 1800, on suitable soils throughout the county, Essex countryfolk took to seed growing. Flower seeds have always been grown in little patches for many of them are tiny, therefore great numbers are contained in each ounce. Furthermore, these crops require individual attention and constant care, both of which are most likely to be received from a grower for whom they represent the main cash crop of the year, and where the hours of labour will not be counted or paid for at anything approaching the going rate — a fact which, from the very beginning, has led to these seeds being sold at an unrealistically low price.

Lore and expertise were built up as observations were made, simple trials carried out and plants, which took the growers's eye, were grown on for seed. Each new piece of knowledge was jealously guarded and revealed, if at all, only to a chosen few. The same secretiveness was found on the merchanting side where, as will appear later, it sometimes assumed almost ridiculous proportions. As might be expected, the practice continues today and whilst deploring the retention of knowledge, it has to be admitted that it would be less than prudent to reveal trade secrets until their capabilities for financial gain had been exploited. The practice does, however, lead to a good deal of repetitious research. Even this, some maintain, is not altogether a bad thing since it allows another checking of the facts which, in the case of such things as spray chemicals and insecticides, provides an additional safeguard.

***

Seed firms and growers tend to fall into several different categories by specialising in different aspects to their trade. Generally, only one from each type that has come to my notice has been described in detail and particularly where they have gone out of their way to provide material during the writing of this book. Each highlights a particular facet of this trade's development.

I hope that those who are just mentioned briefly, or not at all, will not take offence but will understand that time for research and need to keep the book to a manageable size were the limiting factors. (See Appendix C, for chronological list of seedsmen.)

No publishable information which has been given to me, even if not ultimately included within the book, will be wasted. For all my notes and collection of pictures have been accepted for the new library at Writtle Agricultural College, Writtle, Essex, where they will be available as a source of information.

SOME OF THE FIRST RECORDED ESSEX SEEDSMEN

The Cants of Colchester

Ancestors of the rose-growing family of Cant are known to have been in the vicinity of Colchester early in the 18th century and to have been engaged in horticulture by at least 1724. They then continued as general nurserymen and seed growers until Benjamin Revett Cant (1827-1906) started business in what had been his grandfather's nursery in Gutter Street, Colchester (now St John's Street).

By 1858 he was 'budding' selected varieties of roses onto wild briars, taken from the hedgerow or possibly grown from seed, to give the roses vigour. This remains the proper process of propagating sturdy, quality rose trees.

This Benjamin Cant was probably the first member of the family to have actually bred roses as well as to have sold rose trees. Quite soon, if not from the very start, he was crossing various stocks and producing his own seed. Then, in 1853, there occurred what can only be described as a piece of luck.[5] While visiting France, Mr. W. Penrose, of Dedham, called to see 'old Laffay', a celebrated rose grower near Paris. He was persuaded to purchase three roses — Gloire de Dijon, Général Jaqueminot and Jules Margottin (then coming onto the market for the first time). On his return, Mr. Penrose offered these roses as a gift to Benjamin Cant who, although 'discouraged by the opinions of eminent rosarians of the day', backed his own judgment and 'got up a stock' of all three varieties. They were to become popular and started the development of 'hybrid teas', thus creating a revolution in the rose-growing world.[6]

From this time onwards Benjamin Cant devoted all his time to roses and won four silver cups at the National Rose Society's exhibition in 1858. This was all the more meritorious when one realises that he had no glasshouse; the English summer is considered too short for the production of good cultivated rose seed; and there are problems with cross-pollination. Nevertheless, using his primitive method of growing seedlings close together and leaving the rest to insects and chance, in 1875 he produced an extremely popular, rich crimson, hybrid seedling called 'Prince Arthur'.[7]

In 1879, Benjamin discarded his general nurseryman's business and, taking his sons into partnership at that time, moved to Mile End Rose Gardens. When he died in 1906 the firm had 113 acres of land upon which 300,000 roses were grown annually. The trade was both at home and abroad and included cut blooms for London florists. The story of this firm is one of continued success. Some 30,000 catalogues were distributed in the 1965-6 season and today, Benjamin's granddaughter, Miss Joan Cant, still represents the family as Chairman of the Board of Directors, which included her two nephews. (Anyone wishing to probe further into this firm's family tree will find material which may be seen on application to the firm's office at Stanway, Essex.)

John Stow, Lexden, near Colchester

John Stow is first heard of in 1748. In 1768, Morant[8] was quite carried away by the excellence of the auriculas of his successor, Henry Stow, and claimed that connoisseurs considered them 'the finest in the British Dominions, if not in all Europe, some of them having no less than one hundred and thirty-three blossoms upon one stem'.

This fame was not to last, for someone gave Henry Stow 'a fine one that had a worm in the root' which apparently infected all his stock. Nevertheless, Morant continues cheerfully that 'he has been as famous since for tulips'.

Edward and Thomas Evans (junior), Seedsmen and Gardeners, Great Coggeshall

Documents in the Essex Record Office[9] show that, by 1772, Edward and Thomas Evans were both gardeners in Coggeshall. By 1774 Thomas had a mortgage on some land. Perhaps Edward retired or had died. In any event his name does not appear in *Pigot's Directory* of 1823, whereas Thomas Evans is listed with three other gardeners and seedsmen, these latter being King and Company, David Kennet and John Russell (senior). Of the last two, nothing further appears to be known.

John Moss and Son, Kelvedon — by 1780 (?1742)

In the Kelvedon district, the first record of large-scale seed growing is that of the Moss family. In 1907 they farmed some 1,400 acres of land in the parishes of Coggeshall, Feering, Inworth, Messing, Marks Tey, Easthorpe and later at Gorwell Hall, Tollesbury.

The Victoria County History, vol. 2 (1907) describes the Moss's business as 'another old and important firm of the front rank' and then goes on to explain:

> Messrs. Moss differ from other firms noticed herein that they do no retail trade and no seed-dealing whatever, sending out only seeds grown by themselves on their own farms. The produce is sold wholesale to members of the seed trade only. Naturally, therefore, the name of the firm, large though its operations are, is little known to the general public.

Locally they are not now remembered as having been seed merchants, and it seems probable that they were farmers who grew seeds for most of the larger seed houses of their day and who were entrusted with the multiplication and perhaps the cleaning of some of these firms' more valuable stocks.[10] (It is quite possible that a little whiff of snobbery has crept in here. Miss Dorothy Taber remembers one of her aunts saying that when she and her sister were invited to stay with some friends in the seed trade at Plymouth, their hostess, wishing to make the right impression, said to them, 'Now remember to say that your father is a seed merchant, my dears. He is *not* a seed grower!'.) A large, heavy, brown leather-bound book still exists in the possession of B. A. and D. Bonner, its cover laced with thonging of a creamy-white. It shows contracts with various well-known firms between 1890 and 1895.

Sometimes they were committed to growing, and therefore preventing cross-pollination between, up to 19 different varieties of the same crop for one merchant alone. However, there were then no regulations for the isolation of seed crops and probably even the necessity for it was but dimly understood.

In a record of Great Coggeshall for 1742[11] there occurs the name 'Thomas Moss (Uplander)'. He is quite likely to be the same Thomas Moss who became established as a seed grower in approximately 1780[12] and who died at Pear Tree Hall in 1808. Was he, one wonders, also married to a girl named Eleanor and father of the poor little Ann Moss who, in 1799, is recorded in the Coggeshall church burial register as having been 'smothered in a bombey'? The vicar of that time was evidently much moved by the incident and notes furiously in the register that:

> These reeking abominations are to be found within the precincts of nearly every house in Essex, despite the warnings of Dr. Chresh and others. An ordinary cesspool is innocency itself compared to the above.

Mrs. Tom Cullen, of Witham, remembers such a name being given to pits in the garden which were used for the reception of slops and garbage. Others affirm that a 'bombey' was another name for the then usual 'loo' in the garden. But having once inadvertently stepped into one of Mrs. Tom Cullen's remembered garbage pits, I am inclined to her view! Furthermore, the late Mr. R. A. S. Rutkin, of Threshelford's Cottage, Feering, assured me that 'bombeys' were the dustbins of those days and that in winter they were liable to fill up with surface water; also that when a chemical bucket lavatory replaced the 'three-holer' the contents of the bucket was tipped therein. One cannot but agree with the vicar!

In any case, a Thomas Moss's son, John, who followed on in the seed business, was born in 1788 at Pear Tree Hall,[13] which is on the Earls Colne Road some three miles from Coggeshall village (? on the Upland).

John Moss (1788-1871/2)

This John Moss also farmed and grew seeds at Pear Tree Hall, Coggeshall, possibly until he died aged 83 years. The confusion as to the year of his death arises because both the *Victoria History of Essex* and Mr. Eric Deal maintain that he died in 1871, whereas the burial register of the United Reform Church, in Kelvedon, states that John Moss, a member of Coggeshall chapel, was buried in 1872. The date on what is probably his gravestone is too weathered to be absolutely certain but the figure looks more like a two than a one and, although there is another Moss family in Kelvedon, the grave in question is immediately adjacent to two others known to belong to the seed-growing family.

John Moss, J.P. (1826-1912)

By 1846 this John Moss appears to have been living in Feering at Old Will's Farm, built in 1450. There is a plaque in the Mission Hall on the opposite side of the road which proclaims:

> The Feering Mission was commenced in 1846 by John Moss of Old Will's Farm, holding services (for which he had to obtain a licence) in a nearby cottage, later the services were held in a room at Old Will's Farm, until his son, John William Moss, built this Mission Hall to his father's memory. His father opened the Hall on 5 October 1907 that being his 81st birthday.

Rather unusually, this Mission Hall seems to have been opened by the man whose work it commemorates. There exists a Mission Hall Record Book which contains the original licence granted by the Bishop of Rochester and various accounts of happenings such as the opening ceremony in 1907, Mrs. J. W. Moss's parties for children and the opening of the nearby Sunday School room.

Perhaps, when he married, this John moved to Threshelford's, then in the parish of Inworth. Certainly by 1853 he was interesting himself in the building of Kelvedon United Reform Church, of which he was a member and a deacon for 66 years. (Also, by 1880, he was concerned with the building of the original Sunday School room for this same church.)

His son, John William, was born in 1855 and, when he had finished school, this boy was trained as an engineer. John and John William were lucky enough to be seed growing during the boom years around the turn of the century when there was a ready market for almost all kinds of seeds. Their business thrived and it is reported[14] that, in the quarter of a century before 1901, these two trebled their turnover. One of the more unusual seeds that they grew was lavender (see pp.144-6).

8. John Moss, J.P. (1826-1912), from his 1909 Christmas card.

William Deal was foreman for John Moss. He was a large man and a prodigious walker. It is recalled that on most days he would leave Pear Tree Farm in the early hours and would walk, observing the state of the soil or the crops in the fields on his way, to arrive at Old Will's in time to receive his orders, set the men to work and return, via fields where his presence was required, before arriving back at Pear Tree Farm for breakfast. William was also a keen skittle player and, when he moved to Park Farm, Inworth, thought nothing of an evening walk to Maldon and back in order to have a game. No doubt encouraged by his master's success, in due course, William Deal decided to find a piece of land and to start up as a seedsman on his own. So began what was later to become a well-known seed firm in the district.

When William Deal left Mr. Moss his place as foreman was filled by William Wilberforce Moles, a well-remembered lay-preacher at the chapel. This man also founded a seed business and his integrity and honest dealing are spoken of to this day. Furthermore, his son and grandson still have a seed business in Stanway near Colchester.

John William Moss, J.P. (1855—22 September 1938)

Engineering remained John William's primary interest throughout his life. However, after finishing his training he joined his father in the seed business and, no doubt bursting with new ideas, proceeded to put some of his knowledge into practice on the farms. Perhaps he was friendly with Alderman Mechi, a man with similar interests. Certainly he knew Mr.

9. John William Moss, J.P. (1855-1938) with the Darby Rotary Digger and gang.

Darby, of Wickford, who had invented what in those days was a vast machine — the Darby Rotary Digger. It was experimented with on the Moss's farms.

In those days there was still a water mill (Rye Mill) on the river Blackwater at Feering. This belonged to the Mosses and was used to grind or crush all foodstuffs for their livestock. John William soon realised that the mill could also be adapted to generate sufficient electricity to drive seed-cleaning machinery in Threshelford's barn. So this was contrived, the electricity being taken thither by cable for some half mile, and many of the machines for which it was used are said to have been invented by 'Mr. William'. Acting as overseer, this young man lived at Church Farm, Feering. Here the main office of the firm was to be found and it boasted a private telephone rigged up across the fields from Threshelford's.

Although christened Mary Barbara, John William's wife was always known to her friends as Marie. Several of those who remember her confirm that she was a somewhat tall, large, pleasant woman — perhaps a trifle flashy — who almost always wore mauve, and matching make-up! (This mauve, produced from the newly-discovered aniline dyes, was probably a fashionable colour at that time.) Sadly, she had no children of her own, but both she and her husband took a great interest in the Feering Mission, the children of her husband's workmen and of others who attended Mission services. This workforce was comprised of some 110 persons, and all were obliged, if they wished to keep their jobs, to appear in chapel with their families at least once each Sunday. Parties were held for the children at Old Will's and at one there were two Christmas trees 'lavishly hung with gifts'. Perhaps it was at this party that a lady, still living in the district, received a beautiful doll. It was the only one she ever had.

It is not clear when 'Mr. and Mrs. William' moved from Church Farm to Threshelford's but Mr. A. S. Rutkin, their one-time foreman, told his son that Mr. Moss was not always 'up betimes' and that he often had to go and call beneath his bedroom window in order to obtain the key to unlock the buildings.

When work was started on the Tollesbury Light Railway (opened 1904), J. W. Moss immediately became interested and arranged for a line to be extended from Brooklands siding to serve Threshelford's Farm. In-coming trucks full of London stable manure, sprats, or five-fingers (starfish) from Tollesbury, chalk and other goods were shunted off at the siding, and out-going goods such as seeds, returned empty sacks and corn could be picked up and hauled to the main line at Kelvedon. Whatever the weather, loading and unloading could proceed without damage to the goods, as a covered bay had been built onto the end of Threshelford's barn for this purpose. Mr. R. A. S. Rutkin (son of A. S.) remembered that when a single truck was uncoupled at the siding and the weight of its load was not great, it would be given 'a good shove' by the unhooked engine to start it on its way to the farm. Then, with the help of one or two men to push, thus keeping up the momentum, the load could be got to its destination across the road to the unloading bay and barn at Threshelford's. Heavier loads were hitched to two or more horses by a special truck chain, which was strong but not heavy. They also used a brake bar on the wheel which 'could be tricky' in the hands of the uninitiated!

William Moss's engineering course must have finished a few years after 1870 when running water began to be installed upstairs.[15] Perhaps he was even taught the rudiments of plumbing. Anyway, it is remembered that Threshelford's contained a veritable 'flush of lavatories' — so many that in a wet spell the soakaway sometimes failed to cope. Early in the 20th century lavatories flushed clean with water were being installed in most 'better houses'. In the Moss establishment there were four in the house, another in the back yard for the maids, and yet another two in the garden for the gardeners. These were supplied with water from a 60-foot well over which was a windmill that operated the pump that raised it to a large concrete tank over the coach house and bootshed (now demolished). Nevertheless, despite the taps upstairs, Mr. Moss insisted that a supply of soft water from another well be brought upstairs for his use to wash himself. The concrete tank had to be relined several times and eventually became too heavy for its wooden supports. However, before this happened, Mr. William Moss put in the French doors which led from his bedroom to the coach house roof. Through these, in mild weather, he would emerge to plunge into the tank for a morning dip!

Certainly the J. W. Mosses lived in some style. They kept a butler named Gordon, a cook, Metson the head gardener with two or three assistants, one or two maids and a German groom. When Mrs. William wished to shop in Kelvedon she would order out the landau and be driven to the bottom of the High Street. Then, proceeding on foot and visiting various establishments on her way, she would arrive at the top of the hill to find the landau and groom waiting to help with the parcels and to take her home.

As was the custom in those days, the Mosses had the plan for their garden drawn up by a professional. It still hangs on B. A. Bonner's office wall at Threshelford's. Everything fashionable was included: a bridge over a waterfall; a grotto, with a sizeable pool; a fountain; a collection of rare trees and shrubs, including two kinds of nut hedges; a kitchen garden; an orchard and a vast number of many-shaped beds cut into the lawn. There must surely have been some ornamental ironwork although none now remains.

Unfortunately this thriving seed-growing business came to an end in that generation. The couple had no children, John William's eyesight was failing and its seems that they decided to retire and go to live at Tudor Lodge, Frinton-on-Sea. Working for Mr. Moss at that time were two men: J. J. Orst, the son of a Kelvedon schoolmaster, and an able secretary in the office, and a Mr. Catt, a nephew of Mr. Moss, who had married a Miss Darby (of the Darby

Digger family) and was employed as manager. Possibly at some time around 1919 these two were left in partnership having been given, or been allowed to rent, Threshelford's and Old Will's Farm respectively. The deeds of Threshelford's Cottage (formerly a pair) show that in 1919 this farm had been 'released by J. W. Moss to J. J. Orst'. There is a mystery here. No-one remembers a sale of Mr. Moss's farms (and he owned others besides these two). Furthermore, it is said that when he died he left very little money — not enough to pay out all the legacies.

In 1929 the Orst-Catt partnership broke up but each remained in his farm. It is said that Mr. Catt continued to grow seeds and to farm well for some years. 'Jo' Orst died at Rye House, Feering in 1955, by which time the branch line to Threshelford's was practically out of use. He is remembered as a jolly man who always held on to a silk cord on the door panel when being driven around in his automobile. Some children in the district thought this very funny and incorporated the practice into their games, giving it the name 'orsting'![16]

In 1931, Mrs. Moss died, aged seventy-eight. Strangely, both she and her husband were to add one more page to the history of Kelvedon and Feering. There is a plaque in the Sunday School room behind Feering Mission Hall inscribed to the effect that it was built by John William Moss in memory of his wife, who had lived not 30 yards from the site — perhaps before her marriage. In the speech which he made at the opening of this room on 29 May 1937, Mr. Moss said that he had built this Sunday School because his wife had appeared to him in a dream and told him that it was needed for the children of the parish. Upon enquiry, he had found this to be true. On the same day he opened a new Sunday School room in Kelvedon. This he had rebuilt to replace the original room put up by his father. Then on 22 September 1938, this interesting old man died.

Mears and Sorrel, Seedsmen and Nurserymen, Chelmsford — by 1793

Mears and Sorrel were established by the time *The Universal British Directory* was printed in 1793. (This is in the Guildhall Library, London. The Essex Record Office has a photocopy of the Essex section.) In 1837, documents[17] show that a seedsman's shop and dwelling house, occupied by Mr. Thomas Sorrel, Nurseryman and Seedsman, were sold. It appears then to have changed its name to Osborne and Sorrel, Seedsmen, New London Road, Chelmsford,[18] but must have disappeared with the widening of this road in 1839. However, *White's Directory* of 1848 lists among 13 Nurserymen, Seedsmen, Gardeners and Florists in Chelmsford, an Edward Sorrel, of Duke Street, Chelmsford, and Thomas and Maria Sorrel, of Conduit Street, Springfield; so possibly members of the family continued to grow seeds in and around Chelmsford until at least 1848.

William Chater, Nurseryman, Walden Common, Saffron Walden — by 1839 (?1824)

It is the name of Chater which is still quoted when hollyhocks are the topic of conversation. Nevertheless, Charles Baron preceded him in the production of semi-double hollyhocks with flowers in new shades.

Hollyhocks are seldom thought of in connection with blue dye, spinning or weaving, yet when in 1821 some 208 acres were grown on land near Flint, in Wales, and the fibre was subsequently retted, 'a blue dye not inferior to that produced by indigo was obtained'.[19]

Pigot's Directory of 1826, under the heading of Boot and Shoemakers, names Charles Baron and gives his address as The Market Place, Saffron Walden. He was clearly a gardening enthusiast who became interested in the then new method of improving plants by hybridisation. Perhaps he even talked over his experiments with William Chater, for in the *Victoria History of Essex*, vol. 2 (1907), is a statement: 'Later his experiments were continued by William Chater who carried on a general nursery business in the same town.' Of Charles

Baron it is recorded that he became a Town Councillor in 1840 and was also celebrated as a grower of ranunculus and tulips. He died on 3 January 1848.

Pigot & Company's Directory for 1824 list two Gardeners and Seedsmen in Saffron Walden but there is no mention of a Chater, nor have I come across the name until in *Pigot's Directory* of 1839, it occurs under Miscellaneous as William Chater, Nurseryman, Walden Common. However, both the *Victoria History of Essex*, vol. 2 (1907) and an advertisement for James Vert and Sons give the date 1824 as the start of this business.

In 1843 there was apparently no opposition to the removal of trees, for in a description of a walk[20] starting south-east of the Common, it says:

> and at the bridge over the Slade we pass Chater's floral and horticultural grounds — much improved, by the by, and having an abundance of light thrown onto his pleasurable pursuits by the demolition of that grove or plantation originated by Mr. Robinson, sufficiently far back in our domestic history to allow of considerable altitude among the rival trees. But the whole have fallen under the axe; and their removal has given a new appearance to this locality. There is more breathing ground and the flowers acknowledged it by their improved character and greater beauty.

I am indebted to H. C. Stacey, Town Clerk (retired) and historian of Saffron Walden for much of the information on this firm, together with the following:

> 'Mr. Robinson' was 'William', a surveyor who built The Grove (now called Eastacre) on Common Hill in 1804, north of Hatherley, the grounds of which extend southwards to the Slade (water course). Hatherley is a large house which, I believe, was built on the site of Chater's nursery, the latter extending to the east over William Robinson's grove and plantation.
>
> Common Hill East (as it used to be) was renamed Chater's Hill when the Council built some council houses to the east of Chater's nursery site. This was done on the motion of Councillor Carl Gustav Englemann (a well-known neighbouring nurseryman) in the early 1930s. He suggested the new road should be called Hollyhock Road (which was adopted) and Common Hill East renamed Chater's Hill.

Chater's first catalogue of named varieties came out in 1847. It was re-issued annually with constant additions of new forms and varieties of hollyhock until, in 1873, the hollyhock disease *Puccinia malvacaerum* devastated his nurseries and utterly destroyed many of his choicest varieties.[21]

His catalogue for Autumn 1858, *List of Superb Double Hollyhocks* (one copy of which is held by the Saffron Walden Museum and another by H. G. Stacey), shows hollyhock flower heads in the top left hand corner under a caption arranged in a half-circle 'Exhibited at the Great Exhibition, 1851', and after lengthy practical hints as to their culture there follows a long list of hollyhock varieties, together with their breeders. Most were William Chater's but one of Charles Baron's breeding still appears in this list.

An advertisement for Chater's nursery appears in the *Saffron Walden Yearbook* for 1866 and another, for 1870, is preserved in the Saffron Walden library.

For several years after the outbreak of the hollyhock disease in 1873, it is said that[22]

> It is difficult to procure a plant, either from seed, cuttings or grafts, in a fit condition for planting: hence the old method of propagating had to be discarded, both in raising plants and also in cultivation for flowering. The wintering of plants under glass for propagating had to be discarded — and the treatment of the hollyhock as a hardy plant was found to be the only method by which the disease could be combated and the raising of plants from seed the only practicable form of propagation.

By following these new methods William Chater gradually increased his supply of healthy plants and once more became renowned for his splendid hollyhocks.

William Chater was probably the largest producer of hollyhocks in the world when he died in 1885, after which Messrs. Webb and Brand took over his nursery. At this time their own offices were in East Street and they had nurseries and seed grounds in South Road.

Later they appear to have moved from the nursery by the Common to a site opposite the Cemetery, on the Radwinter Road (some two or three hundred yards to the east). In 1907, Saffron Walden was still as famous for hollyhocks as Colchester is for roses. Messrs. Webb and Brand also sold agricultural seeds and were particularly known, in this locality, for seed of a 'Selected Swede Turnip', of which they are reputed to have sold 'as much as one hundred bushels in a season'.

Chater's hollyhocks appear in the catalogues of John K. King from 1896 to 1900 as 'Chater's Superb — Twelve separate varieties — 1/-per ounce'. In 1902 there is no mention of Chater in this catalogue, but Mr. King lists three of his own selections! Evidently he had not mastered the art of keeping stocks free from disease for, from 1904 to at least 1965, this flower is always listed as Chater's stock and latterly as Gold Medal Strain.

In 1892 an advertisement, entitled Webb and Brand (late Chater), still gave the same address as in 1885 and by then they had been awarded a Royal Horticultural Society First Prize (worth £4) for 24 hollyhock heads exhibited at the Show in Newcastle-upon-Tyne in 1888.

At some time before 1924 the firm passed to James Vert. This is another case of a gardener from a large estate setting up in business on his own account, for James had been head gardener to Lord Howard de Walden until the latter's lease of Audley End Mansion expired. In 1924 an advertisement for his firm reads:

> James Vert & Sons, Established 1824, Specialists in Hollyhocks from W. Chater's original stock first grown in these nurseries 100 years ago.

Vert's Fruit Trees won the Royal Agricultural Society's Large Gold Medal in 1922. Their spring catalogue of 1926 (in the possession of L. A. W. Prior) entitled *Farm Seeds*, lists grasses, clovers, cabbages, roots and kales, but no corn. Amongst the roots is a Purple Top Swede described as '. . . a selected stock of the original variety grown for many years by the late W. Chater'.

Fred Vert (James's son) died some time in the 1930s and the business continued under Ernest Robinson, who attended to the nursery, and a Mr. Roberts whose responsibility was the office. By 1949-50 the above advertisement under the name of Vert was reduced to 'Nurserymen, Seedsmen and Florists, East Street' until finally a Mr. Ralph Downham bought the business, which was then closed down and like many another nursery ground became a site for urban development.

Chapter Four

The Kings of Coggeshall

PART I (1793-1919)

Much misunderstanding still exists as to the relationship between these two firms of King. I have therefore recorded the story in some detail, to clarify as far as possible what really happened. It is also a record of how seed merchants' catalogues developed in Essex. (Those wishing to know more about this country's early catalogues are recommended a fascinating book, *Early Gardening Catalogues* by John Harvey (Phillimore, 1972).)

As far as can be traced this country's suppliers of nursery stock, seeds and bulbs have issued catalogues for less than 300 years. The first were simple lists of available plants and seeds sent to the noble clients of a few London firms. They gave no prices. The nobility thought it ungentlemanly to mention money and it was not until after the mid-18th century that the hard-headed middle-class customer required to know the cost before purchasing. In Essex, the largest collection of early catalogues that have come to my notice are those of John K. King, which date from 1895.

John Kemp King

Regrettably, little is known of the John King who, in 1793, founded the establishment which in less than a century was to become the largest seed-growing firm of its kind in Great Britain — a claim which has been repeated without challenge in their catalogues over many years. (The *Victoria County History of Essex*, vol. 2 (1907) refers to the founder as John King and it seems possible that Kemp came into the name with his son.)

Between 1895 and 1918, the history of this firm has been built up solely from its collection of catalogues — after which there were also the Minutes of Meetings held, from which to glean. At first sight the importance of these catalogues was not obvious, and it was only after three separate searches, each time looking for something different, that I began to realise how much information they contained.

Five volumes still exist for the year 1895, one each for wholesale and retail customers; another for farmers; a gardeners' manual; and one devoted to bulbs, and from their sophistication it is clear that they are most unlikely to be the first issued by this firm. In view of this we must assume that earlier catalogues were destroyed, possibly during a move. Coupled with early Directory entries this lends weight to the supposition that the family of John (Kemp) King did not live in Coggeshall until the second or even third generation.

Directory entries

1793	*The Universal British Directory* for 1793 (which would have been prepared in 1792 or earlier) lists no seed growers in Coggeshall.
1823/4	*Pigot's*: lists no King & Company of Coggeshall.
1826	*Pigot's*: lists William and John King, of Coggeshall (Gardeners and Seedsmen).
1832	-ditto -
1839	*Pigot's*: John King, West Street (Gardener and Seedsman); William King, West Street (Gardener and Seedsman).
1845	*Post Office*: no Kings mentioned.

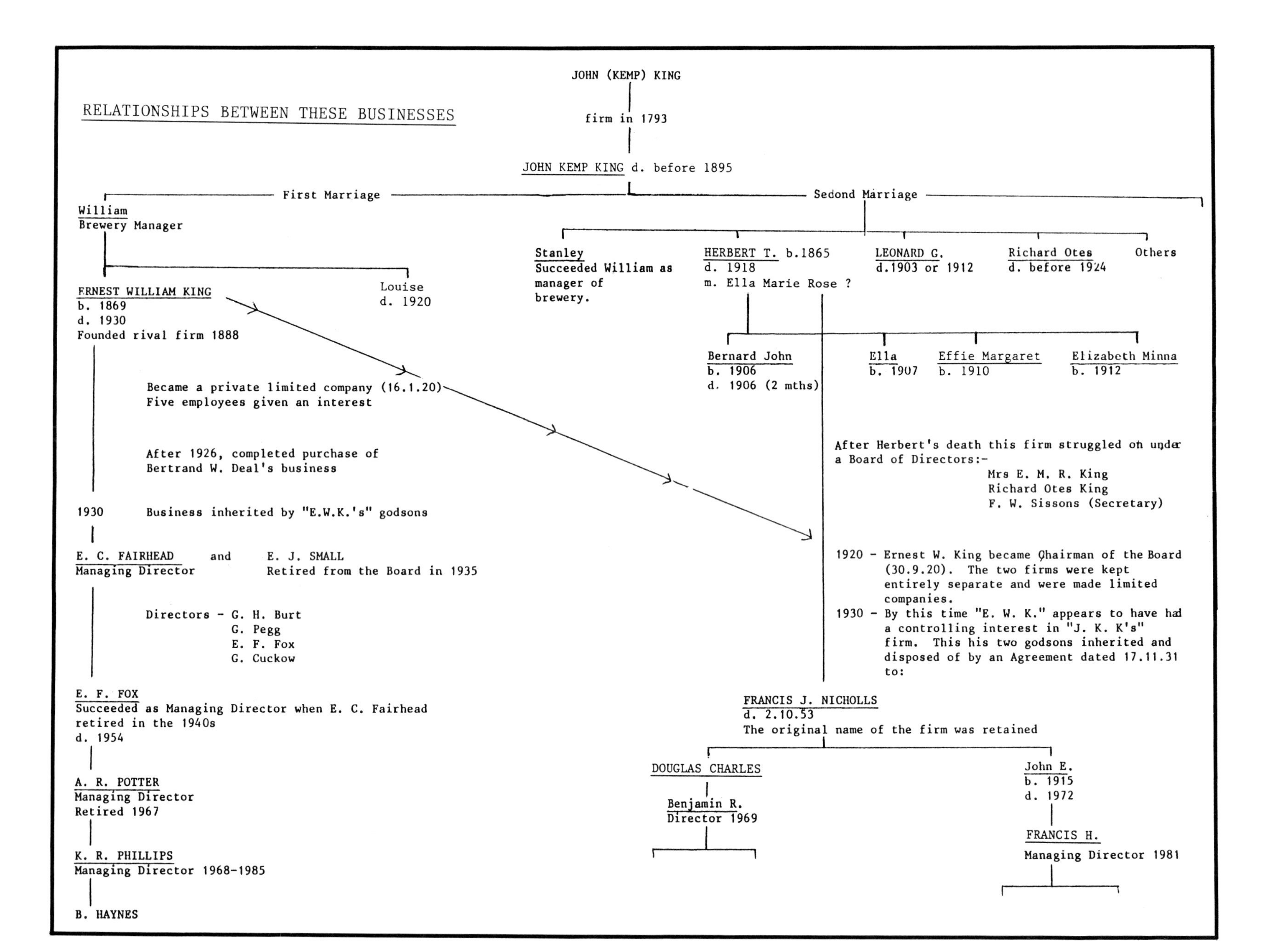
RELATIONSHIPS BETWEEN THESE BUSINESSES
JOHN (KEMP) KING
firm in 1793
JOHN KEMP KING d. before 1895
First Marriage
Sedond Marriage
William
Brewery Manager
ERNEST WILLIAM KING
b. 1869
d. 1930
Founded rival firm 1888
Louise
d. 1920
Stanley
Succeeded William as manager of brewery.
HERBERT T. b.1865
d. 1918
m. Ella Marie Rose ?
LEONARD G.
d.1903 or 1912
Richard Otes
d. before 1924
Others
Bernard John
b. 1906
d. 1906 (2 mths)
Ella
b. 1907
Effie Margaret
b. 1910
Elizabeth Minna
b. 1912
Became a private limited company (16.1.20)
Five employees given an interest
After 1926, completed purchase of
Bertrand W. Deal's business
1930
Business inherited by "E.W.K.'s" godsons
After Herbert's death this firm struggled on under
a Board of Directors:-
Mrs E. M. R. King
Richard Otes King
F. W. Sissons (Secretary)
E. C. FAIRHEAD
Managing Director
and
E. J. SMALL
Retired from the Board in 1935
1920 - Ernest W. King became Chairman of the Board (30.9.20). The two firms were kept entirely separate and were made limited companies.
1930 - By this time "E. W. K." appears to have had a controlling interest in "J. K. K's" firm. This his two godsons inherited and disposed of by an Agreement dated 17.11.31 to:
Directors - G. H. Burt
G. Pegg
E. F. Fox
G. Cuckow
E. F. FOX
Succeeded as Managing Director when E. C. Fairhead
retired in the 1940s
d. 1954
FRANCIS J. NICHOLLS
d. 2.10.53
The original name of the firm was retained
DOUGLAS CHARLES
Benjamin R.
Director 1969
John E.
b. 1915
d. 1972
FRANCIS H.
Managing Director 1981
A. R. POTTER
Managing Director
Retired 1967
K. R. PHILLIPS
Managing Director 1968-1985
B. HAYNES

1848 *White's*: John Kemp King.
1850 *Kelly's*: John Kemp King, West Street (Beer Retailer).
1855 *Post Office*: John Kemp King, Market End (*Cricketers* and Seed Grower).
1863 *White's*: John Kemp King, *The Cricketers*.
1866 *Post Office*: John Kemp King, The Gravel.
1870 *Kelly's*: John Kemp King, The Gravel (Brewer, Wine and Spirit Merchant and Seed Grower).

(The triangle of land at Market End where the B1024 road from Kelvedon meets the A120 road to the west of Coggeshall is known as 'The Gravel'. Upon it stands *The Cricketers* public house and the one-time office of J. K. King's firm.)

From these entries it looks as if John Kemp King (1848 entry) was either the son of John King (1839 entry) of West Street, Coggeshall, or possibly the son of a farmer/seed grower living elsewhere. Coggeshall may only have been Mr. King's seed outlet. There are some grounds for this supposition since neither *Bailey's British Directory* for 1784, nor the *Universal British Directory* of 1793 afford evidence of a seed industry in Coggeshall. However, the *Victoria County History of Essex*, vol. 2 (1907), lists 1,500 acres as belonging to Messrs. J. K. King, on farms in Coggeshall, Feering, Great Tey, Wakes Colne and Chappell, in any of which parishes the original John King may have lived.

One thing is certain: when the time was ripe for the founding of a wholesale seedhouse in Coggeshall, a John King grasped the opportunity and also left a son who carried on and considerably enlarged the business after his father's death. Really firm information about this son is also extraordinarily sparse. The *Coggeshall Festival Souvenir* of 1951 states he was twice married, a fact that may account for the less than friendly rivalry which arose among his grandchildren.

The situation appears as one of discord and dislike between half-brothers and perhaps (though this may be an injustice) a stepmother who wanted nothing to do with either the child or grandchildren of her husband's previous marriage. In any event, the story goes that when, on leaving school, his eldest grandson visited his grandfather to ask for a job with the firm, this was refused and the young Ernest William came away bitterly vowing that one day he would own his grandfather's business. In 1888, when he somehow acquired a small shop adjacent to his grandfather's establishment, the way up that ladder began.

John K. King's catalogues clearly indicate that from its inception, this rival firm was a festering thorn in the side of 'The Oldest and Most Extensive Seed Growing Establishment in the Kingdom'. By 1895, it had caused such annoyance that a perpetual injunction had been obtained against E. W. King by the proprietors of John K. King. Two years later, J.K. King's *Farm Manual* contained a notice, printed in red and attached to the first page, which shows that there was still confusion between the firms of King in Coggeshall; and as late as 1916, the firm of E. W. King was evidently still causing trouble, for every page of that year's catalogue had a line at the top: 'John K. King, of Coggeshall — the original firm' and, at the foot, 'Send your orders to John K. King'.

John Kemp King must have had a keen brain, capable of both understanding and applying the many new horticultural and agricultural practices that were currently in circulation. From approximately 1850 his firm had supplied seeds for the Prince of Wales's farms at Sandringham in Norfolk. The Royal Warrant was received in 1885 when the firm became 'Seedsmen to His Royal Highness, the Prince of Wales'. As this warrant was made out in the names of Herbert T. King and Leonard G. King, we can assume that by this date John Kemp King, son of the founder, had taken two of his sons into the business and retired. When he died is not clear, but it must have been before 1895 because the firm's retail catalogue for that year refers to 'the late John K. King'. However, this same catalogue also

IMPORTANT CAUTION.

A Perpetual Injunction

OBTAINED.

HERBERT T. KING and LEONARD G. KING

the present Proprietors of the Old-established Seed Growing Business of JOHN K. KING, of Coggeshall, Essex, (which was founded in 1793), obtained on the 18th of January, 1895, from the High Court of Justice, Chancery Division, a ***Perpetual Injunction*** against E. W. KING & Co., of Coggeshall, Essex, in the following terms:—

In the HIGH COURT OF JUSTICE, Chancery Division.

Mr. JUSTICE CHITTY at Chambers,

FRIDAY, the 18th day of JANUARY, 1895,

between

HERBERT THOMAS KING

AND

LEONARD GEORGE KING,

TRADING AS

JOHN K. KING, — *Plaintiffs.*

AND

E. W. KING & Co.

AND

WILLIAM KING, — *Defendants.*

"Upon the application of the Plaintiffs, and upon hearing the Solicitors for the Applicants and for the Defendants, and the Plaintiffs and Defendants by their Solicitors consenting to this Order. It is by consent ***ordered*** that the Defendants, E. W. KING & Co. and WILLIAM KING, and each of them, their respective Servants and Agents, be hereby **perpetually restrained** from representing or making statements calculated to mislead and deceive persons into believing that they or one of them are the Plaintiffs' Firm of JOHN KEMP KING, or are connected therewith, or that they or one of them, and not the Plaintiffs, are the Successors in Business to, and carry on the Old-established Business of JOHN KEMP KING, Seed Grower, Coggeshall, or from selling or advertising or offering for sale any Seeds, Roots, or other Agricultural Produce as the Seeds, Roots, or Agricultural Produce belonging to, or grown by, the Plaintiffs' Firm, or the Old-established Business of JOHN KEMP KING, and also from publishing, issuing, selling, or circulating any Catalogues, Prints, Wrappers, Circulars, Labels, or Advertisements, of such a shape, form of appearance, or with such contents as to be copies of, or colourable imitations of, the like ones issued or published by the Plaintiffs' Firm, or calculated to deceive or mislead people into the belief that they are so issued by the Plaintiffs' Firm, and it is ***ordered*** that the Defendant Firm of E. W. KING & Co. do deliver up to be cancelled, all copies of the same which are now in their possession, or in the possession of their Servants, or Agents, and of all Blocks, Plates, and other Materials by which the same are produced."

SPECIAL NOTICE.

The "ESSEX PRIZE WINNER MANGEL," which has obtained such phenomenal success, is only sold by **JOHN K. KING**, Seed Grower, Coggeshall.

In respect of the name "ESSEX PRIZE WINNER MANGEL," the following undertaking has been given by ERNEST WILLIAM KING to JOHN K. KING'S Solicitors:—

To Messrs. PEACOCK & GODDARD.

We hereby undertake that we will not use the word "Essex" in connection with the word "Prize Winner" in the future issue of our Catalogues, nor supply Seed under the description of "Essex Prize Winner."

Dated this 25th day of March, 1899.

(Signed) **ERNEST WILLIAM KING,**

TRADING AS

E. W. KING & Co.

10. 'A Perpetual Injuction.'

H.R.H. THE PRINCE OF WALES'

SEEDSMAN BY ROYAL FAVOUR.

Mr John K King

You are hereby appointed

Seedsman

to His Royal Highness The Prince of Wales.

Given under my hand and seal at Marlborough House, this Ninth day of June 1885

D. M. Probyn. Lt Genl
Comptroller

This Warrant is granted to Mr Herbert J. King and Mr Leonard G. King personally trading under the Firm of Mr John K. King and is to be returned to the Comptroller of the Prince of Wales's Household, on the event of any change taking place in the Firm from death, retirement, or other cause.

OFFICIAL SEAL

11. The Royal Warrant of 1885.

12. 'A blank space was an anathema.'

infers that the deceased John K. King was the founder of the firm, and this must surely be a mistake, since grandfather is mentioned as the founder (1793) in the catalogue of 1908.

Looking through the early Catalogues 1895-1899

By 1894, this firm's trade had increased so much that more accommodation was necessary and the, by then disused, silk mill (with its chimney) was purchased and incorporated into the Orchard House and garden complex. The earliest catalogue that still exists (January 1895) gives details of this on its introductory page.

In the Victorian and Edwardian eras it is very apparent that a blank space was an anathema, every page had to be filled, sometimes even to the extent of being surrounded with scrolls and little decorative patterns and once with the Prince of Wales's feathers in each corner and the Royal Arms at the top. Illustrations in the form of drawings, artists' impressions, engravings and photographs (for this firm all black and white until 1900), even when fanciful or wildly inaccurate provide enormous interest and a window onto another age. Their practical value is a record (perhaps the only one) of corn, vegetable and flower seed varieties which have long since passed into oblivion. (I have been told that, at this date, those wishing for an illustration might be offered a choice from those already in the printer's stock, thus cutting the cost. This practice could account for some of the pictures in catalogues which do not accurately portray the premises of the seedsman in question.)

Most of the documents provide prices and sometimes there is quite detailed cultural advice, including ways of combating diseases and pests, which are often no less mistakenly ineffective, and on occasion dangerous, than those in the earliest gardening books.

January 1895 — Wholesale Seed List

This 20-page volume lists 14 'Specialities introduced by John K. King' and described as 'invaluable for exhibition purposes'. (It was the day of large national and innumerable smaller local shows.)

As well as all kinds of seeds for the wholesalers there were, for the retail trade, 'Illustrated Seed Envelopes' costing:

Filled: with a Penny Retail Pack of Seed, 6d. per dozen; 5/6 per gross. Not less than one dozen of each sort supplied.
Empty: Per 100, 1s.; per 1000, 9s. Not less than 100 of each sort supplied.

This notice was followed by a list of 113 sorts which were kept in stock and 'A handsome coloured show card' was sent with all general orders.

Pictorial Pockets were available for the display of vegetable seeds together with 'Show Cards of Pictorial Vegetable Seed Pockets showing thirty-nine varieties'. These latter were of varnished paper and cost 6d. each. Also offered were 'Everlasting Flowers, Grasses, Wreaths and Bouquet Papers', together with 'Seed Bags, well made and of strong, brown glazed paper' and 'Seed Pockets, well gummed, buff cartridge paper, plain'.

Sweet Peas. At this date only four kinds were available: Mixed, Scarlet Invincible, White Invincible, Everlasting — Red; but the *auricula*, the cultivation of which has been associated with the Huguenot weavers, had reached the height of its popularity by the mid-19th century. It is listed as being a 'Show Strain'. For many decades this flower had a devoted following among factory workers who became very skilled in its cultivation and were able to lavish upon it the care and attention to which it reponds. The auricula shows were usually held at inns, but Thomas Wood, a miller in Billericay, advertised in the local press in April 1776:[1]

13. The premises after the purchase of the silk mill, *c.*1894.

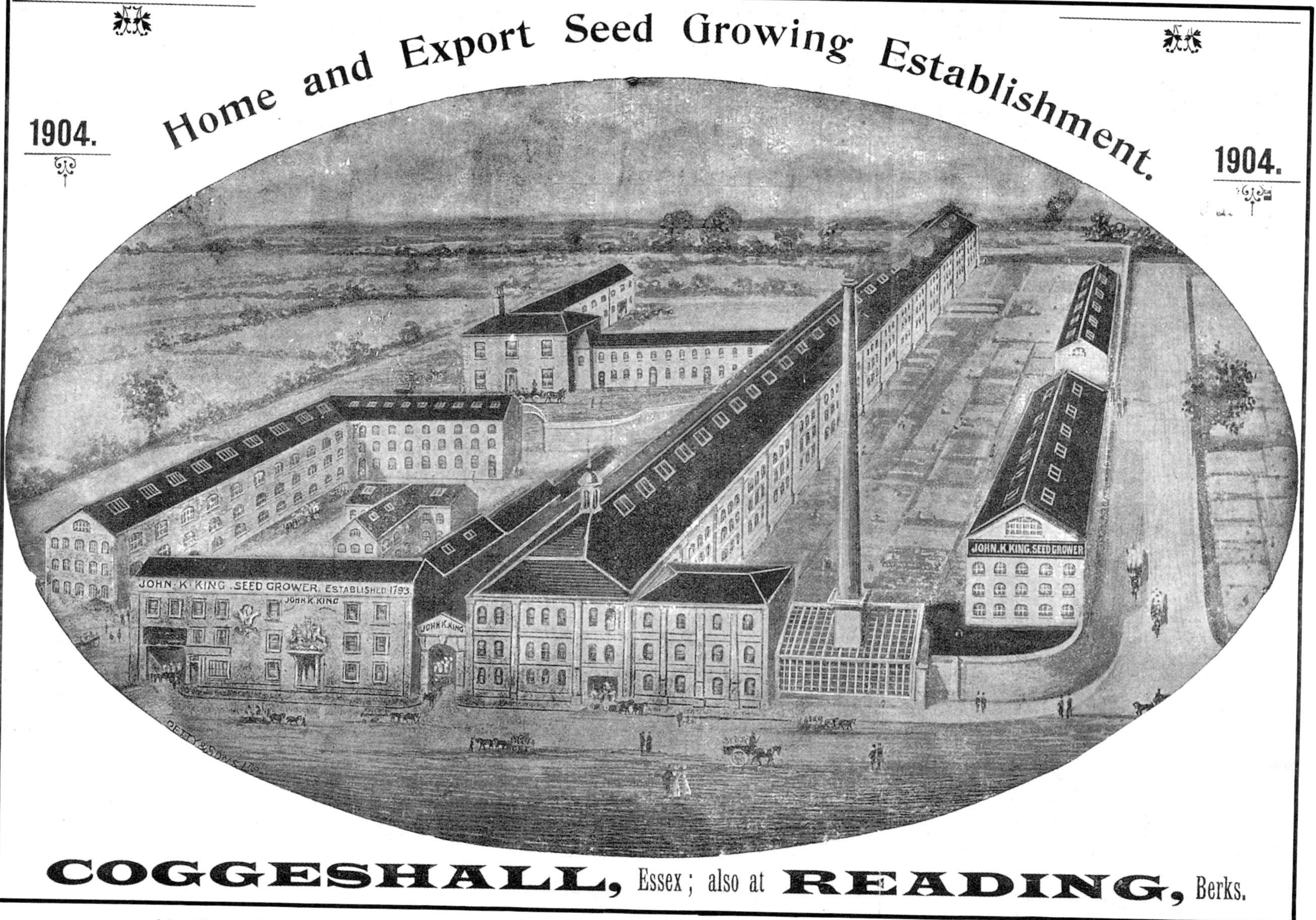

14. 'Even when fanciful or wildly inaccurate.' This illustration seems to have been used in catalogues from 1901 onwards.

15. V.R. post van delivering John K. King's seeds.

> Billericay Mills. The beautiful Show of auriculas will be on the Stage on Thursday the 18th instant. Gentlemen are desired not to bring dogs.

There were also eight varieties of *palm seeds*, with many other varieties available, as well as 16 sorts of *fern seeds*, with often more than one variety of each.

Under insecticides, weed destroyers, etc. there appears:

> *King's Weed Destroyer* A preparation for destroying Daisies and other offensive weeds on Grass Lawns of every kind.
>
> There is nothing injurious in the Weed Destroyer; consequently it will not injure birds, nor anything except the weeds it is intended to exterminate; moreover, it has no objectionable smell and will keep any length of time. In cases where the weeds are not entirely killed by the first application, a second dressing will always be found effectual.

Seven pounds cost 1s. 9d. to the trade and 2s. 6d. retail, 112lbs. cost 17s. 6d. to the trade and 30s. 0d. retail.

Also listed were such items as:

> Beetle Powder, Fir Tree Oil, Flowers of Sulphur, Fowler's Insecticide, various brands of Fumigators, Gishurst Compound, Grafting Wax, Hellebore Powder, Mealy Bug Destroyer, Nicotine Soap, Quassia chips, Styptic, Tobacco:— cloth, powder, paper (Scotch) and Liquor (strong).

The wholesale terms of business show that the problems with accounts were much the same 100 years ago as today. A discount of five per cent was allowed on all accounts settled within one month of the invoice date and interest was charged on overdue accounts. Sacks and bags were only allowed for if returned in good condition within one month from the date of invoice.

In the case of retail customers, payments had to be made within 14 days of invoice to attract a five per cent discount and references were required from new customers. Orders

16. A 1901 memo head, showing the London and Reading offices.

over £1 would be sent carriage paid to any railway station in England and Wales. An order for £2 was required to attract this concession when goods had to be sent to Scotland or Ireland. Furthermore, seed samples would be sent on request.

As yet, there was no telephone and urgent business was all done by telegram, the telegraphic address being 'Seedsmen Coggeshall'. Code words representing words and numbers were introduced to reduce expense. A telegram to John K. King saying 'Enquire instanter Harvest sensitive, Heedless Magnificent, Harrow Pad' decoded would mean 'Quote lowest immediately 400 bushels King's Unrivalled Swede, 100 cwt. King's Prize Winner Globe Mangel, 150 bushels American Wonder Pea'.

'Unrivalled Seeds for 1895' — The Retail list for Growers

A reticent modesty was not a virtue much in evidence among the Victorians, particularly those in trade. The thing was to be a keen man of affairs ever seeking information which might be turned to advantage, extracting every ounce from the work force and ever on the alert for chances to score off a rival. Absolutely every opportunity was seized upon to promote their business and almost no claims were considered too extravagant. So, as may be imagined, as this was the year of the Royal Warrant, both in this and the bulb catalogue for 1895 every conceivable space was filled by the Royal Arms as well as the feathers and motto of the Prince of Wales. (The warrant is dated 1885 but, so far as is known, it is not until the 1895 catalogue that it is particularly featured.)

This catalogue contained a full section on grasses with many beautiful engravings as well as botanical notes on their use.

The first mention by this firm of the useful little pamphlets known as 'Advisory Leaflets', and which continue to be produced by what is now the Ministry of Agriculture, Fisheries and Food, says:

> Until the Board of Agriculture was formed [1793] little was known of the causes of plants 'going off' in the initial stages.

Seed firms also acted as a labour exchange for in the *Bulb Catalogue* of 1895 is a notice to:

> GARDENERS, STEWARDS AND FORESTERS
> I have always on my registers men thoroughly qualified for the duties of GARDENER, LAND STEWARD, or FORESTER, and any Nobleman or Gentleman requiring such may rely on my recommending only those whose qualifications are worthy of confidence.

This was well worth the trouble, for at this time gardeners' wages were at a very low ebb and a seedsman who could recommend a man for a better position would undoubtedly have had his seeds praised to the employer.

The Seed Manual, 1895 — the gardeners' lists

In this volume there is a clear indication that the owners of smaller gardens are being courted by the trade. A competition was arranged for the best collection of vegetables grown from John K. King's seeds. Entries had to arrive by 15 August 1896, and carriage was to be paid by the firm. Seed labels had to accompany every entry and there was a £5 prize to be won.

The 1896 Catalogues

This year the Reading branch, at 6 Blagrave Street, opened under the management of Mr. J. H. Millard, who had previously been with Sutton's and may have provided King's with grassland expertise. *Cos Lettuce* A cultural note advises tying them up loosely, on a dry day, with matting (a type of string) from the top downwards to keep them in good shape.

In the same catalogue is a picture of King's 'Prolific' Cucumbers. These are of such

John K. King's "Royal Sovereign"

MARROW PEA.

AWARDED FIRST-CLASS CERTIFICATE BY THE ROYAL HORTICULTURAL SOCIETY.

I recommend this Pea as pre-eminently suitable for Market Gardening purposes, not only on account of its following closely on the earliest kinds, but for its enormous productiveness and splendid deep green colour. The pods, which are very large, are produced in pairs, and closely filled with from 9 to 11 grand Peas of splendid quality. It travels well, and may be sown with advantage for latest crops. Height 3½ feet.

Per quart, 1/6 Per peck, 8/6 Per bushel, 30/-

JOHN K. KING,

Seedsman to H.M. the Queen and by Special Sealed Warrant to H.R.H. the Prince of Wales,

. . . . . **THE ROYAL SEED ESTABLISHMENTS** . . . . .

COGGESHALL, ESSEX, and READING, BERKS.

Also LONDON, PARIS, and WINNIPEG, Canada.

17. An R.H.S. first class certificate for John K. King's 'Royal Sovereign' marrow pea.

extraordinary straightness that they appear to have been produced by artificial means. Pilkington's Glass Company handmade at about this time some cucumber straighteners for the firm of Clucas, of Ormskirk. One of these has been preserved by Mr. Derek Bonner, of Coggeshall Hall. Similar devices seem to have been in use from at least 1597 as evidenced by John Gerard's *Herball.*

The 1897 Catalogues

Various testimonials indicate that by now the firm was very much 'in' with the gardeners and managers of several well-known estates. They had received a Royal Horticultural Society's First-Class Certificate for their Royal Sovereign marrow fat pea and been allowed to print a three-quarter length portrait of Queen Victoria on the inside back cover of their *Market Growers' Catalogue.* There were by that time also branches at 16 Liverpool Street, E.C.1; in Paris; and in Winnipeg, Canada (more probably, the foreign branches were simple agencies).

The transition of sailing ships to steam is illustrated by a lively picture in the Wholesale Catalogue.

The Farm Manual of February 1897 contains accounts of the firm's displays of roots, seeds and grasses at the Norwich, and Smithfield Club Cattle Shows which had appeared in no less than six newspapers: the *Mark Lane Express* and *The Agricultural Gazette, The Estates' Gazette, The East Anglian Daily Times,* and *The Norfolk Chronicle* and *Norfolk Daily Standard.* There is also a full page photograph of their stand at Norwich which, that year, had been visited by 'no less a personage than H.R.H. The Duke of York, K.G.'

During Victorian times local authority gardening, which provided places for recreation in towns, came into vogue. Miles Hadfield writes that:

> Public spirited owners of family mansions who wished to move further from the city often presented their houses and parks to the Local Authority for use of the citizens.

John K. King's firm very early saw the possibilities here, as witness the next page of their catalogue: 'ANOTHER ROYAL HONOUR . . . Her Majesty's First Commissioner of Works', had entrusted the firm with the order 'for supplying the whole of the grass seeds for sowing the Royal Parks in 1897'.

The grass ley mixtures offered to farmers were, by today's standards, made up of a too numerous and complicated collection of seeds. There were permanent mixtures for Heavy Clays, Rich Deep Loams, Medium Loams and Light Loams, as well as for Brashy Soils on Chalk or Limestone and for Sheep Downs, and all for between 14s. and 25s. per acre.

Mixtures for temporary pastures for six, eight or 10 years' duration cost 11s. 6s. an acre. There followed a note from John K. King which indicated the state of agriculture at the time:

> I was among the first to advocate the laying down of land to Temporary Pasture on the three-fold grounds:
>
> 1. As a measure of relief to landlords who, in consequence of the great agricultural depression, have farms on hand.
> 2. As a means of retaining the fertility of the soil.
> 3. As a profitable reservation in the event of a sudden rise in the price of wheat necessitating the land being put again under corn.

Lucerne, which had received brief mention in 1895, was now allotted three-quarters of a page and there is also a picture of the *New Aspinwall Potato Planter,* with fertiliser attachment, which we are informed 'does the work of ten men'. Its price:

with plain or disc coverers . . .	£15 carriage paid
with fertilizer attachment and plain or disc coverers	£17 10s. 0d. ditto

18. John K. King's display stand at Smithfield Cattle Show, 1909.

19. John K. King's display stand at a Royal Agricultural Society Show at Norwich in 1911.

FAMOUS FOR 108 YEARS.

Separate Natural Grass Seeds.

GERMINATION AND PURITY GUARANTEED.

My Natural Grass Seeds are of the finest quality and have been carefully cleaned by my new and improved machinery. I sell them under a Guarantee as to Purity, Cleanliness, and percentage of growth, as recommended by the Royal Agricultural Society of England.

A corner in one of John K. King's Grass Seed Floors.

Special Notice.

John K. King has been honoured with commands from His Majesty's First Commissioner of Works to supply the whole of the Grass Seeds for sowing the Royal Parks this year. John K. King received similar orders in 1897, 1899, and 1900.

BOTANICAL NAME.	ENGLISH NAME.	Guar'n'd per cent. of gro'th.	Per lb.	Per cwt.
		PER CENT.		
ACHILLEA MILLEFOLIA - -	Yarrow - - - - -	80	4/6 to 5/6	—
AGROSTIS ALBA var. STOLONIFERA	Creeping Bent Grass, Fiorin	90	10d	90/-
ALOPECURUS PRATENSIS - -	Meadow Foxtail - -	70·80	1/- to 1/2	105/- to 120/-
AMMOPHILA ARUNDINACEA - -	Sea Reed or Mat Grass -	80·90	1/3	130/-
ANTHOXANTHUM ODORATUM -	Sweet-scented Vernal scarce	60·70	4/-	—
AVENA FLAVESCENS - - -	Golden Oat Grass, scarce	65·70	4/-	—
CYNOSURUS CRISTATUS - -	Crested Dogstail, scarce -	90·95	1/9 to 2/3	—
DACTYLIS GLOMERATA - -	Cocksfoot or Orchard Grass	85·90	9d to 1/-	80/- to 105/-
ELYMUS ARENARIUS - -	Sand or Upright Sea Lyme Grass - - - - -	80·90	1/6	150/-
FESTUCA OVINA TENUIFOLIA -	Fine Leaved Sheep's Fescue	60·70	1/6	150/-
FESTUCA OVINA - - -	Tall Sheep's Fescue - -	85·95	10d to 1/-	90/- to 105/-
FESTUCA ELATIOR - - -	Tall Fescue - - -	90·95	1/- to 1/3	105/- to 130/-
FESTUCA DURIUSCULA - -	Hard Fescue - - -	85·95	9d to 11d	80/- to 95/-
FESTUCA PRATENSIS - -	Meadow Fescue - -	90·95	10d to 1/-	90/- to 105/-
FESTUCA RUBRA - - -	Red Fescue - - -	80·85	9d	80/-
PHLEUM PRATENSE - - -	Meadow Catstail or Timothy	95·100	5d to 7d	42/- to 60/-
POA NEMORALIS - - -	Wood Meadow Grass -	70·80	1/2 to 1/6	120/- to 150/-
POA PRATENSIS - - -	Smooth-stalked Meadow Grass - - - -	70·80	9d to 1/-	80/- to 105/-
POA TRIVIALIS - - -	Rough-stalked Meadow Grass - - -	80·90	1/2 to 1/4	120/- to 140/-

SPECIAL PRICES PER TON ON APPLICATION.

JOHN K. KING, THE ROYAL SEED GROWER, **COGGESHALL,** ESSEX, and **READING,** BERKS.

20. The grass ley mixtures were, by today's standards, too numerous and complicated a collection of seeds.

The *Bulb Catalogue* was now entitled 'Royal Bulbs' and it was claimed that John K. King's 'Favourite Bird Seed', priced 1d., 2d., 3d. and 4d. a box was then being sold by 'Grocers, Corn Merchants, and Store Keepers throughout the world'.

In 1899, John Kemp King described himself as 'wholesale and export seedgrower'; his firm had added a branch office on Wall Street, New York; and there was another order for grass seeds for the Royal Parks. In the *Gardening Manual*, several pages are devoted to the cultivation of vegetables, on one of which some 47 varieties of potato are said to be 'Disease-proof'! However, if the potato information is somewhat suspect, their instructions for making and maintaining a lawn is still, on most points, remarkably sound. The history of culinary peas in Great Britain has not yet been published in any great detail and so an observation referring to garden peas that 'of late years a very great improvement has been made in this most useful vegetable, especially as regards earliness, cropping properties and flavour' is worth recording.

Sweet Peas were gaining more prominence but the frilly-edged Countess Spencer had not yet been found. The bird seed was, of course, by then renamed Royal Favourite. The black and white flower illustrations are particularly good and lists give the name, price per packet, hardiness and duration (for example h.h.p. = half-hardy perennial) as well as colour, height and remarks for each item.

His Royal Victorian Era Boxes of seeds, one containing 16 kinds of flowers and the other containing 30 varieties of vegetables were an attraction for the retailers.

At this stage the *Manual* almost became a Gardeners' Guide with articles written on various subjects by well-known authorities.

John Kemp King was not only selling to the wholesale trade but also had retail customers and claimed that by selling direct from his farms he was able to charge twenty-five to fifty per cent less. There was also an engraving of a seed shop, showing seed bins, drawers, packets and glass cases together with customers in frock coats — a veritable Harrod's of a seed shop.

1900-1920

Surviving stories of John Kemp King closely follow those from other firms' employees. Today, for better or worse, there is little control of staff and certainly none outside working hours. Then, if any of J. K. King's work force patronised a public house in Coggeshall other than his own, *The Cricketers*, they were severely reprimanded and even in danger of dismissal. Needless to say, employees of E. W. King drank in the nearby *Porto Bello*. On Mondays and Fridays work started at 6 a.m. and finished at 5 p.m. and on Saturdays they generally finished by noon. Anyone arriving late would find the gates shut and had to wait outside until they opened again for breakfast break at 8 a.m. Then, according to Mr. Percy Rayner, a former employee, 'they had to go on the carpet'.

In company with most seedsmen of his day, J. K. King seldom bred an entirely new variety. He was a prolific and evidently gifted selector of plants which took his eye in his own and other people's crops. These he would grow on for a few years, each season 'roguing out' any plants considered unworthy of further trial. Once satisfied that he had found a reasonably stable and good stock, the combined seeds from the remaining plants, the 'mother' seed, would be multiplied up on his own farms or on chosen fields of farmers who could be relied upon to do a good job. The practice continues today. It could easily be eight, 10 or more years before there was sufficient seed to be offered for sale in his catalogue and always there was the fear that some adverse genes would appear — perhaps even in the last year of trial. This would necessitate still further years of careful work to breed it out, or another hopeful line having to be put on the scrap heap. Reader, do not grudge the price asked if the seed be good.

JOHN KEMP KING'S Wholesale Catalogue of Vegetable and Flower Seeds for 1899.

The Royal Victorian Era

BOXES OF Unrivalled Seeds.

Box No. 1.

Box No. 2.

FAC-SIMILES OF BOXES FROM PHOTOGRAPHS.

21. Boxes of seeds for display in shops.

22. 'A veritable Harrods of a seed shop.'

After John K. King's death, his son Herbert took control of the business. Somehow one senses that the hand on the tiller was no longer that of a practical grower, with an eye for a good plant. Some of the keen business acumen was still there but we now had a man who had been educated at Sir Robert Hitcham's School in Coggeshall; a keen player of football and cricket; a parish councillor; a church sidesman and a proprietor of his firm who regularly attended Mark Lane and who would emerge to greet and exchange pleasantries with parties of visitors but, it seems, seldom made time to be with them in the fields or on trial grounds.

Hitherto publicity had been almost entirely dependent upon the catalogues. This was now backed up by demonstration in the form of visits from various groups of interested people from this country and abroad, who came to see the trial grounds and hear about 'J. K. K.'s' method of 'Pedigree Breeding'. They also gained publicity by their support of Horticultural and Agricultural Shows, with exhibits and prizes as well as an almost premeditated opportunism in that, at shows where there was to be a visit from someone of particular note, they invariably had a new variety on their stand. If, by happy chance, the new introduction was admired by the visitor it would, of course, be found to be just waiting for a suitable name! So, when the King visited their stand at the Royal Show held at Norwich in 1912, a sweet pea received the name 'Prince Edward of Wales'. At the National Sweet Pea Society's Show in 1927, E. W. King did the same thing when the cricketer Jack

Hobbs, visited his stand and on that occasion there was even another new variety for Mrs. Hobbs.

After 1906 increasing emphasis was placed on selections of cereal, root and other agricultural seeds. Indeed, the winning sack of Chevallier barley, which they had purchased after it had won the World Championship at the Brewers' Exhibition of 1897, remained a leading line in one or another of King's selections until 1932. Surely this must be a record for the popularity of a barley variety. (See Appendix D.)

The Increasing Demand for Seeds of Fodder Roots

In the 19th and early 20th centuries root crops became a considerable feature of Essex seed growing and merchanting and, for many years, they figured prominently in farm seed catalogues. Therefore, it is worth discussing how and when a demand for these seeds arose and the part they played in the history of John K. King and Company will serve as an example of the many firms who, in varying degree, have dealt in these seeds.

Turnips (*Brassica napus*)

In England, turnips appear to have been the first root crop grown to feed cattle and, for a number of years, to have remained the complete answer to the winter feeding problem for this hitherto grossly underfed class of animal. During the 17th century, although in Holland better types had already been found and were being extensively used for this purpose, still only a few crops were recorded in this country and these were for sheep folding.

The writings of Sir Hugh Weston who, around 1644, was living in Holland and observing their ways, aroused some interest in the crop. About the same time, Sir Hugh Platt was also advocating roots as food for cattle in winter. By 1722, Daniel Defoe[2] noted that turnips were extensively cultivated in England and very suitable as cattle food. However, one of the earliest references in agricultural literature to turnips for cattle, occurs in 1723[3] and the writer says, 'raw turnips chopt or whole, are given by some' which hardly indicates extensive cultivation. Nevertheless, the undoubted benefits of the crop were such that it could no longer be ignored and after Lord Townshend started to grow and enthusiastically to promote this root, the acreage considerably increased.

23. 'This Grand Turnip is acknowledged to be the handsomest and best stock of Imperial Green Globe Turnip in the Trade.' It was advertised in 1899 at 5d. to 9d. per pound.

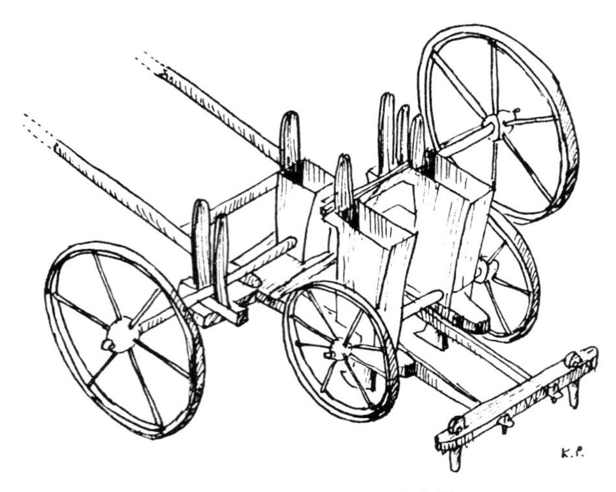

24. Jethro Tull's seed drill.

It was not only useful as animal feed. Selected varieties were required by the greengrocers of London and the larger towns, and seeds were needed for kitchen gardens. It became popular as a 'break' crop and once Jethro Tull's drill came into use, as a 'cleaning' crop also, for the crop could then be sown in rows and so could be horse-hoed frequently. This not only benefited the immediate crop but, by freeing the land of many weeds, it also lengthened the time before the need for a fallow year. Yet again, when folded off, this crop provided an excellent preparation for wheat because of the manure dropped by the sheep while grazing and the possibility of an early ploughing of the field. Even this was not the final virtue. Crops 'to improve the land' were coming into favour; the practice of 'green manuring' was being advised and what better for ploughing in than a thriving crop of tennis-ball-sized turnips complete with their abundantly leafy tops?

Seemingly, the market for turnip seed knew no bounds for, by the 19th century, trade with our colonies was also building up and contracts were proliferating in all the seed-growing areas. At that time there was no seed zoning legislation. Matters of cross-pollination would, if worried about at all, have been settled more or less amicably by mutual agreement between the growers, merchants and owners of any garden plots nearby. For quite a long time turnips remained the sole root crop grown for animals in this country, but gradually their undoubted success led to ventures into the growing of other roots for this purpose.

Swedes, formerly called Swede Turnips

Although some form of swede is said to have been in this country for hundreds of years it seems that it was not until 1755 that seed of an improved variety was imported from Holland for use on our farms. This root has the advantage of a better feeding value and of withstanding storage for a longer period than the turnip. Therefore, it fits in nicely for cattle feeding in the after-Christmas period. It is better adapted to the cooler and more moist conditions in the north and south-west of Great Britain. A check by drought often results in an attack by mildew so, in the eastern counties, where spring drought is often severe, swedes are not much favoured. Perhaps this accounts for many seed firms having contracted for their swede seed to be grown in Holland where, if drought conditions arise, the physical properties of many of their soils allow control of the water table and they therefore have a greater chance of producing a satisfactory crop.

Kohl Rabi (*Brassica oleracea canlo-rapa*) or Turnip-Rooted Cabbage

Grown mainly in the eastern and south-eastern counties of England, as a replacement for swedes. It has an ability to withstand both drought and frost, so is seldom harmed by mildew and may be left longer in the ground than the swede.

Mangel Wurzel

The introduction of this root into Great Britain was at least partly due to a mistranslation of its original German name.[4]

25. 'The heaviest cropping oval shaped Swede in cultivation, and has yielded over 50 tons per acre.'

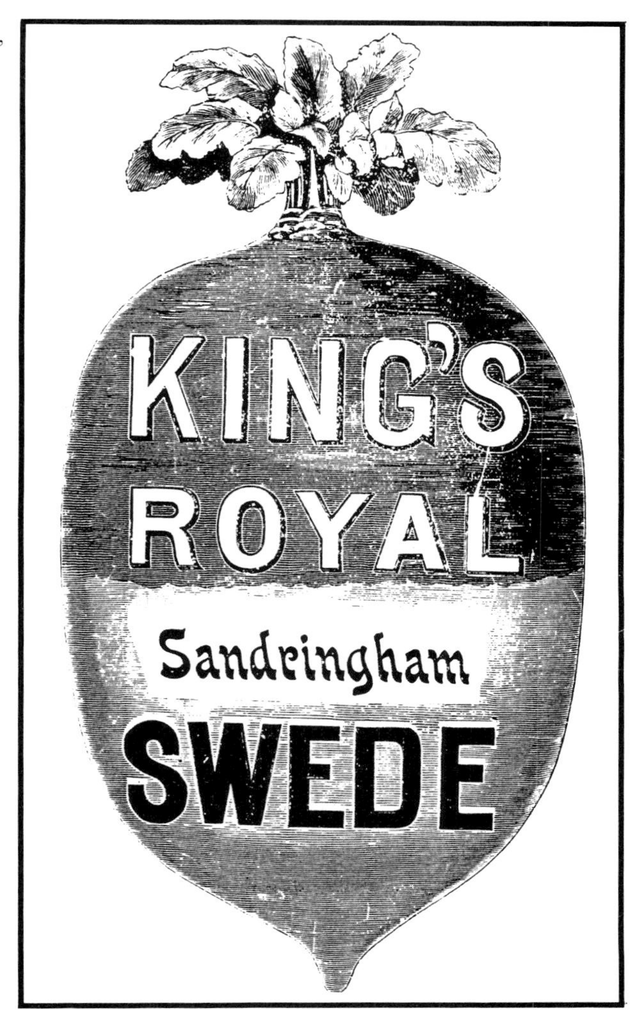

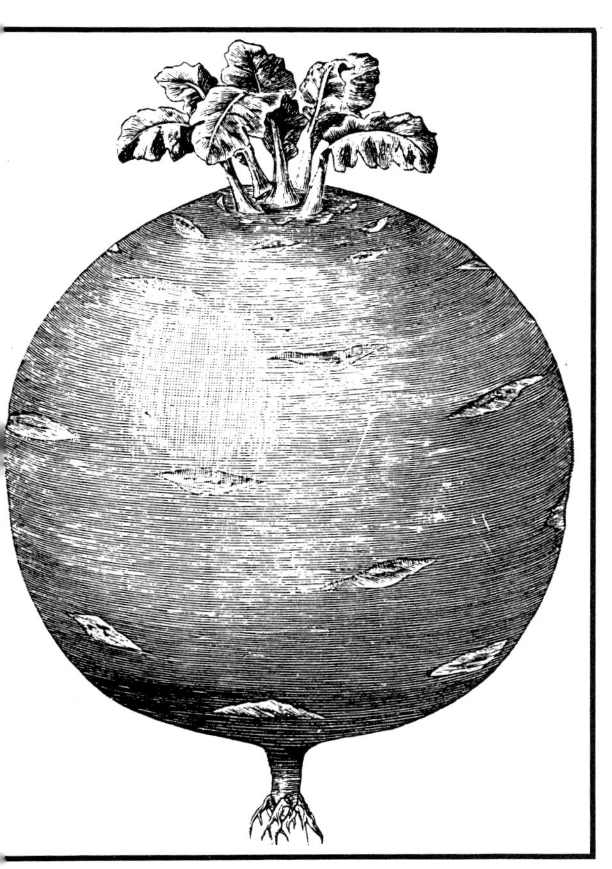

26. John K. King's Kohl Rabi: 'a splendid drought-resisting root'.

27. 'Grown on the farms of H.R.H. The Prince of Wales.' Price 9d. per lb. or 75s. per cwt.

In North Germany and Holland a cultivated variety of the sea-beet (*Beta maritima*) had been grown for a century or more under the name 'mangold wurzel' or, in our language, beet root. This crop spread to France where, in the 'terrible eighties', it was often the only food available to the half-starved peasants. Confusion between the German words 'mangold' (beet) and 'mangel' (dearth) led to the French giving the root what was thought to be a French equivalent of its German name (i.e. 'racine de disette' — root of the needy). There were periods of dearth in England in the latter part of the 18th century and it was suggested that this crop should be grown to provide cheap food for the hungry. At a meeting of the Society of Arts a letter was read on the virtues of 'racine de disette' and seed was distributed for trial.[5] Mistakenly, the seed supplied from Germany was that of the 'mangel' (cattle food) and not the 'mangold wurzel' (beet root) and so the resulting crops were pronounced more fit for animals than for men.

Even for animal food it was some time before mangels became popular in England. However, by early in the 19th century they were being grown fairly extensively and perhaps the root competitions, held by many seed firms, were first instituted as an incentive for the adoption of this crop.

It is probable that root crops were amongst the first seeds to be grown for sale by the original John King. The first catalogue record of his firm having supplied these seeds to H.R.H. The Prince of Wales's farms at Sandringham, indicates that this was not later than 1850 and may have been earlier. Testifying to the excellence of King's seeds, in 1896 Henry Cannock of Spanish Fort Company, Utah, wrote: I have pleasure in stating that the produce of your seeds has given immense satisfaction far surpassing in quality and quantity anything that I have previously purchased in this country' and, from Essex in the same year, Percy Wood, agent to Lord Rayleigh stated: 'we usually grow about four hundred acres of mangels per year, and have had a large proportion of this seed from you, for several years. I may say your seed has always given every satisfaction'.

The firm held Root Shows before the depression of the 1870s during which they were dropped, to be revived again in 1899. The competitions were limited to customers of the firm. In fact an extract from *The Land Agent's Record* of 1 November 1902, and quoted on page four of the Spring Catalogue 1902, states:

For many years past — Mr. John K. King had a small exhibition of the produce grown from his Seeds so long ago as 1797 — the Coggeshall Royal Root Show has been an important agricultural event in Essex and this year it partook of the character of a county function.

There is a long account of their 'Royal Root Show' in the *Agricultural World* of 9 November 1901. On this occasion 'luncheon was provided for a large company' on the first floor of the Coggeshall seed store and a speech was made by the Member of Parliament, the Honourable C. H. Strutt. Another such show, reported in the *Land Agent's Record* of 1 November 1902 gives an insight into the number and different types of prizes that it was expected would be provided for such an event. In 1902 their total cost was said to have been £108 and included 'The Three John K. King Coronation Challenge Cups, each value 25 guineas' which were presented for the best mangels, barley and vegetables. There were, besides, prizes of plate for each of the five mangel classes in which 12 roots of a specified variety had to be shown. Swedes received similar treatment. For turnips, kohl rabi, red wheat, John K. King's 'Improved Pedigree Chevallier Barley' and King's 'Pedigree Black Oats', and also for White Oats there were First and Second prizes of pieces of plate, and 59 cash prizes for potatoes and other vegetables. Mention in this account that 'the genial Mr. Millard, manager of the Reading branch', was very much in evidence helping Herbert King with the arrangements may indicate that Leonard King, reported as 'not present having been confined to his house for the previous four months', was then near to death.

From 1902, King's continued to gain publicity from their exhibits and prizes presented at agricultural shows. From their catalogue of 1908 it is evident that this firm still firmly believed that the largest roots gave rise to the best seed. They had not then adopted the practice of drilling the seed in a seed bed during the previous autumn, but were continuing to sow in the spring and to select and to store the largest roots over winter, before planting them out again in the field during the spring of the seed year.

Still, in 1912, two gold and four silver cups and other prizes were being offered at the principal agricultural shows in the kingdom, for roots grown from King's seeds, but the writing was on the wall. In the catalogue for that year, this firm which had hitherto printed testimonials from the United States of America praising their root seeds, now inserted a warning cautioning customers not to buy 'inferior foreign seeds' (the earliest seeds imported from America were of poor quality but this was soon remedied).

***

Amongst much else, the 20th-century catalogues provide evidence of this firm's widespread export and import trade and to whom some of these seeds were supplied. By 1900, there were exports to Europe, America, Canada, Japan, India, Australia and New Zealand. A contemporary Australian newspaper stated that 'No firm dealing in seeds holds a higher position than that of J. K. King from whose establishment at Coggeshall seeds are sent all over the world'.

In the same year, some beet, cabbage and turnip seeds which had been sent to the United States of America in 1899, were favourably reported upon by Cornell University of Agriculture, Ithaca, the experimental department of Michigan Agricultural College, and the Agricultural College of Illinois. From Ireland came testimonials of further success with farm seeds which had been supplied to His Excellency the Lord Lieutenant and no less than 15 Irish Co-operative Societies. Then, by 1906, there were added to the list of 'seeds for exportation' the countries of Persia, Egypt, Tasmania and East, South and West Africa. *The Farm Seed Catalogue* for 1901 contained two well-balanced full page notes on the 'Pure Beer Bill' and 'The Testing of Seeds by the State'. (Appendix E.) English barley is boosted in the former and wholehearted support given to the latter. It is also emphasised that this firm's seeds are already tested for their percentage germination and points out what the more enlightened seedsmen and growers had to repeat for many years to come, namely:

28. 'A Consignment of our Pedigree Seeds being shipped for a Distant Port.'

It is only to be supposed that the creating of Seed-testing or Seed-control stations in this country will be strenuously opposed in some quarters, but those Seed Merchants who have gained a reputation by always supplying seeds of the highest germinating power will regard any measure with satisfaction if it will prevent the distribution of the immense quantities of practically worthless seeds which are sown every year.

A Market-Garden Seeds Catalogue for 1902 reveals that King's then had 130,000 catalogues printed each year. There are also reports of success with their seeds from customers abroad. For instance, the President of the Board of Agriculture in Tokyo reported individually on seeds of cabbage, carrot, endive, leek, lettuce, onion, pansy, parsnip, radish, savoy and tomato supplied to His Imperial Majesty the Emperor of Japan. One can only guess at the reason for the inclusion of the pansies, perhaps they were his favourite flower or were meant particularly for the Empress. There is also a report of their seeds' success from the Scientific and Forestry Department in Uganda.

At some time around 1903 the Reading branch was closed and its manager, Mr. Millard, was moved to Coggeshall where, it is said, on Sundays he could often be found outside the Chapel exhorting men to attend Divine Service rather than visit the nearby public house (this was not *The Cricketers*!).

The destination of some of the imported bulbs is revealed in *The Garden Manual* of 1905 which informed patrons of yet another command from His Majesty's First Commissioner of Works, this time for a supply of bulbs for the Royal parks and gardens. In that year there were planted in St James's and Regent's Parks, St Margaret's Square, Greenwich and Hyde Parks, Buckingham Palace, Marlborough House, Hampton Court and Osborne House (Isle of Wight) gardens, as well as around the Queen Victoria Memorial, some 380,000 bulbs. The public press described the result as 'a magnificent display'.

In the 1906 *Manual* we learn that the 'Early Rose' potato, supplied by J. K. King, was being grown in South Africa. In fact, by that year the potato was quite a feature of their catalogues. The frilly sweet pea, the 'Countess Spencer', appeared in King's catalogue for the first time. *The Farmer and Stockbreeder Magazine* of 8 August 1907 gave an account with a splendid photograph of a July visit by horticultural and agricultural experts and journalists to John K. King's trial grounds.

The 1906/7 Corn Catalogue contained a statement that John K. King being deceased, the present partner and his sole successor — Mr. Herbert T. King — not only still carried on the system of 'Pedigree Selection' for fodder roots but had extended it to cereals and other crops. A photograph of a 15-acre field of 'Emperor' White Wheat showed a straw height of 5 ft. 11 ins. and an estimated yield of 64 bushels an acre.

The Garden Manual for 1908 had an unusually uncluttered cover of dark green with gold embossed lettering and the Royal crest. In this year they were visited by parties of French and Danish agriculturists. In 1909 their sweet pea trials contained nearly 150 varieties.

1910 provided the only surviving catalogue of 'Indian and Colonial Trade only' and a medal was won at the Brussels International Exhibition, for Seed Corn and Farm Seeds.

Although the visit of the Chinese minister and his attaché, each accompanied by two of his daughters, occurred in 1912, it was not until the *Gardening Manual* of 1914 that customers were given an account of this event. A photograph taken at the time provides possibly the only surviving picture of that flamboyant character, referred to in the press as 'the genial Mr. Millard' but who, one suspects, may sometimes have been a bit of a nuisance.

This manual, issued early in the year, gave no hint of the impending war. The 130 pages

29. Visit of His Excellency the Chinese Minister to John K. King's seed farms, 27 July 1912. Mr. Millard is the gentleman in the back row and Herbert King is on the extreme right of the front row.

of good glossy paper listed a great number of different flower and vegetable seeds as well as sundries. The visit of Edward, Prince of Wales to the firm's stand at the Royal Show in 1912, was made much of and it is evident that the sweet pea, nasturtiums and possibly also wallflowers were then the flower seeds being produced in bulk on their farms. On page 64 was an article on 'French Gardening or Intensive Culture', a book upon which 'will be forwarded post free on receipt of three postage stamps'!

In 1915 customers were sent a catalogue of reduced size and inferior quality paper which, nevertheless, proclaimed 'Business as Usual' and that seed quality was the same, despite the fact that they were short of 50 or so employees between the ages of 18 and 40 years, who had, or would shortly 'obey the call of King and Country and join the colours'.

In 1916, apart from reminders at top and bottom of each page of the name of John K. King, to differentiate them from their long-time rivals, E. W. King, there was also a warning that seeds needed to be ordered early because of possible delays, caused by use of the railways by the military.

On 18 July 1917, the *Essex Chronicle* newspaper reported that Dr. Voelcker, the renowned chemist and analyst to the Royal Agricultural Society, and Professor Armstrong, of Cambridge University Experimental Farm, visited the firm to discuss methods of plant breeding and selection. The catalogue theme for that year was 'The Production of Vegetables in Wartime'.

The year 1918 was a fateful one for the firm. On 17 March, George A. L. R. Paterson, aged only 45 years, their manager of seed warehouses and an employee of 20 years' standing, died. Then, on Wednesday 13 June, with the death of Herbert, the line of Kings in this firm came suddenly and dramatically to an end. Extraordinarily, the account of his death and funeral in the *Coggeshall Almanac* of 1918 has provided one of the very few positive sources of information that have come to light on this family over three generations. It tells us:

> DEATH OF MR. H. T. KING — In connection with the tragic death of Mr. Herbert T. King, Coggeshall, who was killed by a German bomb at a London Railway station on Wednesday, June 13th, it may be stated that that gentleman with his manager, Mr. J. H. Millard, was on his way to the Midlands to inspect his seed crops. The two gentlemen were waiting on the platform when, at 11.45, a bomb dropped some distance away. They had only gone a few yards when another bomb of high explosive dropped not far from Mr. King, who fell on the platform. Mr. Millard was not struck, but reeled forward, and on regaining himself he looked round and saw Mr. King in a pool of blood. Mr. Millard returned to his friend, and while in the act of lifting Mr. King up, another bomb dropped closer blowing him some yards away, when he fell unconscious with a wound at the back of his head, from which the blood was streaming. Mr. Millard remained in this position for some time, but was ultimately picked up and taken to St Bartholomew's Hospital where the wound was dressed and bandaged. Mr. Millard subsequently made search for his friend among the killed and wounded at several London hospitals and it was only during the evening that Mr. King's body was found at a mortuary.
>
> Mr. King's funeral took place on Saturday, June 16th, at the Coggeshall Cemetery, in the presence of a large concourse of people. The cortege left Orchard House, the coffin being borne to the grave on a hand-bier. Blinds were drawn and shutters closed along the entire route. The flag on the Church tower was at half-mast and the bells rang muffled peals.
>
> At the time of his decease Mr. Herbert King was the sole proprietor of the business of John K. King and Sons, in which he was formerly in partnership with his brother, the late Mr. Leonard King. Mr. King was fifty-three years of age, and he leaves a widow and three young children . . .

With the warehouse manager and Herbert King dead, Mr. Millard a severely shocked and ageing man, Herbert's brother, Richard Otes King, too inexperienced to take responsibility for the running of the family firm; the widow, with the help of her brother-in-law, Frederick Waite Sissons (an accountant) attempted to keep the business going.

Fate struck this firm for the third time in 1920. Just after 1.00 p.m. on 6 May, a disastrous fire broke out at their largest warehouse then full of seeds.[6] £50,000 worth of damage was done. Three floors of the warehouse were quickly alight. Smoke was seen by workmen living near and first the Coggeshall and then the Kelvedon Fire Brigades were summoned. A high wind quickly spread the flames and within 20 minutes the 200-foot long, 10-foot wide roof fell in. Thousands of pounds worth of valuable seeds were lost in the holocaust. The huge warehouse on the north side of West Street was completely gutted and the adjoining stores and seed-testing house were also destroyed.

The following week the *Essex Weekly News* and the *Essex Chronicle* published an announcement:

> THE LATE FIRE:
> Business as usual
>
> Although the disastrous fire on Thursday, the 6th inst., completely destroyed one of our large seed warehouses with its contents, yet we are glad to say that our other warehouses containing Large Stocks of our Choice Pedigree Seeds were untouched.
>
> With the loyal help of our Employees and other friends, we are quite prepared to execute all orders and despatch them without a moment's delay.
>
> JOHN K. KING
> The King's Seedsman
> Coggeshall, Essex

Before leaving this generation of Kings mention should be made of their football prowess.

Coggeshall Town Football Club[7] — 'The Seedgrowers'

On 27 September 1878, this football club came into being. It received great support from all including the town's seed merchants, growers and nurserymen. Names like John K. King, E. P. Brown, E. W. King and Humphrey Brothers all played their part and the support continues to this day.

Early records reveal that the subscription was originally 1s. 0d. for players and 2s. 6d. for non-players. It seems that the 'gear' could not always be afforded for,

> There were no good nets. Each side fielded an umpire and sometimes disputes arose between them. Players wore caps, some even played in bowler hats. Heading was unknown — when unable to kick the ball it was received on the chest.

Mr. K. R. Phillips, a one-time player and until 1985 Managing Director of E. W. King and Company, remembers that another Coggeshall seed merchant, Mr. E. P. Brown, who was known to fall for hard luck stories, was 'put upon by many a player to supply a pair of boots for the game'. But if quaintly attired their enthusiasm was boundless. Once, rather than miss playing a cup tie, one Alf Beaumont walked 12 miles to the ground.

From the *Church Magazine* for April 1886 we learn:

> The Football Season has come to an end, and Coggeshall Team has greatly distinguished itself, not having lost a single match. The play has been good throughout, but special praise must be bestowed on the really fine play of Messrs. H. T., S. J. and L. C. King . . .

Again in the February 1887 issue:

> The goal was kicked by H. T. King, who, during the game was well backed up by his two brothers, L. G. and Harold King. The two first named are widely known as football players and have represented Essex on more than one occasion, and when 'the Kings' are playing for Coggeshall it means that there will be a good match.

In the early 1900s another seed merchant's family rose to fame in this and other clubs. Walter G. and Ernest Turrall (both deaf and dumb) and Charles, Percy and Edgar Turrall, all played for Coggeshall and their father, a corn and seed merchant, was Vice-President of Coggeshall Town from 1903. Charles, Walter, Percy and Ernest together with another brother also played for Essex.

No wonder this club became known as 'The Seedgrowers' for throughout the years these, and many other seed-growing names appear in its team lists.

PART II (1920-39)

The fire seems to have been the final disaster which decided Mrs. Herbert King to give up trying to run her business and to attempt instead an amalgamation with that of her half-nephew; Mr. Sissons, her accountant brother-in-law, most probably told her that if the shares in her company were to retain any value, some new arrangements must quickly be made. The firm was already on a downhill course; it was, as a consequence of the fire, terribly short of warehousing and Richard Otes King showed no signs of having the ability to put matters right. Somehow her income had to be made more secure, for she had three daughters to bring up, all less than 14 years of age. So, in the summer of 1920 Ernest William King was asked to consider an amalgamation of their two firms.

Private correspondence from this time until his death has been retained by E. W.'s firm. These letters are the carbon copies from a tear-out memo book which was kept in his office safe; obviously written as thoughts came into his head, with little regard to formal composition, indeed often in a kind of shorthand of his own. As such they are invaluable to an historian since, being quite free from embroidery or deviousness, they almost bring their reader into the presence of this shrewd, fundamentally straightforward and honest bachelor who, despite his many activities, had, one suspects, often suffered much from loneliness.

Whatever his early aspirations with regard to his grandfather's firm, this correspondence shows clearly that the opportunity to control it was, by then, not a job for which he had the slightest relish. He foresaw that there would be much spiteful talk and besides he had been suffering bouts of illness and indisposition. He often felt tired and had no wish to add to his commitments. In fact, he was even then considering looking for a personal assistant to take some of the burden of his own very considerable business from his shoulders. The very last thing that he desired was to have to contend with all the family squabbles and ill-feeling that would inevitably ensue. Nevertheless, although he had not yet seen the books, he guessed that if Mrs. King's shares were to retain any value, someone who knew what they were about must soon assume control. So, very reluctantly, he shouldered the burden.

The two companies were always run as two entirely separate entities and so few people knew that 'E. W.' was the Managing Director of both, that there was even an occasion when one of his employees actually wrote to the Managing Director of J.K.K.'s in answer to an advertisement for a position, This employee received no acknowledgement and subsequently no promotion came his way! There never was an amalgamation of these two businesses but, from 4 November 1920 until his death, Ernest William King was Chairman of the Board of John Kemp King's firm and, from 1926, he held the controlling interest.

As has been mentioned, Herbert King had been guiding his firm's business towards farm, rather than garden, seeds and under 'E. W.'s' management this policy continued.

Their catalogues, after 1918, very soon lost any hint of war-time austerity but their former exuberant flamboyance may be said to have faded away after a statement, in the 1920 catalogue, to the effect that their connections with the Far East were as good as ever and seeds had been sent to: The Imperial Government of China; His Majesty the Emperor of Japan; His Highness the Maharajah of Mysore; His Highness the Maharajah of Aliwar; His Highness the Rajah of Chitandepur; and further, an exhibit of King's seeds took first prize at the Horticultural Show held in Government Gardens, Bangalore, India.

Today as one browses through this collection, and particularly the earlier editions, the reaction is first one of amused disbelief, perhaps followed by some disgust and thought that John Kemp King and his sons were altogether too boastful. However, search a little further and try to find a claim which cannot be reasonably substantiated and you are left wondering (with more than a tinge of admiration) what manner of men these were. Certainly, during John Kemp King's lifetime and for some years after, the achievements of this firm were prodigious and there are still lessons to be learnt from its sales promotion by publicity. Press reports and customers' testimonials from far and wide continued to praise for many decades, and it appears that the catalogues' extravagant claims were no greater than those of their contemporaries and they have never been refuted.

(What a pity it is that so many catalogues have been, and still are being, destroyed. Even more sad is the way that many firms fail to take proper care of even those, as well as other papers, which have survived. Many collections are lost when offices are moved, or a firm is amalgamated, or changes hands. *May I here make a plea* that anyone with such material should let the County Archivist, Essex Record Office, know what they have. Even if they do not wish to part with it, the Record Office will be most grateful to know that it exists and where it is housed; and if the material is not connected with Essex, the information can still be passed on to an appropriate centre.)

The Story from the Minutes (4 November 1920 to 23 August 1938)

On 4 November 1920 the first Director's Meeting was held at which E. W. King took his position as Chairman of the Board of John K. King and Sons Ltd. There were two other Directors, namely Mrs. E. M. R. King (Herbert's widow) and Mr. F. W. Sissons, Secretary.

E. W.'s private correspondence shows that he subsequently received £200 a year for his service as Managing Director of this firm.

At another meeting held on 1 November 1923, it was agreed to print an unusually large number of catalogues, 20,000 Garden Manuals, 8,000 Wholesale Garden Catalogues, and 45,000 Farm Catalogues. At the same time authority was being sought to carry out officially-recognised seed tests and it is stated that some 3,000 trials were laid down on their farms each year. Amongst these trials were several for sweet peas. The 1924 catalogue informs all customers that the firm had won a 50-guinea cup for a display of their sweet peas at the Leicester Show. This was, however, the end of their day with this flower for in the Minutes dated 18 September 1925 it was decided that J.K.K.'s should discontinue growing sweet peas.

The first telephone to be installed in Coggeshall was that of the Post Office. In 1925 the installation of what was soon to become Coggeshall 2 was delayed until the Directors had been appraised of the cost. During this year, also, Mr. F. W. Sissons died and Mrs. Sissons took his place on the Board.

Over the years, until it was bought by Francis Nicholls, there were several attempts to sell the whole, or at least the farms and retail side, of this business.

On 20 February 1926 E. W. wrote to a Mr. Danby, in which letter he states 'The shareholders (three) are very keen on liquidating the business and think they can get their money out (it shows so on paper)'. Then at an Extraordinary General Meeting which was called on 27 July 1926, Mrs. King and her sister, Mrs. Sissons, proposed the voluntary winding-up of the company. E. W. King did not vote.

Mr. T. G. Fairhead, who farmed at Hoo Hall, Rivenhall, was a longstanding friend of E. W. King — indeed E. W. was godfather to his son. Probably as early as 1920, Mr. Fairhead was overseeing the J. K. K. farms and helping to subdue (the perhaps troublesome employee) Mr. Millard. Certainly, in a letter from E. W. to Mr. Beaumont, the Coggeshall solicitor, dated 10 September 1920, there occurs the sentence:

> I had a chat with Mr. Fairhead last evening and think he would be agreeable to put £5,000 in business . . . it would strengthen business considerably as his practical knowledge on farms would be great asset . . . further Mr. J. M. would listen to him.

E. W. continues that at least £40,000 will be required to set this business on its feet again, and that he does not know 'whatever is to be done in warehouse accommodation . . . time is getting on and contracts coming in and unfortunate contracts being so much overdone will have to be kept a year or so before realized'.

Exactly when T. G. Fairhead put money into this firm is not certain. However, after an Extraordinary General Meeting held on 11 March 1927, he became a member of the Board of Directors and it is apparent that the business of this firm was under the management of E. W. and himself until, on 20 March 1930, Ernest William King most unexpectedly died.

It is said that E. W. left both his own and J. K. K.'s business to his godsons, Edwin Cyril Fairhead and Edwin James Small. The next meeting of John K. King and Company Ltd. was held on 15 April 1930. Edwin C. Fairhead took the chair and also present were: 'Mr. and Mrs. Royle — and Mr. E. J. Small, all of whom were made Directors of the firm'. Mrs. Royle was a cousin of E. W. King, and her husband was a most able industrialist from the Midlands. Had Mr. Royle lived it is said that he had the ability to manage this firm so that it could once more have become a viable concern. However, ill fortune had not yet run its course in this business for, in 1931, he died and the decision to sell the company was made.

Through a distant relative who had married into the seed-growing family of Small, in Taunton, Somerset, Francis Nicholls of Hasler's, Dunmow, heard the news. (Everyone says 'Frank' but 'Francis' is on the legal agreement.) He had four sons, two of whom still required positions in the seed trade. His eldest son, Henry, was already working for Hasler's and therefore, in order not to overburden this firm, he decided to purchase the Coggeshall business.

On 17 November 1931, an 'Agreement for the sale and purchase of shares in John K. King and Sons Ltd.' was signed between 'Messrs. Edwin Cyril Fairhead, of Hoo Hall, Rivenhall, in the County of Essex, Farmer, and Edwin James Small, of 'Wild Oak', Taunton, in the County of Somerset, Seed merchant, and Francis Joseph Nicholls, of Dunmow, Essex, Seed Merchant'.

E. C. Fairhead was to continue as a Director of the Company at a salary amounting, after deduction of any income tax payable thereon, to £200 a year for a period of two years. Should Mr. Fairhead wish to sell his shares, they were first to be offered to the company. Mr. Fairhead's shares were in due course all sold back to the firm, except for one, which he retained for many years in order to remain entitled to a copy of the Company's Annual Balance Sheet. Provision was also made for a pension of £52 to be paid to the retired Company Secretary, for a period of five years. Further, Mrs. E. M. R. King was to retain a life interest in the tenure of that portion of Orchard House then in the occupation of Herbert George Watson.

So, with these constraints, Francis Nicholls and his two sons set about pulling together an establishment, which for some years had lost impetus. From the moment they took over the atmosphere was brisker and more purposeful and, although in the early years profits were virtually non-existent, the decisions taken were sound and a steady progress was maintained. Items occurring in the Minutes show what happened and the difference in costs between those days and the present.

On 22 November 1932, it was reported that, subject to the addition of a few more items, the Ministry of Agriculture would grant a licence to carry out Official Seed Tests in their laboratory. A contract for grass seed had also been obtained from Barking Corporation.

During 1933, holders of 10s. shares were paid out at 7s. 6d. and new shares were issued for £1 each, fully paid. E. W. King and Company evidently purchased 1,000 shares. In the November a second-hand Morris Cowley car was purchased for Company use. It cost £41!

Seed corn, which had previously been dressed with copper sulphate against seed-borne disease, was now to be dressed with the safer and more reliable 'Ceresan' powder and in December 1933 a dry-dressing machine was purchased for £38.

In March 1934, four cottages had been done up and the tenants 'had agreed to a rent increase of 1s. a week'. These years cover a period which has become known as 'The Hungry Thirties' and in May 1934 the Directors were told that despite a slight improvement in the trade of their company for the year ending June 1933, there was no doubt that the depressed state of agriculture continued to be felt and many farmers were not disposed, or even able to spare money for high grade seeds. Also many owners of large private gardens had to curtail their expenses and sometimes to close their large country houses altogether. The demand for mangel and turnip seed was reported to have fallen because of the increasing acreage of sugar beet then being grown. The sugar beet crop provided by-products of pulp and tops, both of which provided food for cattle and sheep and so reduced the acreage of mangel and turnip crops required for this purpose. Nevertheless, in August 1934, 17,500 Garden Retail and 10,000 Wholesale Garden Catalogues were to be printed whereas the Farm Catalogues had been reduced to 17,500.

As from 1 January 1935, staff wage increases were as follows:

NAME		
—	from 34s.	to 36s.
—	from 30s.	to 32s.
—	from 17s. 6d.	to 20s.
—	from 10s.	to 12s. 6d.
—	from 26s.	to 27s. 6d.
—	from 7s. 6d.	to 10s.

At the Annual General Meeting in 1935, there was a statement that prices were having to be kept down because of unrealistic price cutting by competitors. This was then a common complaint from the more reliable seedsmen. They realised the folly of too much competitive undercutting and had learnt from experience that what was best for producer, distributor and consumer, was a fair, and not a low, price for all. In the very short run consumers may sometimes obtain a bargain and the seller filch some of his rivals' trade. Ultimately, no-one gains. For if a producer receives too low a price he grows a different crop the next year, thus creating a shortage and higher consumer costs. The merchant also cannot afford the numbers, or the quality, of staff necessary to maintain seed standards, and growers lose a satisfactory return on their crop by the purchasing of inferior quality seeds. Yet the practice remains rife especially during a depression when those firms with insufficient capital reserves compete (rather than co-operate) with one another in an attempt to keep their heads above water. The solution is no simple matter.

By February 1936, the firm's Morris Cowley was replaced by a Hillman Minx saloon car at a cost of £177 10s., less an allowance of £32 10s. for the old car.

This was a disappointing year for there was a glut of peas which brought the price right down and so although sales remained the same, there was but a small margin of profit. Furthermore, yields from the farm crops had been disappointing. By November, another lorry driver was engaged for a wage of 45s. a week and six employees received wage increases of from 1s. to 1s. 6d. a week. More warehousing was required for the increasing corn trade and after receiving tenders from various firms, in March 1937 another 3,000 ordinary shares were issued at par, to provide the necessary capital to meet Messrs. E. R. & F. Turner's charge for the erection of a silo and warehouse to accommodate 1,450 quarters of grain. The cost was to be £3,875.

The question of market expenses had arisen and in August 1937, it was considered reasonable to allow both D. C. and J. E. Nicholls the sum of 10s. a week for this purpose.

At the Annual General Meeting, it was recorded that, although turnover had been the greatest so far under the Nicholls' regime, the small demand for root and picking pea seed had curtailed profits to the extent that nothing could be added to the reserves. Moreover there had been a considerable falling-off in the demand for garden seeds.

In 1938, after 66 years' service, the Company Secretary, Harry Taylor, retired and was replaced by another at an increased wage of £4 a week. Olive Rudkin was in charge of the laboratory and G. R. J. Blackwell was the second of this firm's employees to be sent on a Course and Examination in Seed Testing, arranged by the N.I.A.B., at Cambridge, on 20 June.

At the Annual General Meeting held in August 1938, everything appeared 'set fair' for the future of the business. Orders were increasing all round, the Balance Sheet was the best yet and the new warehouse, together with the necessary machinery, had been completed for a total cost of £4,089. Nevertheless when the Account Book, which had been started by E. W. King in November 1920, ended in April 1939, there was a small farm loss.

1939-1984

By the time war was declared in 1939, this firm's policy to phase out its trade for private gardens and to concentrate on cereals and other farm and market garden seeds, had placed it in a good position to give wholehearted support to the Government's campaign for more cereals. Indeed, the firm's catalogue for 1941, then a simple, austere, black and white publication with almost no illustrations, was exhorting all to 'Grow Still More Food and Dig for Victory' for, despite the loss of imports, this firm was still able to offer its customers over 90 per cent of normal seed supplies.

The year 1940-1 was the period when high explosive bombs, for which raiders had failed to find any better target, started to be jettisoned more or less indiscriminately onto the East Coast before the enemy planes left to cross the Channel and return to base. After this time, many a field changed its name to 'Bomb-hole'! The effects of such random bombing are clearly portrayed by the tapestry which was sewn to commemorate the war: particularly that section which depicts an expanse of marsh pasture in which is a large bomb-hole with beside it, lying dead, one poor old British Friesian cow. (This most telling piece of work, the 'Bayeux Tapestry' of our time, was commissioned by the brewers, Whitbread and Company Ltd. It is now housed in the City Museum, Portsmouth. Not to have seen it is to have missed something very worthwhile.)

J.K.K.'s did not escape, for the Minutes state that on Tuesday 5 November 1940 an H.E. bomb demolished the house at Purley Farm. There were evidently other bombs dropped in the fields, for the Estate Agents, Messrs. Surridge and Company, were instructed to prepare a claim for compensation to 'include loss of the farm house, and damage to the land in consequence of bomb craters'. By 14 November, Everett's of Colchester had been engaged to camouflage King's grain store. This cost £35.

All over the country members of War Agricultural Committees, with officers of the Ministry of Agriculture, were preparing what was almost another Domesday Book of farm land, labour, equipment and livestock. Sometimes a farm or an odd piece of land was found to be in such a bad state that, if the population was to be fed, strong action had to be taken and arrangements made for this land to be farmed by someone other than its occupants. Such a case was Hop Green Farm, which Messrs. J. K. King were asked to take in hand to improve the conditions and to grow food. The firm still has this farm which, in 1983, was said to be highly productive.

In February 1941, the much-prized Royal Warrant of Appointment was renewed by His Majesty George VI, and there was an accompanying letter to state that the Warrant would be reviewed again in 10 years.

Essex was a county which was not only having to meet its Government quota for food crops, but also to find land upon which the seed crops required for sowing these extra acres, both in the county and elsewhere, might be grown. To increase the acreage of tillage, permanent pastures had to be ploughed. This was a process fraught with difficulties, especially when the pasture was a marsh, where the grass 'matt' had frequently built up over many generations, often to a depth of 10 to 12 inches. In those days there was nothing with which to combat attack of wheat bulb fly, even if the thinning had been traced to this pest. However, the catalogue of 1941 lists 'Terrasan' as a killer of wireworms, and 'Drymac' and derris dust were on offer for use against flea beetles.

In March 1942 it was noted that malting barley was making the record figure of 300s. a quarter, and for seed lots even a premium over this.

With many of their staff in what was then known as a 'Reserved Occupation', this company was fortunate in having a fair proportion of trained labour to carry them through the war years. However, as one Director had indicated, it is probable that, like others in reserved occupations, the staff sometimes felt that life might have been less arduous in the armed services because, not only were they expected to do a full and hard day's work, but on most nights they were up and on duty with the Home Guard or some other form of Civil Defence.

It was unfortunate that the Company's 150th anniversary came during a period of war-time austerity. Nevertheless, in 1943, the occasion was marked by each employee receiving a bonus of 10s. for each year that had been worked for the Company.

Francis J. Nicholls (Frank) was forced to retire from active participation in the business in 1946. He had been suffering the crippling and painful effects of rheumatoid arthritis for very many years. Nevertheless, it is remembered that his brain remained keen, and that he took an unflagging interest in the business until he died in 1953. His place as Chairman of the Board was filled by his second son, Mr. Douglas C. Nicholls.

Minutes of 18 December 1947 record with some acidity that 'after seven years, agreement had now been reached with the War Damage Commission that the farm house at

30. Francis J. Nicholls.

Purley Farm, which was destroyed . . . in 1940, should be replaced on a cost of works basis'.

At the end of 1952 Mr. L. R. Raven, an employee for 53 years, the last 14 as the Company's Secretary, retired on a pension. Oddly, he was replaced by a Mr. E. W. King, who claims to have no relationship with the family who founded the other Coggeshall firm. In 1954 another long service employee (63 years), Isaac Potter, was forced to retire through ill-health. He was allowed to remain in his cottage, rent free for life, and was given a pension of 30s. a week.

In September 1954, this firm once again qualified for a Warrant of Appointment, this time to Her Majesty, Queen Elizabeth II.

From the catalogue it appears that 1955 was the start of the fodder beet growing campaign. The Minutes record that on 3 February 1958, Francis H. Nicholls, the present Chairman of Directors, was accepted into the firm. By February 1958 Mrs. Herbert King had probably died. In any event it was then that Orchard House, Coggeshall, came into the ownership of the Company, and that plans were put in motion to transfer their offices from the noisy and cramped conditions of an old building facing West Street to the more spacious Orchard House, which also has the advantage of having been built well back from the road. This move was made, after alterations had been completed, in May 1959. It is also recorded that 1958 was most probably the worst harvest in living memory, and in consequence most seeds produced in this season were of poor quality. During this most difficult time the benefit of their drying and cleaning plant was appreciated to the full.

J.K.K.'s, in common with many other firms, increased their representation throughout the 1950s. A page-long list of representatives began to appear in each year's catalogue so that by 1962 there were 24 of their 'reps' operating in areas throughout the British Isles, from Coggeshall to Cornwall.

Clearly by 1960 a dressing had been found to help combat the wheat bulb fly problem, for 'Heptasan W.B.' appeared on their list. The Annual Report for 1960 claims steady progress and a widening of this firm's activities. The garden seed trade, which had scarcely been resumed after war ceased, had been completely given up in 1958. Herbage seeds were booming and cereals continued to increase with demand for the improved varieties then becoming available.

The firm enjoyed a record turnover in 1962 and very wisely, because competition in the grain trade was increasing, decided to use this opportunity to increase their facilities for wholesale trading and bulk handling. (This competition arose from the formation of such things as Farmer's Buying Co-operatives, and the increase in agricultural co-operative buying and selling, both of which particularly affected the smaller agricultural merchant and seed establishments.) Once again Messrs. E. R. and F. Turner of Ipswich were given the contract which, it was estimated, was to cost £35,000. Most fortunately this plant came into operation in time to handle the particularly wet and difficult harvest of 1962. The drying plant alone was in continuous use for several months. Minutes of May 1965 announce the arrival of the 40-hour working week. There were to be no changes in wage rates, but it was expected that changes in job rates would increase the wages of some employees.

A further expansion of this company's trade in cereal seeds, and in the seed of peas and beans to be grown for the dried market, took place in the 1960s. In the 1970s the position was consolidated when the company became the main supplier of East Anglian growers. This was particularly the case in regard to seed for dried peas and for cereals in 1977. As a further diversification into pulse crops, the company helped to establish Pulse and Commodity Traders Ltd. This separate unit removes the tough outer skins (a process known as decortication) from several hundreds of tonnes of dried peas and lentils. The result is a highly marketable product used in the making of soups and other canned products.

Mr. John E. Nicholls, who had been a director of the company since July 1941, died

31. Francis H. Nicholls.

before the Board meeting of July 1972.

In the Minutes of February 1976, Mr. D. C. Nicholls reported that he had received on behalf of the company notification that, after review by the Royal Household Tradesmen's Warrants Committee, the Royal Warrant of Appointment as Seedsmen to Her Majesty the Queen had been renewed until December 1985. During the 1970s, horticultural sundries had become part of this firm and, if he were alive today, John Kemp King would be happy to learn that a considerable part of this trade is concerned with regular deliveries to Buckingham Palace and the Royal Parks of Central London.

On 30 June 1978, Mr. D. C. Nicholls retired from full-time work with the company, but he remained as Chairman of the Board until 1 July 1980. Mr. F. H. Nicholls then took his place as Chairman and Mr. D. C. Nicholls remained on the Board as its Consultative Director.

In the 1980s, Francis Nicholls was making a name for himself in the dried pulse trade. Here, as a past Chairman of the Essex and Hertfordshire branch of U.K.A.S.T.A., a past President of the British Edible Pulse Association, for several years the United Kingdom's representative for this sector during the E.E.C. negotiations in Brussels, and a current (1983) vice-Chairman of the G.A.F.T.A. Pulse Committee, in June 1983, he became the first Briton to be elected President of the Confederation Internationale du Commerce et des Industries des Legumes Secs.

When, back in July 1969, the third generation of the Nicholls family were made Directors of the firm, it was a clear indication to the farming world that the firm founded by John (K.) King had every intention of remaining an independent family concern. In 1983 its Chairman wrote:

> The Company still jealously guards its independent status and by diversification with new crops and by innovation and ingenuity Kings look forward to their bi-centenary in 1993.

GRASSLAND OVER TEN CENTURIES

Grassland has always provided food for animals and from at least the 11th century has played a major part in our people's leisure and sporting activities. Yet it was not until comparatively recently that seeds, rather than turves, were used to establish a lawn or a sporting area. As for grass for hay and grazing, this was something that was already there or which, if a piece of land was left uncultivated for long enough, established itself. The herbage of both was determined by such factors as geographical location, drainage and the numbers and types of animal by which they were grazed.

John (K.) King's firm was founded in time to experience the increasing demand for grass seed mixtures and was early in the field of grassland improvement. Therefore, before passing on to the separate story of Ernest William King's firm, there follows a brief history of lawn, playing field and agricultural grassland development.

Even today, that which most impresses any air traveller, and particularly the English returning home after a period abroad, is the fresh greenness of so much of our island. For centuries, climate and geology have ensured that this is so, yet although there are previous references to 'closely mown' grass, expanses of close-cut, level and weed-free lawn did not become commonplace, and indeed, almost a fetish, until after the invention and widespread distribution of the mechanical lawn-mower.

In the early days, grass used for recreation was not regularly or closely cut but, 'rejoicing in invasion by daisies and blue speedwell for most of the year'.[3] The hay fields, grassed orchards, flowery meads and the grass patch in the herber or the cloister garth were scythed twice yearly in spring and autumn, unless growth became too luxuriant — as might happen in a wet season — in which case they were cut again. Similarly, nothing approaching modern grassland management was practised on farms earlier than the mid-1700s. Before that, when hay was required, an area of meadowland was enclosed in a temporary fence of thorn branches, to prevent grazing and treading down by deer or domestic animals. The enclosed area was then cleared of fallen branches and any other obstruction to the mowers, before closing the gate-gap with more thorn branches and leaving the grass to grow until it was ready to be cut.[9]

Mention of areas of grass which were used for relaxation occur by the 11th century. In the 13th century there is ample proof that grassy areas were considered as a necessary adjunct to noble houses and monastic buildings. For instance, at the King's garden at Windsor, in 1262, 'a pool of water was to be made and the King's herber turfed'.[10] Herber, translated from the medieval Latin word *herbarium*, may mean, according to its context: close garden with lawn, flower garden, or garden of medicinal herbs.

'Even turf ready for laying could be bought from a dealer by 1300'.[11] This was not only required for establishing new areas of grass but also for repairs to jousting grounds, grass seats, worn patches in lawns and at archery butts. The jousting grounds were mown twice yearly and their turf had to be entirely renewed every third or fourth year.[12]

Detailed instructions on turf laying may be found in books on gardening from at least the 13th century and moles must have been as much of a nuisance in 1344 as they are today because the accounts of Clare Priory, Suffolk, show that Thomas 'Mollere' was paid 4d. for catching moles in their meadows at Bardfield, Essex.

Possibly it was the game of bowls that first emphasised the need for a better quality turf. During the 16th century this game became so popular that it not only superceded archery as a pastime but also led to so much gambling that, in 1541, an Act was passed by Parliament whereby any who played bowls outside their own orchard or garden were to be fined, and landowners, with land above the rental value of £100, must have a licence to play on their own private greens.

Camomile lawns and later camomile banks and seats also became popular. It is thought probable that it was on a camomile turf that Drake played bowls while waiting for the tide to turn in his favour before setting off the meet the Armada. There is a camomile lawn in the garden of Buckingham Palace to this day.

Although, in the 17th century, there is still no mention of grass seeds the frequent cutting of lawns by sickle or scythe was already in vogue by 1625. In his essays, Francis Bacon recommends 'closely mown lawns . . . because nothing is more pleasant to the eye than grass kept finely shorn'. About the same time the diarist John Evelyn recommended that grass walks and bowling greens be cut and rolled every 15 days. In the 18th century a skilled workman, using a scythe, could produce a fairly even sward and three experienced mowers could cut an acre of lawn a day. At this period, betweeen one mowing and the next, a 'daisy rake' came into use to clear the lawn of flowers.[13]

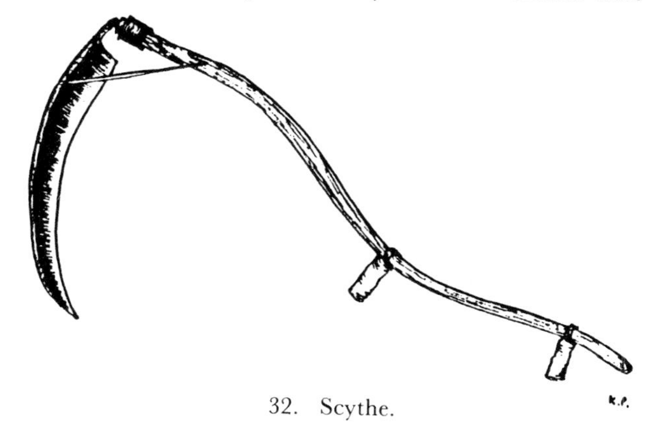

32. Scythe.

In 1706, suggestions for different types of sward occur in what was originally a French book which states that these may be obtained by the use of 'Turfs, by Spanish Clover Grass, by Hay Seeds, by seed of Sainfoin and by that of Medick Fodder'. In 1719, there is record of grass seeds, namely 'fursee and meason', coming in from Aleppo — whatever these were, they sound roughish material.

With the advent of landscape gardening in the 1720s came a need for a much larger area of closely cut, as distinct from meadow, grass. 'The scythe, now wielded with increasing precision, aided by brush and roller, and shears and edging irons, came into general use',[14] and a description of the rather stupendous gardens at Canon's, in Middlesex, says that the turf was scythed two or three times a week and weeded every day.[15]

It is in 1758 that one of the first mentions of lawn seed occurs[16] together with the information that 'there is great difficulty in getting good seed; for that from a common haystack is by no means proper' and 'grass of a clean upland pasture' is what is required.

Although there were still no lawn-mowing machines, it was not long before the aid of a horse was enlisted for rolling the grass and it is recommended that, for this purpose, the horse must be unshod and wear 'Woolen mufflers' on its feet.[17] By Queen Victoria's day the mufflers were superceded by a set of four leather slippers, which again helped to prevent hoof depressions on tennis, croquet and other lawns. (Mr. Noel Blyth of Wick Farm, Wick Lane, Ardleigh, Essex, says that when he took one of these slippers apart, to see how it had been made, he found that a double thickness of leather had been sown in around the front and that the pocket so formed had been tightly packed with lead shot. No doubt this both helped wear, at a point at which it was most likely to occur, and also deterred the horse from swinging its feet too much.) Furthermore, it is not just the 'mad English' who do these things. In 1977, and I expect still today, I saw a herd of sleek black buffalo cows progressing purposefully down a macadamed road in the vicinity of Kathmandu airport, in Nepal, each wearing a set of neatly plaited grass slippers, no doubt to prevent damage to the tarred surface softened by the heat of the sun.

At roughly the same time as the garden lawn was coming to the fore, farmers were becoming interested in the improvement of pastures for their livestock and in crops, such as clover, which not only fed their stock but which also has a restorative effect upon the soil. A market for such seeds then opened up and because, no doubt, the seeds from Aleppo

33. Lawn mowers and rollers advertised in John K. King's Manual of Gardening for 1914.

had been rather unsuitable, seedsmen and scientists were taking a closer look at the grasses in our meadows as a source of seed supply. By the turn of the 18th century differing mixtures of especially selected grasses and clovers began to be offered by seedsmen, for grazing and for hay.[18] Even then, because of the high cost, poor type and quality of the seeds, and the lack of knowledge as to their successful establishment and subsequent management, it was years before temporary leys gained favour. Indeed, there were many respected farmers who, during the Second World War, still firmly believed that permanent grass was superior to temporary ley.

The inventor of the first cylinder reel lawn-mower was Edwin Budding. He was an engineer in the cloth trade and had the idea from a machine used to trim the nap of cloth. By 1830, after some nocturnal experiments, the sound of which puzzled his neighbours,[19] he had made his machine, which he patented in 1832. After several improvements, including grass delivery and methods of traction, there appeared in 1890 an early version of the 'ride-on' mower. On the market from 1900 was the first gasoline-powered cylinder mower, and by 1986 we have rotary mowers, air-cushion or hovercraft mowers, together with very elaborate developments of these upon which the operator may ride.

As may be imagined, Essex seedsmen soon discovered that although the county, because of clay and climate, was one of the most difficult places in which to produce grass for grazing, it was very suitable for growing grass seed.

John K. King, and Sutton's Seeds of Reading (established 1806) were early in this trade. From 1895 the catalogues make it clear that for many years King's had been noted for their grass seeds. A testimonial from Cambridgeshire speaks of the customer having, 'some twenty-one years ago', had excellent results and requesting a further supply. Of exports we are informed that: 'Grass seeds, clovers, turnips, mangel and lucerne, together with other kinds of seeds, are being sent to Australia, New Zealand and other colonies' and also 'all my seeds are carefully packed by a new process in hermetically sealed cases and delivered free to any port in the United Kingdom'.

1897 marks the first occasion upon which grass seeds were supplied for the Royal Parks and both Mr. King and Mr. Millard were travelling far and wide to act as consultant advisers to those wishing to seed down new lawns, tennis courts (as at Sandringham), golf courses (as at Cambridge), and cricket grounds (as at Essex County Cricket Ground at Leyton), or even to repair the damages to park grass after a disastrously wet Agricultural Show (as at Prospect Park after the Royal Counties Show of 1902).

In 1900 grass seed was supplied for the Royal Parks for the third time. Included were Kew Gardens, Green Park, St James's Park, Hyde Park and Kensington Gardens. The first recommendation for laying a lawn was that the land be well drained and that there be a good outfall. This advice cannot be bettered and is still having to be hammered home today.

Advertisements for ley grasses and clovers were still much in evidence together with another interesting item: '*Furze, Whin or Gorse* — for cover, line fences or for feeding. crushed it is excellent for milch cows. Sown in April/May,

For forage (drill 15 in. apart) 40-50 lb/acre

For cover (drill broadcast) 30 lb/acre

Cost 130s. per acre'.

So the grass story has developed, with the acreage of closely cut lawn at its greatest during the 'landscape' era and starting to decrease noticeably from the early 18th century until today, when it is reduced to a mere grass patch or has been replaced by concrete slabs.

On the other hand, there has never been such a development of amenity and agricultural grasses and all are being bred with a specific purpose in mind. The production of Certified Herbage Seeds in this county enjoyed its heyday between 1945 and the 1960s. In 1966 some 18,000 hectares were grown here, after which apart from an unsustained rise to 25,000 hectares in 1974 (mostly rye grasses), the home production of these seeds dropped to 14,000 hectares in 1984. Few acres of clover are now seeded in Great Britain, the bulk being imported from New Zealand, Holland and Denmark.

Some comparisons can be drawn between today's amenity parkland and the 12th-century hunting grounds and flower-bespangled meadows; also between the more intimate flowery mead-herber once situated near to palace and castle and the small flower-bordered lawn found adjacent to houses in today's suburbs. But today, flowers in grass are frowned upon and our lawns are slavishly mown and weeded from spring to winter.

PART III — THE FIRM OF ERNEST WILLIAM KING, 1888-1914

After the unsuccessful visit to his grandfather, the disappointed and furiously resentful Ernest William King, in 1888, somehow managed to set up his own establishment in a small house on the same side of the market end of West Street — indeed in the same block — as John K. King. Here, as well as selling a few seeds, he hired out boats on the nearby river. By 1893, and possibly three years earlier, he had moved over the road to premises on the corner of West Street and the Kelvedon Road, within a few yards of his grandfather's public house, *The Cricketers*. Here he had a small but double-fronted shop behind which was a three-storeyed warehouse, with access from West Street.

His business must have got off to a good start for in his introductory letter to his Wholesale Catalogue (January 1898), he writes:

> The great proof of the quality of our seeds is the fact that our business during the past five years has *increased enormously, beyond all expectation*, and that we have had again to increase our warehouse accommodation; also hire more land for our extensive cultivations. In addition to Vegetable and Farm Seeds, we grow largely Flower Seeds; in Nasturtiums alone our annual sale is 2-3 Tons. We export them to all parts of the World.

34. E. W. King, *c*.1905.

In 1900, he bought his first piece of land — the Tenterfield in Little Coggeshall. This was the field where, in former days, cloth was stretched to shape on tenter hooks. It cost him £262 for three acres, one rood and 19 poles.

By 1904, he had given his corner shop to the District Council to enable the road to be widened and had moved to Grange Hill, Coggeshall. Furthermore, by the time of his death E. W. King owned some 300 acres irrespective of 1,200 acres of rented farm land. An engraving in his catalogue of 1904 shows a tall chimney on the site of what then became the main establishment of this firm. No such chimney ever existed there. It is thought to have been drawn in as yet another dig at Grandfather, whose premises included the quite useless (to a seed business) tall chimney of the onetime silk mill. Another catalogue engraving, in 1908, shows windows in the top storey of his premises. Again, there never were any, and still are no windows here. Perhaps he had intended to put some in later and wished to save the expense of another engraving. This would have been in character.

At this period the firm of J. K. King, because of its earlier start, its retail customers, and having been honoured with a Royal Warrant, was much in the public eye. It is, however, a fact that quite early in its history E. W. King's firm became the largest family firm of its kind in Essex to be dealing only with the wholesale seedhouses. Nevertheless, because he had no connection with the retail trade, few people realised the extent or importance of his business.

As a rule Ernest's catalogues (in 1985, early editions were extant for the dates 1894, 1896, 1897, 1898, 1903, 1904, 1905; all give prices and, after 1894, are illustrated) are not on such a lavish scale as those of John K. King and in 1901 he took the opportunity to reduce his printing costs by £500. On the pretext that as the year had been a bad one for farmers, the cost of seeds must be kept down, therefore, he was sending out only a simple price list and demanding cash payment upon delivery; as this would further keep down the price by saving bookkeeping charges. In addition, no show prizes were to be given in that year.

Even if unnamed, his catalogues would be distinguishable from those of his grandfather, although they follow the pattern of all such for this period. It appears almost as if, once his catalogue had been set out, he amused himself by filling every blank space with

35. E. W. King's 1888 premises.

36. E. W. King's 1893 premises.

37. E. W. King's 1904 premises.

'advertising doodles'. These were written in at any angle which would allow the blank piece of page to be filled to the best advantage. He dealt in root, grass and clover seeds as well as cereals and pulses, but it is in the field of garden seeds for the wholesalers that this business steadily gained in status.

The Catalogue for 1896

'Renovating Mixtures' consisting of Rye grasses and clovers were offered. Also, 'Ice Plant seed — useful as a garnish' cost 3d. a packet.

Testimonials, presumably from farmers who had been chosen to multiply his seed stocks, tell of successes with his root seeds. H. Speakman, Esq., of Woodham Walter Lodge wrote: 'The seeds I had of you have done remarkably well, beyond all expectation', and W. H. Smith, Esq., of Blamsters Hall, claims that 'the seeds are v.g. I took 2nd Prize at our Dunmow Show', while Mr. Wiffin, the steward at Stanway Hall, had gained a first prize with some 'Monarch' swedes.

The Catalogue for 1898 — wholesale vegetable, flower and farm seeds

From this catalogue it can be seen clearly that, 10 years after founding his firm, Ernest had already become a considerable seedsman. Items were listed under 50 different headings. The following extract list gives some idea of the range. (I have inserted figures in brackets to indicate the number of varieties on offer.)

1. Specialities recommended for exhibition and market
2. Peas (52) also gives height and price/peck and /bushel
3. Broad beans (11)
4. Dwarf beans (7)
5. Runner beans (7)
6. Asparagus (1)
7. Beet (12)
8. Borecole or Kale (5)
9. Brussels sprouts (9)
10. Broccoli (19)
11. Carrot (8)
12. Capsicum and Chili (6)
13. Cabbage (19)
14. Cattle cabbage (5), incl. Thousand Head kale
15. Savoy (4)
16. Cauliflower (5)
17. Celery (9)
18. Cress (4)
19. Cucumber — Frame (5), Ridge (6)
20. Endive (4)
21. Egg plant (1)
22. Gourd (3)
23. Leek (7)
24. Lettuce — Cos (7), Cabbage (8)
25. Mustard (3)
26. Melon (4)
27. Onion (20)
28. Parsnip (4)
29. Parsley (4)
30. Radish (12)
31. Rhubarb (1)
32. Salsify (1)
33. Scorzonera (1)

34. Seakale (1)
35. Spinach (3)
36. Tomato (8)
37. Turnip (8)
38. Vegetable marrow (5)
39. Sweet and Pot herbs (18)
40. Potatoes (17)
41. Lawn grass (3)
42. Bird-seed mixture
43. Choice flower seeds (230)
44. Imported flower collections
45. Pictorial-packet flower seeds
46. Bulbs and roots: Gladioli (3), Ranunculus (2), Anemone (2), Liliums (2)
47. Sundries
48. Agricultural seeds
49. Grass seed mixture
50. Rye grass, clovers, lucerne

His own flower seeds were packed in 'Pictorial Seed Packets' but those sold in 'Blue Sealed Packets', although field-inspected by his experts during the growing season, had been obtained from abroad.

In the 1898 catalogue seed of the 'Pink Cupid' sweet pea was being offered. Subsequently, this sweet pea disappeared for about 50 years. At that stage, when none could be found, interest was re-aroused by plant breeders who wanted specimens for hybridisation. Dr. Keith Hammett, a plant pathologist in New Zealand, interested in pre-Spencer sweet pea types, heard of this, and on visiting an old lady's garden, unexpectedly saw a whole row. They had been grown from home-saved seed which had originally come from England!

A report tells that E. W. King had staged an exhibit at the Smithfield Show in 1897; bulbs were now listed and sundries included tobacco paper at 9d. a pound. Furthermore, he claimed to be one of the largest growers of nasturtiums and to be exporting between two and three tons of this seed to all parts of the world. In 1901, this firm was said to have grown 10 acres of nasturtium seed which, during September, had required 80 to 100 hands to gather up the 500 bushels of seed.

By 1897 he, too, was having difficulties with his firm's identity, for in a notice to customers giving his address his initials were now heavily underlined.

The Selected Home-Grown Seed Catalogue for 1903

The Findlay bred 'Eldorado' potato was given a considerable write-up. Small quantities of these 'seed' tubers had been released at prices of between £60 and £300 for one pound. E. W. King had managed to obtain a few pounds for £150 and actually sold one tuber for £50 — at which price one ton would have realised £440,000! There is a story in the trade that one purchaser sold two bullocks and with the proceeds bought one pound of these potatoes, took them home, put them on the kitchen table and then went out again. When he came back his wife had peeled them for lunch! In desperation he scraped around in the dustbin for bits of peel which he planted. Eventually a few tubers were produced but by this time the popularity of the Eldorado had almost vanished for unfortunately the variety did not fulfil its early promise and in only one year the price dropped to £3 a pound. As could be expected, in their catalogue of 1906, the firm of J. K. King was not slow to point out the folly of buying from those who put varieties onto the market before they had given them a thorough trial.

By 1905 'Ernest William' was distributing a range of wholesale catalogues:

A Gardening Manual— ready 1 January
A Farm List — ready 1 March
A Bulb List — ready 1 October
A Fruit and Rose List— ready 1 October

This was his 'Year of the Sweet Pea'. They appeared in colour on the front cover of the Gardening Manual. They took up a full eight acres of trial plots, in which there were trial rows of 160 varieties, as well as 60 plots of the more choice sorts. Grandfather gave prizes for roots but his grandson now offered cash prizes for sweet peas in every parish (presumably limited to Essex) amounting to over £1,000 and this was in addition to 'Show Prize Money' all over the country. It was certainly an era when gardeners competed and seed merchants vied with one another in their show exhibits and the prizes they presented.

38. Sweet pea trials, *c*.1906. 'Messrs. Bolton, Jones, Hogan and Brown with our Mr. King.' Note that the sweet peas were grown unsupported at this time.

From then onwards this firm had a name for sweet peas. Since 1906 it had introduced upwards of 120 novelties, 54 of which had received one or more awards, and by January 1913 was already described in *The Nurseryman and Seedsman* as 'Great Britain's largest growers of Sweet Peas'. Their collection of show prizes, cups and medals has long been impressive and continues to increase. Any sweet pea with a name which was topical in the year of its introduction is probably one of E. W. K.'s. There are, for instance, such names as 'Nippy' (after the Lyons Corner House waitresses); '2L.O' (the then newly-established wireless broadcasting station); 'Amy Johnson' (the pioneer airwoman); 'Buy British' (after the advertising campaign); 'All Clear', 'Princess Elizabeth' and many others.

Apart from its normal items the Manual of 1905 also offered flower seed collections — labelled somewhat patronisingly 'For Ladies and Amateur Gardeners' and 'Artisans and Cottagers' Collections'. The vegetable list includes rhubarb seed, and capsicum 'All the best sorts' and, under Bulbs — gladioli, described as hybrids. (Rhubarb appeared in this country as an ornamental plant in the 16th century. It was not until the 19th century that it appeared in the London markets as a food.) The list of sundries had also expanded to include a miscellany of manures, potting materials, labels and flower sticks, barometers, fumigators, Fir Tree oil, Floral cement, Gishurst compound, gloves, knives, pencils, shears, syringes, Summer Cloud (for shading greenhouses), Tiffany (another shading), thermometers, virgin cork, weed killers, lawn mowers, rollers, garden chairs and tents.

This year was enlivened by the coronation of King George V. To mark the occasion E. W. King presented the town with a magnificent 32-mantle gas lamp for the illumination of the market square. Unfortunately, what was thought locally to have been the first automatic street gas lamp to be installed has now been taken down and lost or destroyed.

1914-18

During the First World War this firm is said to have packeted seeds in the buildings at Coggeshall from 1,400 acres of land. This will have been done mainly by women, using a

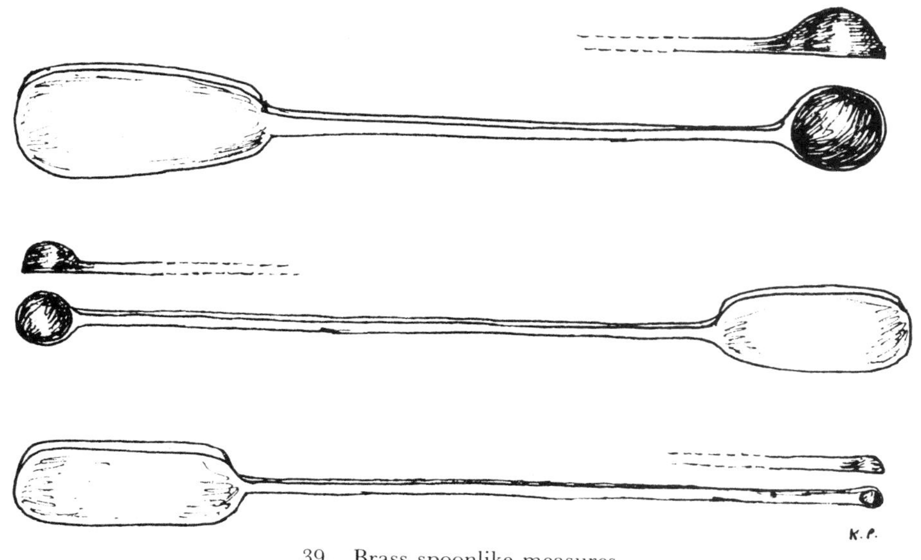

39. Brass spoonlike measures.

set of hemi-spherical, spoonlike measures. At that time there were 14 in a set and they ranged from one fiftieth to one quarter of an ounce. Previously, seeds had been packaged by cottagers in the villages and then a child's thimble was often used as a measure.

At this time E. W. K. drove a Fiat car and Bert Saunders (then employed by the firm) remembers how dusty it was travelling in the dickey to the Dengie Marshes to help to rogue E. L. Attenborough's radish seed crop. Macadamed roads were then few and far between.

Although he remained a bachelor, E. W. King was 'rather partial to the ladies' and during the war he had printed a postcard of some land girls working on his farm at Bocking Hall, West Mersea. It bore the caption 'Seed Growing, War Time, on 1500 acres'. The back of the card was divided into two, a space for the address and, on the left-hand side the message and a list of places where he owned or rented land:

FROM TO

E. W. KING & CO. Seed Growers

Seed farms: Coggeshall, Kelvedon, Feering, East Mersea, West Mersea and Wethersfield

We beg to acknowledge receipt of yours which is having our attention.

About this time also, Hutley's bus is remembered as putting on a bus trip from Coggeshall to Clacton. It was on Sundays during the summer months. Passengers were required to change their seats from the lower to the upper deck at a half-way point on both outgoing and homecoming journeys. This was instituted so all should have a share of the better view from the top. This deck had no roof; there were oil cloth sheets fastened to the backs of the seats which, in bad weather, might be fastened across the passenger to a hook on the opposite side. The driver had no windscreen and no lights except candle lamps fastened to the front. There was, however, an electric dynamo which produced a light under the destination panel, which was hooked on to the front, and also provided one dim light inside the lower deck.

1918-30

In order to appreciate what happened to the seed trade between the wars it may help to be reminded of the way of life and some of the developments of the previous 20 or so years. Before 1914, labour was plentiful and accustomed to working long hours for little pay so that all but the very poorest households were able to keep servants. The number varied according to income from households where a 'skivvy' came in daily, through a middle group supporting a cook, parlour-maid and back'us boy with possibly a groom/gardener, to the more well-to-do who maintained a veritable retinue of both indoor and outdoor staff. All had to be fed, including members of the immediate family and often dependant relatives as well as guests.

Most of the staff would still have known, even if that generation of employers did not, something of life in the country, and had perhaps been brought up there. They were still used to having a vegetable patch and some fruit to fill the cooking pots and they would have known the difference between freshly-dug celery and the pathetic cold-stored or canned apology currently offered for this once delightful comestible.

There were no supermarkets with their shelves crammed with dried, canned, chilled or frozen foods. Apart from 'ice-houses' in the shrubberies of the larger estates there was no domestic refrigeration and town pantries and shops tended to be relatively small, airless and too warm to keep food in good condition for more than a short period. Therefore seeds were needed to grow produce in one's own kitchen garden or to supply the market gardeners, who sent their goods into the city by horse-drawn cart or by water. Of these latter, complaints were made when it became obvious that the boats which had taken manure and other filth from the cities, for use on the fields as a fertilizer, returned with a load of green-grocery without having been cleaned!

After 1918 both the country and most of the population were suffering reduced circumstances. Three quarters of a million of our young and able-bodied men were dead and those who returned did not find the country as they remembered it but were faced with a harsh reality of shortage and want. Many had not even their former good health to enable then to do a full day's work. Gardeners were still required, but in decreasing numbers, and quite soon market gardeners began to suffer from the competition of cheaper food from abroad. A refrigerated shipload of pears and green peas was sent from Italy before 1898 and, soon after this, refrigeration was used for fruit coming in from Australia.

Our seed trade was particularly badly hit when, after 1918, the United States 'slapped a 6d./pound duty on all seeds imported'. It killed our very considerable root seed exports to America as, being low-priced seeds, they were unable to absorb the duty and still leave a profit. However, between the wars a root seed outlet was opened up with New Zealand which, in its turn, has been reversed since the Second World War.

The replacement of horses by machines revolutionised agricultural and horticultural practice for, particularly in the urban areas, horse manure for the market gardens was no longer to be found in any quantity and ways of using the different kinds of 'artificials' were having to be found out.

Labour, in short supply after 1918, had formed its Unions and found itself in a position to demand improved conditions. The 'ladies who picked over the pea seed' at Nutting and Sons, London, actually revolted! For years they had been expected to pick over a two hundredweight sack each day for 10s. a week. Then, if the overseer was not satified with their work, they had to stay behind and were not allowed home until the job was done properly. They went to Mr. Nutting asking for a rise to 12s. He is said to have protested that he had never heard of such a thing and that it would break the firm. However, being a wise man, he granted their request and the firm continued to prosper.

This sorting of the damaged from the sound pea and bean seed was a winter occupation but it had to be contracted for during the summer. In the spring, after the sorting was completed, some of the ladies repaired to the docks to pick over cocoa beans. Poor women — the ends of their fingers were often cracked, raw and bleeding, worn away by continuous movement on the benches. In their eyes the inventor of Elastoplast (which stayed put so much better than adhesive tape) would surely have been high on the list for canonisation.

The inter-war catalogues tell us that there was much happening in the field of hybridisation, seed testing and other legislation. Machinery usage continued to increase relatively slowly, and fungicides, insecticides, bacteriocides and weed killers were still confined to such substances as 'Bordeaux Mixture', Sulphuric Acid, Derris Dust and Calomel.

Unlike his grandfather, E. W. King became a local character about whom stories still abound. Locally he was known, more or less affectionately, as 'the one and only E. W.' and, in the trade, universally as 'The Sweet Pea King'. Every Monday morning he drove his Fiat to Kelvedon station to catch the train to Mark Lane, sometimes almost hidden by a colourful bunch of sweet peas tucked into his buttonhole. Today, nicknames seem to have gone out of fashion but then you were a nonentity indeed if you did not acquire one.

By the 1920s he was living at Abbeyfields, a pleasant house with a large garden above the River Blackwater, in Coggeshall. Negotiations for this house and garden together with four cottages, outbuildings and an adjoining property (Miss Cant's), finally came to an end in 1921, when he paid £1,250 for the lot. It is still possible to look into this garden from the firm's trial grounds and to imagine it as it must have been, beautifully kept by its owner.

On the domestic side, E. W.'s life became lonelier as the years progressed. His sister Louise E. King, died in 1920. In the same year he wrote to a friend saying that he had bought a new chair for his mother, Ellen Jane King, in the hope 'that she would recover from her illness and get downstairs again'. She was his last close relative.

Clearly a very fussily busy person he was 'into everything': a member of the Rural District Council and of Little Coggeshall Parish Council, an overseer of his parish and of Marks Hall, a Governor of the Coggeshall Council Schools and also of Sir Robert Hitcham's Foundation Exhibition, a Trustee of Paycock's Charity and, in the realm of sweet peas, a long-standing member of the Society, who won the Eckford Memorial Medal, and was twice its President. *The Nurseryman and Seedsman* of 8 November 1928, reinforces the indications in his personal correspondence that, latterly, E. W. was not in robust health for it reports from the N.S.P.S.'s Annual General Meeting (at which he was to have been presented with the Eckford Memorial Medal) that,

> 'Special and flattering reference was made to this year's trials, conducted by Messrs. E. W. King and Company, of Coggeshall, which were designated 'the best in the history of the Society' . . . It

was a matter of regret to all present that Mr. King, owing to indisposition, was unable to be with them that day . . . A telegram of sympathy and thanks was sent to him.

Politically a staunch Conservative, who was for years President of the Constitutional Club and a member of the Coggeshall Working Men's Conservative Association, he was also Vice-President of the Town Football Club, although he preferred hunting and cricket. He regularly rode to hounds with the East Essex until, three years before his death, riding had to be given up. However, he continued to give his support both to the hunt and to its point-to-point meetings at which his favourite horse, John, had had success. Cricket he followed with interest and is reported as being a most generous President of the local team. Time was found to set up a fund for ex-Servicemen and for widows and orphans. The latter fund is administered by the Parish Council to this day.

In his will, money was left to build a house for the district nurse — it is still in use — as well as eight almshouses for retired employees. There was also money for Colchester Hospital to which, in season, he would go to deliver a load of grapes from his own vines

40. Ernest W. King's N.S.P.S. trials, *c.*1930. By this time the sweet peas were supported on wires.

41. E. W. King with his favourite horse, 'John', which is being ridden by Mr. 'Rip' Browning.

on his way to the Corn Exchange on Saturdays. Truly he was a public benefactor and one hopes that the niggardly little meannesses, still recalled amongst his workforce, may be explained by the fact that he never quite came to terms with the changed money values after 1918. Many older people, today, have the same trouble since decimalisation.

1930-86

By the time of his death Ernest King had rebuilt, in brick, his original wooden warehouse near to Kelvedon railway station. On 21 August 1920, the firm became a limited company in which five of the employees were given an interest and at least some of them also became Directors of the Company. This proved a wise move because, at his unexpected death in 1930, his business was able to continue without faltering, to a steady expansion so that today the firm is still a totally wholesale establishment retaining the name of the founder. In 1986 it remained one of the very few privately-owned limited companies to be producing flower and vegetable seeds, whose employees and management show a proper pride in maintaining the very high standards set by their predecessors.

Before he died E. W. agreed to have the N.S.P.S. trials on his ground for the second, and what proved to be the last, time for in 1931 the N.S.P.S. decided that henceforth the trials should be laid down annually at the National Royal Horticultural Society's grounds at Wisley.

The exact terms of Ernest King's will are not remembered locally, but it is believed that his two godsons were left a substantial interest in both his own and J. K. K.'s businesses. In 1935, Mr. E. J. Small, one of the godsons, left the Board although he remained a shareholder. It is the other godson, Mr. E. C. Fairhead, of Hoo Hall, Rivenhall, Essex, who is remembered as being the 'hard but just' Managing Director of the two firms. Under his guidance, with the aid of the other Directors, namely G. H. Burt (the flower seed expert from 1912), G. Pegg (a firm's representative of long standing), E. F. Fox (E. W.'s personal secretary from 1929) and G. Cuckow (who joined the firm in 1914 and remained until he died in harness in 1948), the firm continued to flourish.

During the Second World War period progress in breeding and other programmes was officially halted but, behind the scenes, the selection of both flowers and vegetables was continuing so that, by 1949, the Company was able to resume, in full, its pre-war programme. It was fortunate that the post-war staff was almost identical with that of pre-war as those who had been serving in the forces returned, releasing those who had loyally continued beyond retirement age, many having completed well over 50 years with the firm.

Back in 1920 an orange/cerise/pink sweet pea named 'Doris' won an R.H.S. Award of Merit and a Silver Medal at Chelsea Flower Show. This was followed by another named 'Gladys' which achieved the same honours in 1921. Later came 'Mavis' and 'Dinky'. All came from the firm of Ernest King and had been named after the four daughters of G. H. Burt. Apart from Doris these girls had worked for the company for many years and, indeed, Mavis and Dinky were still doing so in 1986, and can look back with pride to the many occasions when their skill in arranging a floral exhibit has contributed greatly to the firm's winning a major award.

Looking at the present day catalogues with their impressively long lists of available seeds one cannot but reflect that, neat and concise as they are, the stop-press titbits are missing which deprives them of their former historical value.

It is refreshing to find a firm which is not wholly geared to the supermarket trade. Here, there are plans to grow some of the perennials not currently available in any quantity in England and which are now expensive to buy from overseas. Again, the cost of foreign herbs has risen sharply over the last few years and this firm, like the Emperor Charlemagne in A.D. 802, has decided to grow some of its own.

In 1980 Mr. Campbell Bowring became the firm's flower seed expert, having spent some years gaining experience in Holland. He is full of energy and new ideas for the development of his department and the firm has already succeeded in gaining a Gold Medal for their display of over 100 varieties of sweet peas at the 1982 Amsterdam Floriade.

Mr. Bowring volunteered the information that F1 hybrid begonia seed has been known to be worth more than gold dust and on very rare occasions it has commanded a price of over £2,000 for one ounce (28 grams). Mr. K. R. Phillips added that the seed is extremely tiny, just like fine dust, and may be sold in amounts as small as one-tenth of a gram (one two-hundredth of an ounce). (Appendix F.) In case the reader is gaining the idea that all seed growers are, or should be millionaires, it must be strongly emphasised that such seed is in only limited demand and therefore no great acreage is grown. Also, in most cases, such gains are almost invariably off-set by losses made on other crops through disease, pest or weather. For instance, Altenaria has in the last few years caused great losses within the Brassicae genus — a crop may look like yielding four or five hundred kilos in June, but one month later, following an attack by Altenaria, the yield may be reduced to a mere 50 kilos of shrivelled seed of very poor germination ability. In the case of a seedsman's crop this may mean the loss of his particularly valuable 'mother' seed, plus the cost of cultivations, weed and pest control chemicals, disease control sprays, rent and such like for the acreage of land which the crop has occupied for, perhaps, two years, leaving all to be paid for by the profits from some other crop; as Mr. Phillips remarked, 'It is almost safer backing horses!'.

Also in 1980, C. B. Phillips, who had been running the farm and seed-growing side of the business, was made a Director. He is grandson of W. T. Phillips, who came to Coggeshall to work for the rival firm of J. K. King in 1915, and son of K. R. Phillips, who started with E. W. King as an apprentice in 1933, became Company Secretary in 1953 and Managing Director from 1968 to 1985.

A walk round the E. W. King trial grounds with K. R. Phillips revealed an interesting selection of vegetables including their 'Crusader' runner bean renowned for its length of pod. From their large range of cucumber is one called 'Apple'. It is spherical, creamy white, and said not to be indigestible. They also persist with parsley seed crops despite the hazard of virus disease which has recently deterred many other growers. Here there are seed plots of lavender; a new annual hollyhock, 'Summer Carnival', from the United States of America; a strain of tobacco, the large leaves of which will provide food for the predator *Encarsia formosa*, now used to control whitefly in tomato houses. It is on the trial grounds near the office that the sweet pea hybrids were cherished, together with items which for the moment 'are being kept dark'. Returning through the packeting department and the store with its walls lined with the original drawers (made from Hudson Soap boxes) full of every sort of seed, one feels the spirit of E.W.K. still permeating the building. On getting back to his office, Mr. Phillips remarked thoughtfully 'I wish that I had known him. I should like to think that he would approve of what we are trying to do'. Surely he would.

E. P. BROWN AND SON, COGGESHALL, ESSEX

The following is all that has survived of another good and thriving little seed business, built up by Mr. E. P. Brown, who had first been apprenticed to John K. King. His premises were on the site of what was once the doctor's house in Church Street, Coggeshall. As is so often the case his attempt to give his sons what he felt he had missed in his youth led to these children growing up with no real understanding that work was a necessary part of life. So while all agreed that they were keen sportsmen, good-natured and generous boys, it was also said that they were no businessmen.

An undated catalogue sent out by this firm survives in the collection of Ernest W. King and is of interest as showing the very large range of seeds handled by quite a modest firm. The probable date is around 1923.

New Annual Special Offer
(Wholesale)
Catalogue of Pedigree Vegetable, Flower and Farm SEEDS

After the introductory letter to customers, which is signed by Edward W. Brown, there are listed the following Vegetable and Flower seeds for the garden. I have inserted figures, in brackets, to indicate the number of varieties on offer in each case.

1. Peas — wrinkled (44)
   — round (12)
2. Broad beans (16)
3. French beans (8)
4. Runner beans (16)
5. Artichoke (2)
6. Asparagus (3)
7. Beet (17)

8. Borecole or Kale (14)
9. Broccoli (22)
10. Brussels sprouts (14)
11. Cabbage— garden (37)
    — cattle and drumhead (6)
12. Savoy (7)
13. Carrot (23)
14. Cauliflower (9)
15. Celery (17)
    Celeriac (1)
16. Cress (5)
17. Cucumber — ridge (9)
    — frame (12)
18. Endive (6)
19. Gourds (4)
20. Leek (8)
21. Lettuce — cos (16)
    — cabbage (23)
22. Mustard (4)
23. Onion (34)
24. Parsley (4)
25. Parsnip (8)
26. Radish (20)
27. Rhubarb (seed) (4)
28. Spinach (8)
29. Tomato (22)
30. Turnip (12)
31. Vegetable marrow (7)
32. Alphabetical Flower List — $3\frac{1}{2}$ pages — Priced per oz. and per lb.
33. Superior coloured Pictorial Seed Packets for Vegetables and Flowers

The farm seeds are confined to the back cover and include

clovers (6) plus lucerne and sainfoin.
Grass seed mixtures — permanent pastures and 3-8 year leys for heavy, medium and light soils
Herbs and sundry seeds (42)
Kohl Rabi (6) King's selections
Mangel Wurzel (19)
Lawn grass seed mixtures

There are also manures, the list of which emphasises the limitations of such in this era. Customers are, however, offered a good selection of what would have been available:

1. Our special fertilizer — used for all crops
2. Bone meals (raw)
3. Clay's Fertilizer
4. Fish Compound (Eclipse)
5. Hoof and horn
6. Nitrate of Soda and Sulphate of Ammonia
7. Sweet pea and Tomato Compound (Extra Good)

Mushroom spawn, strong paper seed bags and plain seed pockets and raffia were also offered. They were followed by:

Rape or kale seed — (Dwarf Essex)
Kale (for cattle)
Swede turnip (5) — Purple Top varieties
Turnip (farm varieties) (5)

On the back cover they claim to be:

> The cheapest and best growers of Finest Home-Grown Selected Seeds especially grown for the MARKET GROWER, FARMER, FLORIST OR SEEDSMAN ETC., at lowest wholesale prices for the present season.

And further:

> We have the very best the world can produce and for which we will not be undersold by any reputable firm.

The last son, Walter, who had been sponged upon by many, and particularly for football boots and other gear, finished up living in a ramshackle shed with no door, on the side of Tey Road, Coggeshall. Finally, he had to be taken in by the 'Poor House' at Braintree, where he remained, amiable and cheerful to the end. When a visitor, who went to see him just before he died, asked, 'Do you regret your life?', he replied firmly, and in some surprise, 'No, I enjoyed it'. One cannot but believe that such a one received a welcome in Heaven.

Chapter Five

An Interweaving of Businesses

PART I — TABER TO COOPER TABER

George Taber, Rivenhall and Witham, Essex

> The family crest of Taber, one of the oldest of Essex names is described as:
> 'TABER, ESS., a griffin's head, erased, ppr.'[1]

George Taber, the founder of the firm of Cooper Taber and Company Ltd., Witham, is first heard of in a letter from Louis Gowlett, his niece by marriage. It was written in 1936 to George's grandson Walter Taber, who had evidently asked what she remembered of the family. She told him that a Mr. Sparrow-Bigg had married 'a pretty poor girl', probably of lesser social standing than himself and that one of their children was a daughter called Mary, who was Louis's aunt. Mary married a Mr. Ralston who was killed, perhaps in the Crimean War, after which she returned home to Great Baddow. There she became housekeeper to the Reverend Mr. Hamilton by whom George Taber was also employed as groom or, more probably, groom-gardener. From her niece's account we get a picture of a kind woman who, although remembered as 'very much older than him', had a little money and in due course Mary and George were married.

Nothing is known of George's family but it must have had some social standing for he obviously had manners acceptable for one who was to become head gardener on a fair-sized estate. Furthermore, his education was sufficient to have at least given him the capability of teaching himself the many facets of the art of gardening, to plan for and advise his employer, to speak in public, and to control and instruct those under him. Certainly, a later photograph of George is of a gentleman in a grey top hat and a neat dark coat — a personage much more likely to be giving orders than to be told to 'go dig that border'. Perhaps he was a younger member of a not very affluent family of the gentry. At any rate, when he applied for the position of head gardener to the Du Canes, of Great Braxted Park, he was considered suitable and got the job.

It was the custom to provide such employees with a cottage on the estate and an office, usually within the main house, from which they conducted their business. On his appointment, the pair moved into the park to the cottage by the lake. George is known to have laid out the Fan Garden (now replaced by a rose garden). Perhaps he supervised the planting of the long avenues of limes that lead from the road to the house. Certainly he will have had to know the rudiments of surveying, about stoves, hot beds and glass, as well as how to look after fruit and vines. Did he, perhaps, also supervise the planting of at least some of what is said to have been a very fine collection of imported trees and shrubs set within the high walls of the Park?

A directory of 1848 lists George Taber as head gardener at Braxted Park; another of 1855 describes him as market gardener and seedsman, but he was probably still with the Du Canes. In the 1863 directory he had moved to (or at least gives his business address as) Rose Cottage, Rivenhall, and he is now described as gardener, florist and seedsman.

Meantime, in 1811, Dr. Dixon had come to Witham as medical practitioner and by 1816 was living at 129 High Street (the present doctor's surgery). In 1850 he moved out of

Witham to the small estate of Durward's Hall, Rivenhall. He was a man of many interests and perhaps needing some horticultural guidance he made the acquaintance of, and in time became very friendly with, the head gardener at the Park. In fact, from his diaries (now in the possession of Dr. J. G. Denholm, Witham) he seems to have made it possible for George to enlarge his seedsman's business in 1864. Whether the help was financial, or by allowing seeds to be grown on part of his land for a nominal rent, or both, is not clear.

Dr. Dixon was aware that George interested himself in good works and so when Dr. Barnardo came to Durward's Hall they were introduced to each other and perhaps became friends. At any rate, his great-grandchildren still report that great-grandfather knew Dr. Barnardo!

In 1872 George Taber produced a 'Select List' in which he announced 'purchasers of quantities will be liberally treated with', and in 1873 he moved his family into Matchyn's Farm, where there were numerous outbuildings suitable for seed storage and trading. The first lease for this property, between George Taber and Colonel Sir Samuel Brook Pechell, Bart., is dated 1880, but it seems that George Taber had been farming this land since 1862.

A directory for 1874 lists him as Seedgrower, Rivenhall, and also contains an advertisement for his 'Gate Post' mangel. Root seeds were to remain a main commodity for which this firm had a name.

As a result of the move, Rose Cottage became vacant for his recently-appointed assistant, Thomas Cullen. All went well and in 1881 Thomas Cullen was made a partner with a third share in the business which was re-named Taber and Cullen, Rivenhall.

By now George was clearly a pillar of the district. He attended church (probably because his wife was Church of England), preached in the Chapel and regularly consulted an astrologer in Ipswich. (A study of the stars was very much in vogue and many a family's telescope dates from this time.) It is said that on astrologically inauspicious days this gentleman, with his almost 'stage prop' spade-shaped beard, retired indoors behind drawn blinds, lit the lamp and would not come out until the signs were more favourable!.

In 1884 George Taber was still Managing Director of the business and on hearing that Robert Cooper's firm was looking for more capital he at once saw the chance to link a merchanting business with a prestigious London address to that of the seed-growing firm of Taber and Cullen. His diary for 16 April 1886 (in the possession of T. A. Glover of Thorrington, Essex), includes this entry:

> Webster, Hodges, Thorburn and Huggins came to Rivenhall with a view to establishing a seed company. Cold with Hail Storms.

This is almost certainly a reference to the formation of Cooper Taber which took place the following year.

His partner, Thomas Cullen, did not agree with this proposed amalgamation but George was determined, with the result that, although for financial reasons Thomas remained with the firm for another seven years, he soon started his own business and finally broke away in 1894. (See pp.116-17)

In 1886, the 1880 lease of Matchyn's Farm, which had been extended to 1901, was further extended to expire in 1915. This allowed for the rent (£116 per annum in 1880) to vary with the yearly average price of wheat at Ipswich market. This lease was also transferred from George Taber to his Administrators and Executors, which probably indicates that he was already suffering from cancer of the throat, and that he had retired from active participation in the business by that date; a supposition further supported by the first Annual Report of Cooper Taber and Company Ltd. (in the possession of Essex Record Office (D/F 90)), which shows that by August 1888 George was listed amongst the Directors but was no longer Chairman of the Board.

At the time of George's death on 9 February 1895,[2] his only son, James, was living and

42. Messrs. Taber and Cullen's staff at Matchyn's, Rivenhall, just before the business moved to Avenue Road, Witham, *c.*1887. Back row, left to right: unknown, 'Pug' Ager, Walter Taber, Arthur Mann. Next row (standing): Alfred Springett, Albert Wallis, George Taber, Thomas Cullen, William Rushen, 'Bubbly' Cook, Charlie Ager. Seated men: Tom Gurton, Alfred Gooch, Chralie Tuff, ? Avey. Seated boys: ? Rushen, Tom Ager, unknown.

43. George Taber with his spade-shaped beard.

farming at Little Braxted Hall, from which he later moved to Evelyn House, 129 High Street, Witham. James's son, Walter, continued farming at Matchyn's, but the seed business was now almost entirely carried on in the Witham establishment into which two other firms, Henry Clarke and Sons of King Street, Covent Garden, London, and Waite, Nash and Company, 79 Southwark Street, London, had already been incorporated.

On Monday 28 May 1900, Matchyn's delightful farmhouse was burnt to the ground. The *Essex County Chronicle* of 1 June 1900 gives a splendidly detailed account of all that happened:

LARGE FIRE
at Rivenhall

MR. W. TABER'S HOUSE
burnt down

narrow escape of the inmates

exciting scenes

On Sunday night the household, which consists of Mr. and Mrs. Taber, a baby daughter, and two servants, retired to bed at the usual time, Mr. Taber being the last to look round the premises and lock up. At five o'clock on Monday morning P.C. Smith, stationed at Rivenhall, went past the house, when all appeared to be safe. A few minutes later a man named Cutts saw smoke issuing from the back part of the premises, and a messenger was at once sent for the constable, who was about to return after his night's duty. The constable set to work to save the inmates of the doomed building, and in this he was successful, although not a moment too soon. Mr. Taber only had sufficient time to slip off his nightshirt, and Mrs. Taber to put on her dressing gown, and they just managed to catch up the sleeping baby from its cot and rush to the staircase. One of the servants, Annie Sewell, had a perilous adventure. The staircase being in flames she made for a back window and scrambled out, falling into her master's arms. Neither was seriously hurt.

In a very short time the whole house was enveloped in flames. From the drawing room several easy chairs, a pianoforte, table and other articles were rescued, and from the office a safe and three guns.

By seven o'clock nothing remained of the fine old house except the chimney stacks. All the contents, with the exception of the articles mentioned, were destroyed.

Shortly before seven o'clock the Witham Fire Brigade received a call, and went to the scene as quickly as possible, but it was apparent that no good could be done by playing upon the *debris*. After pushing over the chimney stacks, which were in an exceedingly dangerous condition, the brigade returned. . . . The outbreak is supposed to have originated in the kitchen chimneys.

Miss Dorothy Taber, the 'sleeping baby' of the report, remembers being told by her mother how distressed she had been to see the men struggling to bring out large items such as the piano and easy chairs, when they might have saved far more valuable and easily transportable items such as silver christening mugs and other treasures. She also adds that although it is true that her father removed his nightshirt, he did manage to drag on his trousers before making his escape!

On 22 June 1903 James Taber died, leaving four sons, all in farms, and six daughters. One son, James, was a Director, but when he died, although they still held shares, none of the family took an active part in running the business.

His son, Walter, remained farming at Matchyn's and was much interested in the new machines then coming onto the market. He bought one of the first pea-shellers, which was driven by a Ruston Hornsby engine. The shelled peas were packed into cardboard boxes in which, although they had ventilation holes, the peas heated. On another occasion he tried attaching a strongly-built car to pull a self-binder. When Walter died, in 1965, Matchyn's Farm went out of the family.

Cooper Taber and Company Ltd., 90-92 Southwark Street, London S.E.1, and Witham, Essex
1887-1962

When George Taber's firm became Cooper Taber and Company Ltd., its character changed from that of a local seed grower's company to that of a wholesale seed merchant. It was now a seed house of standing in the City of London, owning little land of its own, except the Witham trial grounds, but contracting out with selected farmers and smallholders for a large acreage of seeds to be grown.

Moreover, through the link with Cooper, the new company could claim connections back to several of the oldest-established firms in the country, including those of Mr. Child and J. Field (see pp.17-18).

At some time around 1920, George H. Dicks, then this firm's General Manager in London, drew up the firm's family tree. It is still the basis of the 'tree' which was brought up to date some time after 1962, and which is still used as an historical record by Hurst Gunson, Cooper Taber Ltd. (see p.110). Some of the dates in this tree do not agree with those in other documents quoted in the text. I have done no research to find which is right except in the case of George Taber, who is recorded as selling seeds in 1861, and the date of the Taber and Cullen partnership is certainly 1881.

The connections with other seed firms before 1962

In 1880, one of the oldest of the London seed firms, Minier and Company (1760), came into the family tree. In 1813 Daniel Nash joined the Minier's firm which, by around 1820, became known as Minier, Nash and Nash. Probably the last Minier died, or retired, before they became Waite, Nash and Huggins after amalgamating with Waite, Burnell and Huggins in 1880. This firm, as Waite Nash, joined with Cooper Taber in 1887. The Cooper firm also has a link with Minier and Company through the John Mason who appears in their lineage. Minier and Company started at 'Ye Signe of the Orange Tree', No. 60 Strand, where from 1760 they carried on a thriving business with those who attended Covent Garden, which was by then the premier London flower and vegetable market.

Their business remained in the Strand for over a century, undergoing several amalgamations and consequent changes in name. Often these came about because a seedgrower had been taken into the business on having agreed to grow for the firm such seeds as were required. It was during a particularly unsettled period around 1781 that John Mason, an employee and by then a partner in the Minier firm, left to set up his own establishment at 'The Sign of the Orange Tree', 152 Fleet Street. Edward Cross's business was at 'The Sign of the Orange Tree' and it looks as if Mason took over his business. At best the similarity of this address with that of Minier's must sometimes have led to confusion!

An article in *The Grower* (16 April 1966) states that Mason issued a 110-page catalogue in 1793. This catalogue is now lost. The title page read:

> Fine Double Hyacinth and other various flower Roots and Seeds, Imported chiefly from Holland, France, America, Italy, Botany Bay, etc., by John Mason, Orange Tree, 152 Fleet Street.

A trade list of John Mason and Son, dated 1826, also now lost, was shown by D. O. Morris to the writer of an article in *The Grower* of 25 October 1958. A photoprint of this list heads the article and shows the date and prices for 1826 filled in by hand. The original was last seen by D. O. Morris in a tea chest which, with several others full of books and documents, was sent to be stored in a London cellar.

In 1827 Mason's nephew, surnamed Noble, and a Mr. Goude, took over the business, which became Noble and Goude. By 1830 the sole proprietors were W. and J. Noble, who carried on the business until both died of cholera in 1848. The surviving son of W. Noble then brought into the business as partners two men who had long practical experience with the firm, which now became known as Noble, Cooper and Bolton. By 1867, it seems that Mr. Noble had died and Mr. Bolton retired, leaving Robert Cooper as sole proprietor. It was he who wrote to his customers in 1872:

> I beg to hand you my Price Current for the ensuing season . . . If any articles are quoted lower by respectable houses, have the Kindness to inform me, as I will not be undersold . . .

Cooper carried on in his own name at 152 Fleet Street until the lease ran out. Then the business moved to 90 Southwark Street, London, and not many years later, in 1884, Robert Cooper died. Not much is known about him but by the way he built up this business he must have been a man of considerable acumen, for by the time this firm joined with Taber and Cullen the trade with America was remarkable.

Mr. D. O. Morris, who became a director of Cooper Taber Ltd. (*c.*1955-60) says that four generations of Morrises worked for Robert Cooper. That he had a kindly nature is shown by the family story that when Grandfather Morris died from scarlet fever at 33, his eldest son, aged 12, was immediately found a job as an office boy to help the family finances. This lad became a commercial traveller selling seeds for the firm until he died, aged 82, having seen his own son, D. O. Morris, come into the Southwark Street warehouse in 1922. Mr. Morris has an interesting relic of the past — a wooden quart measure — which belonged to Samuel Mason's firm. It is stamped with a William IV crown, and a W on the outside, presumably the employee's initial.

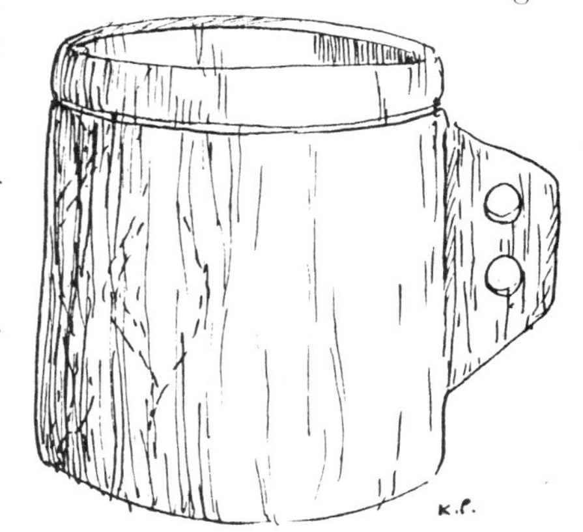

44. A quart measure from Samuel Mason's firm, made from a single piece of wood.

By 1899 Cooper Taber's had connections with 10 old-established seed houses each of which, in its day, had introduced new and specially selected strains of different seeds. There was R. Cooper's 'Sparkler' radish, George Taber's 'Rivenhall Giant' mangel, Jacob Wrench's variegated hollies and the 'Cup and Saucer' Canterbury bells (*Campanula Medium Calycanthema*) of Waite, Burnell and Huggins.

A few other points of interest have survived regarding some of these firms. For instance, Jacob Wrench, taken over by Howcroft in 1905, was the oldest wholesale seed firm then existing in the City of London. It had been founded at the sign of 'The Three Sheaves' in 1750. This sign, recently re-painted, now hangs over the door of Hurst's canteen at Witham.

Howcroft and Watkins claim to be the originators of pictorial seed packets and brought to the Cooper Taber business their connection with Dutch bulbs. Daniel Nash was a miller and seedgrower in Biggleswade.

J. G. Waite started as a market gardener in Camberwell in 1830 and as his seed business increased he moved first to Hatton Garden and later to High Holborn. At his death it was his stepson who carried on the business, in partnership with Huggins and Taylor. This firm became known as Waite, Burnell, Huggins and Company and moved to 79 Southwark Street. As already stated, in 1880 Waite, Burnell, Huggins and Company amalagamated with Minier, Nash and Nash, and when their Southwark Street lease expired, they became incorporated with Robert Cooper's firm to which they brought personnel, stock and additional capital.

In 1834, George Charlwood issued a seed catalogue from his premises in Tavistock Row, Covent Garden (the street is no longer there), and, as Charlwood and Cummings, also did business from premises in Hart Street (now Floral Street) and the adjoining James Street,

Covent Garden. In 1871 he sold out to William Watkins whose firm subsequently became Howcroft and Watkins.

Henry Clarke and Sons joined Cooper Taber's in 1887 from King Street, Covent Garden.

Premises

From time to time the premises of Cooper Taber have become the subject of written articles. A reprint from a newspaper of 12 December 1891[3] described those in Southwark Street as:

> A very fine and capacious warehouse is that occupied by the Company . . . It is of great height showing a substantial frontage of six storeys besides being of large depth. The shop [on the ground floor was] a splendidly appointed and conveniently fitted up department.

The reprint continues,

> An interesting industrial feature of these warehouses is that on several of the floors, ranged in front of the windows, may be counted over 100 women busily engaged picking [over] peas . . . A large amount of plant and machinery, driven by gas engines, is distributed over the floors for fanning, cleaning and in other ways manipulating the seeds.

A later description by D. O. Morris of the yearly programme and working conditions of these women shows that the floor on which they worked from October to March was, even by 1923, very far from being 'splendidly appointed and conveniently fitted up'. He told me that from 8.30 a.m. to 5.30 p.m., with hardly a break, 'the ladies', as they were called, sat on wooden benches wrapped in a cocoon of assorted clothing (supplemented by sacks on the worst days), their eyes fixed on the dry peas on the table immediately in front of them, their mitten-clad, chilblained hands darting forward to remove any discoloured or damaged peas as they were noticed.

There was no heating, even in the bitterest weather. To make matters worse, as soon as one lot of peas was finished, the doors at the end of the building were thrown open while sacks were hoisted to and from a horse-drawn cart in the street below. If such a thing were possible, the temperature in the warehouse then dropped.

When the dry peas were finished, usually by March, the women were paid off. Then, as soon as green peas came, they were off to Covent Garden Market, to shell peas. Once this was finished it was the family's holiday to go hop-picking in Kent before returning to the £1 weekly wage in the warehouse, where the doors were opened to let them in at 8.30 a.m. If they arrived even a few minutes late they would find the doors locked against them, not to be opened again until 11.00 a.m. when they were admitted but docked a quarter day's pay. Yet despite the hardships they are remembered as 'Good old Girls, who swore like troopers' and no wonder! Today, split, holed and discoloured peas can be removed from a dried sample by a machine. This may be said to have removed a chore or to have taken away several people's jobs, according to which way you look at it.

Of the Witham premises, in 1958, there is mention of a recently-gained architectural award for the most modern and up-to-date building of its style for that year. It was judged by a committee under the chairmanship of the then Mr. Basil Spence, and a commemorative plaque was presented.[4] The three architects concerned, Chamberlain, Powell and Bon, now perhaps better known for their involvement in London's Barbican development, described the Cooper Taber job as 'lovely engineering and the client only wrote four letters'.[5]

Dutch Bulbs

A bulb business, partly in London and partly in Holland, came to Cooper Taber's through Mr. Howcroft of Howcroft and Watkins, in 1912.

The business was then enlarged and the firm had its own staff and premises at Bennebroek, near Haarlem, Holland. Two or three of the staff were always sent out from London to help pack and invoice the crop at harvest time. This continued (with a break during the First World War) until about 1921. Afterwards, packaging in Holland was discontinued but a buyer still went out each year to purchase bulb crops. These were then shipped direct to the warehouse in London for packaging in this country.

About 1930, D. O. Morris, from the Cooper side of the business, took over the London bulb department. He considered that the former method of packaging in Holland was better than bringing the bulbs to England in bulk and handling them twice, so, for the first time, he hired land for the firm in Holland on which bulbs were grown and packaged. When the Dutch stopped this practice by foreigners, a Dutch company, known as Cooper Taber and Company n.v. Holland, had to be formed.

After the First World War, J. C. G. Van der Laan, a Dutchman, was the Bulb Manager in Holland. He remained in this post until about 1950. During the Second World War, this man was allowed by the Germans to carry on since he was considered to be too old for their Labour Camps and of more use to them by keeping the business going until they had won the War. When they lost it and Cooper Taber's once more had contact with Van der Laan, they were able to appreciate just how great his loyalty to them had been for the firm's affairs were still in perfect order.

Sadly, soon after Cooper Taber's joined Hurst Gunson in 1962 this Dutch bulb connection lapsed.

The American Trade

As soon as European emigrants settled in America an export trade in seeds from Europe began. First the settlers required seeds to plant their fields and gardens. Then in 1736 came their export of American tree, shrub and flower seeds for Europe's gardens.[6] By the 1850s the bigger firms in the U.S.A. were growing some of their own seeds, but at this stage the quality still left much to be desired. However, gradually the necessary expertise was acquired either from European visitors who decided to stay to grow seeds, or from those who were induced to extend their stay to clean up someone's American stock.[7]

Nevertheless, in 1887 the trade from Europe was still mainly one of export and Robert Cooper's firm was able to bring to the partnership with Taber and Cullen a quite considerable American trade for the export of turnip, swede, mangold, cabbage and flower seeds.

To quote D. O. Morris,

> Coopers did an enormous trade with the States, as did Johnson's and Sharpe's — you had to be in the big side of the business to deal with America. Samuel Dicks was the first traveller to America, of whom I have heard. He was followed by his son George who was perhaps the best firm's traveller in America that there ever was.

With this reputation it is not surprising that George Dicks became managing director of the firm. That the export trade was large is confirmed by a story of Cooper Taber's American and Canadian representative, Mr. W. A. Sim.[8] One season he obtained from one firm alone an order for three million pounds of turnip seed. It was with Wood's of Richmond, Virginia, who required two million pounds of Purple Top, White Globe Turnip seed, and one million pounds of Golden Ball Turnip seed.

Before the First World War, as soon as harvest was over and the seeds dressed and weighed up, it was quite common for whole train loads of seeds to leave ports such as Liverpool and Southampton to be shipped to both North and South America. There were even occasions when the quantity was so great that the railways had to refuse to move more until the seed already at the ports had been cleared.

Mr. A. H. Cutts, once a warehouse manager with Cooper Taber's, remembers that during most of his time with the firm there was an annual order from D. M. Ferry and Company of Detroit for anything between 25 and 50 tons of Purple Top, White Globe Turnip seed.

The first real blow to this trade was the 1918 import duty of 6d. on every pound of seed imported into the United States. This made it very difficult for a profit to be made on seeds such as roots which were in the low price range. From then on this trade gradually tailed-off until during the Second World War America, through Lease-Lend, was supplying England with seeds grown in their country. Without this aid our farmers and seed merchants would have had great difficulty in carrying on, but it meant that after the War our seed exports were decreasingly required — even more so because by then they had learnt our way of growing root seeds.

The fire of 1953

On Friday 18 September 1953, when the 16-page *Braintree and Witham Times* could still be bought for 3d., the Company suffered another fire. This time the headlines read:

£250,000 DAMAGE BY FLAMES
Seed Warehouses a Roaring Inferno
Girders and glass melt in heat

Firemen were on the scene in four minutes, more rapidly than at Matchyn's, but unluckily there was no water available. The pressure was down to 30 pounds per square inch and 40 minutes were lost before a full supply could be obtained from the River Brain in Guithaven Valley, a quarter of a mile away.

About 1.15 p.m. one of the office staff, Miss Pamela Lines, of Kelvedon, first noticed smoke coming from a warehouse window. As it was lunch-time there were only four people on the premises, the Manager, Mr. C. F. Hawkins, Miss Lines, Mrs. Chaplin and Mr. Kenneth Cutts. The Manager at once called the fire brigade and turned off the main gas supply. Soon members of staff arrived and helped to carry the firm's record books to the lawn of a house across the road. The already made-up weekly wage packets were also saved with a few items of office furniture and a few sacks of seeds.

The staff were then told by the police to keep clear because of the danger of falling walls. So intense was the heat that the apples and pears on the trees of my nearby garden were roasted in situ and the wall of the house remained, like a brick oven, hot for days.

Despite the presence of 10 fire brigades very little could be done during the 40 minutes they stood by helplessly with a mere trickle of water issuing from the hoses. When at last an adequate supply of water did come through, many of the 50 or more waiting firemen were so surprised that they dropped their hoses. In any case, it is doubtful if much could have been done as it was but a matter of minutes before flames took hold of the entire weather-boarded building and roared on to the next and larger warehouse built of brick. On one window-sill, a large ball of twine was encased, like a huge paper-weight, in the molten glass.

There is fierce rivalry between all seed firms but they have a tradition of coming to one another's aid in times of difficulty. So we read that after the fire 'The neighbouring firm of Thomas Cullen and Sons immediately offered Cooper Taber temporary accommodation and storage for the seeds which had been rescued'. However, in order to preserve their business privacy, the office continued to be run from a garage on the old site. The fact that Cullen's came to the help of Cooper Taber's is not based on a newspaper report alone, for members of Cooper Taber's staff recall 'how very good' Cullen's were, not only at the immediate time but also later. One hears such remarks as 'We were desperate for kale seed. You see, we had almost the whole supply hereabouts and dozens of orders to fulfil. It was all burnt. But I remember Cullen's let us have what they could and only charged a fair price for it.[9] And again, 'when we had our new buildings up and had installed a new machine — a Kipp Kelly separator (it can, amongst other things, remove stones from

45. Fire at Cooper Taber's, 18 September 1953. 'On one window-sill a huge ball of twine was encased, like a huge paper-weight, in the molten glass.'

samples of peas) some of their [Cullen's] men came over to help us get it going — as they already had one, and knew how it went'.

Another firm which came to the rescue was E. W. King of Coggeshall. They dried all the seed which had got wet but was otherwise undamaged.

When the fire engines finally departed, after something like a week, the peas that could not be saved by drying began to germinate and smell. In order to clear up and remove the smell, lorry loads of rotting peas and turnip seed were carted out to Blue Mills gravel pit at the bottom of Wickham Bishop's hill. When complaints about the ghastly stench started coming in from this 'superior' residential area the carters covered the pit with a layer of soil every night.[10] Nothing quelled the smell which pervaded the whole area for weeks if not months. Then, what was described as 'a plague of silver fish' occurred in the pit. The local newspapers had a field day reporting complaints and queries from far and near. Would the silver fish invade the houses? Were they really silver fish? Was it a plague? Was the smell catching? Would the disease spread? Would there be an epidemic? and so on.

Sometimes, on a late summer evening, very local Witham residents still fancy they can smell rotting peas!

After the fire of 1953, although they rebuilt the premises by 1955, the firm of Cooper Taber Ltd. are said to have been looking for a way out of their difficulties, for it is thought locally that they had been under-insured. There were rumours of a proposed take-over by Thomas Cullen and Son which, it is said, was rejected. Certainly, this proposal, if made, came to nothing, for in 1962 it was as Hurst, Gunson, Cooper, Taber Ltd. that we next hear of the firm (see Part III of this chapter, p.109).

Meanwhile, in Part II, the history of William Hurst's firm will be brought to this date.

PART II — THE HURST, McMULLEN, SHERWOOD AND GUNSON CONNECTIONS

Hurst and McMullen 1843-57

On Monday 13 April 1843, an interesting advertisement appeared in the horticultural trade press:

> NEW HORTICULTURAL & AGRICULTURAL SEED ESTABLISHMENT
> 6 LEADENHALL STREET
>
> William Hurst and William George McMullen for many years past engaged with the house of Warner & Warner, 28 Cornhill, beg respectfully to acquaint their Friends and the Public that, circumstances have arisen which induced them to leave the service of that establishment, they commenced business as Wholesale and Retail SEEDSMEN and FLORISTS at the above named premises on Monday, the 13th inst., and they can confidently assure all who may kindly favour them with orders, that from the numerous resources they possess, through extensive connection with the best Seed Growers both in this country and on the continent, and from many years practical experience in various branches of the Business, they are enabled to offer every article of first rate genuine quality, and no exertion will be spared in giving prompt attention to every order, and endeavouring to merit a continuance of their support.

This was followed by a short list of what they had to offer. It included, as well as seeds, collections of Asters, Zinnias, Balsams, Hollyhocks and Larkspur from 'the finest German growers known', together with other plants such as Myatts New British Queen strawberries (10s. 6d. per 100 plants) and Grayson's Giant asparagus (3s. 0d. for 100). Seeds cost 6d. and 1s. a packet, with common varieties for 3d.

It is this William Hurst's surname which now heads the amalgamation of firms under the title Hurst Gunson Cooper Taber Ltd., of Witham.

W. G. McMullen left the firm and returned to his brewing and seed grower's business in Hertfordshire. This perhaps happened in 1857, when William Hurst took his son, another William, into partnership, for the firm then became known as Hurst and Son.

Hurst and Son 1857-1939

Nathaniel Newman Sherwood, J.P., V.M.H. (1846-1916) was born at Maquise, near Boulogne, for at the time his father was employed on the completion of the North France Railway. Later, when both father and uncle were employed on the construction of the London to Brentwood section of the Eastern Counties Railway, Nathaniel left school. He was at once apprenticed to his uncle, an engineer, but showed no aptitude for the work and in 1862 joined the firm of Hurst and Son, Houndsditch, London. Evidently this young man was received socially by the Hursts, for he married Emma, their youngest daughter. In 1864, William Hurst (senior) died and in 1868 Nathaniel Sherwood was made a partner in the firm. Then in 1871 his brother-in-law, William Hurst (junior) died and this left Nathaniel in control of the business.

By 1874, Hurst's were in the forefront of the seed world. A wholesale catalogue for 1874/5 is preserved which lists garden, agricultural and flower seeds. The head office was still at 6 Leadenhall Street, and by then this firm had Stand No. 38, in the Seed Market, Mark

Lane, as well as offices at 152 Houndsditch, with warehouses behind in Gun Square and another, for grass and clover seeds, in Church Street, the Minories.

In 1892, more buildings were acquired in Butler Street (now Brune Street), Spitalfields, to which the then expanding Grass and Clover Seed Department was moved from the Minories. About the same time the head office was transferred to 152 Houndsditch and the original Leadenhall Street premises were discarded. A picture of these Houndsditch premises shows that the ground floor received very little daylight for there are large mirrors set at an angle above each window to reflect light inside. Present-day City workers can have no conception of how little sunlight penetrated the smoke-laden atmosphere of street and buildings before the days of smokeless zones. In fact, it was not until after the 'smog' in 1952, when many citizens, as well as fat stock on show at Smithfield, died, that any effective action was taken to reduce London's air pollution.

As John Keeling reminisces,[11]

> One of the biggest changes in the City of London since the War [1939-45] is the effect of the smokeless zones. We so seldom speak of our achievements. London must be one of the cleanest cities in the world today.
>
> Then, a pea souper fog was just that. One of Hurst's staff once walked into Aldgate pump in a thick fog. He was quite sober. A bowler hat was really necessary against the smuts. As also was a small scarf to cover the gap between face and edge of overcoat, otherwise your shirt and collar could be dirty after but a short walk. Even in summer the sun was never more than a red ball in a hazy sky.

Trial grounds became a feature of this firm in the 1860s, First they were in Croydon and afterwards at Boreham, Essex, until they moved to Feering about 1890. Two of the greenhouses which were moved from the Boreham trial site were still in use in Feering in 1981.[12]

By all accounts, and there are many, Nathaniel Newman Sherwood became a much liked and respected member of society and today his portrait still looks down with an air of confidence, wisdom and kindly amusement. No doubt it was he who encouraged Hurst's employees to form the cricket team which, in 1895, defeated a team from Sutton's seed-house — 'the first defeat they had sustained that season'. In this year also, his two sons, William Henry Charles and John Edward Newman Sherwood (b.1876) were made partners in the firm. William, the elder brother, was frequently unwell and took no active part in the business. Therefore, when Nathaniel's health began to cause concern, it became necessary to curtail Edward's education at Cheltenham College in order that his training to take over the management of the firm could be brought forward.

So, aged 17½, Edward was apprenticed to the old-established German firm, Benary of Erfurt, and also spent some time with his father's friend and business associate Edmund de Maunthnea, a large landowner and seedgrower in the Budapest area of Hungary. In fact, the de Maunthneas remained friends with the Sherwoods and grew peas for Hurst's for two generations. Mrs. Edward Sherwood recalls that on at least one occasion, when her husband went over to look at his pea stocks, she accompanied him and they stayed on with the de Maunthneas for a holiday.

Nowadays, we forget the apprehension with which early users of the telephone approached this instrument. In Hurst's Houndsditch office, everyone knew when their pea manager was telephoning the de Maunthneas' pea manager in Hungary for, so overwhelmed was he by the distance of the call, that he felt it necessary to shout his loudest into the telephone in order that he might be heard!

This was the age when, for both social and business reasons, 'a place in the country' was a necessity for the up and coming man. Here he would invite his friends and business associates to shoot, to play tennis and in the evening (if they had good voices) to sing

46. Nathaniel Newman Sherwood (1846-1916).

and perhaps even to dance with his daughters. Certainly there was music in the Sherwood house for Edward both wrote music and conducted concerts for the firm's own Music Society. The musicians are reputed to have performed with a large choir for which, on one occasion, Mr. Sherwood composed an alternative tune for the hymn 'Lead Kindly Light'.[13]

In both 1896 and 1897, Nathaniel was appointed Master of the Worshipful Company of Gardeners whose Fraternity, it will be remembered, dates back to 1345. It was then that he found his property in Streatham Hill, S.W., inadequate for his needs and so bought Prested Hall, Feering, Essex.

Nathaniel became a founder of the Sweet Pea Association in 1900 and the year 1912 was the fiftieth anniversary of his association with Hurst's. To mark this occasion, a large garden party was held at which staff from all the London premises and from the Feering trial grounds gathered on the lawn at Prested Hall. Those who came by train were transported from the station by farm wagons, and a photograph of this event not only gives an idea of the number of employees, but also what it was then considered proper to wear for such an occasion. In later years a staff garden party became an annual summer event, held after the main summer party for friends and business associates.

Nathaniel was made a Justice of the Peace for Essex in 1915 and some 17 months later he died.

This family's succession as partners in Hurst's had, from 1905, been in the capable hands of the younger son Edward Sherwood, a 40-year-old bachelor in 1916. At this point it was thought unlikely that either he or his elder brother would marry, but their sister May had become Mrs. Campbell and had a son and a daughter.

In 1923, John Edward Newman Sherwood, J.P., astonished everybody by marrying the young and beautiful Miss Sybil Keeling from the Priory, Earls Colne. It was even more of a shock when the couple produced two children — a boy Nathaniel (the present 'Nat' Sherwood, of Easthorpe Green) and a daughter Sybil. It then seemed that the name of Sherwood, as partners in Hurst's, was assured.

In 1929 Edward Sherwood became the second member of his family to be made Master of the Worshipful Company of Gardeners and, like his father, had become a very well-liked and prominent member of the seed world in both London and the country.

47. The staff garden party at Prested Hall in 1912, held to mark the fiftieth anniversary of Nathaniel Newman Sherwood's association with Hurst's.

Well before 1939, Hurst's Dutch bulb connection is reputed to have been perhaps the biggest in England. It is also said that they were the first firm to use containers to transport these bulbs by ship to Harwich, then on by rail to Bishopsgate station where they were transferred to a van which was pulled by four horses to the firm's premises in Houndsditch.

A catalogue, the cover of which proclaims it to be the

Bulb List — (Wholesale) June, 1936, — No. 555

Hurst and Son. Sole Proprietors W. H. C. Sherwood, J. E. N. Sherwood, 152 Houndsditch, London

is still in existence at their Witham office. There is a note to say that where prices were not given, these would follow. Species tulips were on offer; there are various cultural instructions and between each page of this substantial list there is the luxury of a blank sheet of lined paper for notes. At some time around 1970 Hurst's decided to give up importing Dutch bulbs and to concentrate solely on their seed interests.

Until 1944 the business, large as it was, continued as a family partnership. When Nathaniel died, William and Edward had been left equal partners in the business. Edward, despite having to shoulder all the work and responsibility, was content to take only half of the profits because the arrangement was that on the death of one partner his assets in the company were to be transferred to the other. Edward, being considerably younger than his ailing brother, relied upon out-living him. In the event it was the younger brother Edward who, in 1939, died first. His death was a great blow to all and materially changed the history of Hurst's.

In September of this eventful year the Second World War began. The last Sherwood garden party had been held and early in 1940 the family had to leave their home very hurriedly. Prested Hall had been requisitioned by the Military, for use as a Brigade H.Q.

At the time of Edward Sherwood's death the staff at this residence consisted of: six women in the house; six men in the garden; one chauffeur; one groom; three gamekeepers, and their total wages amounted to less than it would cost to employ one man in 1982. In fact, the average wage was £1 10s. per week.[14]

Hurst and Son 1939-44

Because it is sometimes wondered why John Keeling and 'Nat' Sherwood did not stay in the firm, and reasons given for their not having done so are frequently incorrect, a brief summary is given of what happened in this firm between the deaths of Edward and William Sherwood. This and much other information relating to Hurst's has been obtained through correspondence and meetings with the late John Keeling and Nathaniel Sherwood. I am greatly indebted to them both for the trouble to which they have put themselves to ensure that, as far as is known, the facts which have been included are true.

On 10 May 1930, Mrs. Edward Sherwood's young cousin, John G. Keeling, had become an employee of Hurst's, a firm in which, apart from his wages, he had no financial interest. When Edward Sherwood died on 11 April 1939 John was asked by the executors of the will if he would take over as the firm's General Manager. This would place him in a position of authority and it was expected that by the time 'Nat' was ready to join the firm a place would be found for him. Unfortunately, not all of the Sherwood family saw it that way and apart from other objections, through clashes of personality, no-one knew if John Keeling or Nathaniel Sherwood would prove capable of managing the firm and safeguarding the shareholders' interest.

With hindsight they would most probably have done better to have had more faith. John G. Keeling, O.B.E., amongst other seed trade achievements, became Chairman of the Directors of Elsom's Seeds Ltd., Spalding, Lincolnshire, and in 1982 was appointed Master of the Worshipful Company of Gardeners. Nathaniel Sherwood still farms the family land to which he had added considerably (in 1983, 1,650 acres) and remains in the seed world as a successful grower of cereal seeds for both Pertwee's and John K. King.

After careful consideration John felt it would be beneficial all round if he accepted, but only on condition that Vernon Leslie Roscoe, the 52-year-old and very able manager of the firm's Flower Seed and Bulb Department, was made joint general manager with him. At the time it seemed a good idea because by the early 1930s Vernon Roscoe had established a particularly profitable seed growing connection with Yugoslavia. These crops were under excellent management and the wages and climate in that country enabled crops to be grown more cheaply and with more certainty of success than would have been possible in Great Britain. These seeds were even sold to leading Dutch seed houses at a good profit. In fact, as manager of the Flower Seed Department, it had been said that for a run of several years he had doubled the profits and, today, older men who were apprentices at the time still speak of the wizardry with which he built up this department.

The dual appointment was agreed by the solicitor trustee of Edward Sherwood's will and by the only remaining partner in the family firm, William Sherwood. From then on, however, neither help nor encouragement appear to have been offered to John Keeling for the rest of his time with this firm. Very soon difficulties of management began and they were not just due to import restrictions and the loss of seeds through bombing. Quite soon after war was declared the ailing William Sherwood decided to live in Scotland and, without even consulting his joint-manager, John Keeling, he made Vernon Roscoe his partner in the firm. This act effectively reduced John to unconsulted second-in-command, a position which was quite untenable, and after attempting, unsuccessfully, to find a means by which his young relative Nat might in due time enter the family firm, he left with every intention of joining the Army, in May 1943. In fact, as soon as Mr. Elsom of Spalding heard of John Keeling's intention, he immediately approached him with the suggestion that he would be of more use to his country if he joined Elsom's Seeds Ltd. In this both the Ministries of Labour and of Agriculture agreed, and so John started with Elsom's.

As for young Nat Sherwood, he served his country in the Royal Air Force from 1942 to 1944, after which he was invalided out and for a short while joined Sutton's Seeds of Reading. This experience persuaded him that he would do better to take an M.A. Agriculture course at Cambridge as his father had wished. This he did in 1945-47 and afterwards found that Hurst's, a limited company since 1944, had changed. Those who had been juniors at the time of his father's death now held positions of authority and no place was open to him. In other circumstances he would very much have liked to enter the firm but as things were he decided to put his agricultural training to the test and to become the first Sherwood to farm any of their land.

The bombing in 1941

Before the days of modern electrical installation, dust extractors and brick or concrete-built warehouses, seed firms were very prone to disastrous fires. However, Hurst's fire, like that at Mark Lane seed market, was neither accident nor act of God — but caused by German bombers during one of their night raids on London.

On 10 May 1941, John Keeling walked from King's Cross towards his office in Houndsditch. Almost there, at the corner of St Mary Axe, he found the road sealed off and on explaining to a police constable that he wished to reach his place of work beyond the barrier, was told bluntly 'That's gone, Sir'. Collecting his wits, he realised that a warehouse at the back of Gun Square was less damaged than the offices at the front. Therein were some particularly valuable seeds, but no-one was allowed to go through. Nevertheless, with the aid of some other employees who had by then arrived, a plot was hatched.

Amongst other things John Keeling was in the Auxiliary Fire Service. He went away, changed into his uniform and then returned to walk down the street with a pretended air of authority and escorted Hurst's horse and van through the arch to the back warehouse. Here, the seeds were loaded with all possible speed, ceremoniously escorted out and sent on their way to be looked after elsewhere. By no means all the seeds could be salvaged and for days 'the air was rent with colossal reports', as small radish seeds within their hessian sacks, having been drenched with water from the firemen's hoses, swelled and began to grow until such was the force they exerted that the sacks split asunder with a sound like gunfire.

As day followed day the employees and management set about restoring some kind of normality. The offices were moved to the Butler Street (near Spitalfields) warehouse, where room was made on the first floor under an unplastered ceiling of bare boards over joists. Dust, grit and the few odd seeds, filtered and rolled through the cracks in the floor above, bouncing onto the papers and people beneath, as sack barrows pushed by Mr. Lock and Mr. Key rattled and squeaked to and fro with their loads.

For some time there was no office furniture. Desks and filing cabinets were not to be found. Like all who had been bombed out, Hurst's improvised. Gradually orange boxes and tea chests found their way into this warehouse, scrounged from no-one enquired where; they were just about the right height for a desk. Other boxes became stools, and planks supported on bricks, picked up from bombed buildings, were useful for holding the innumerable cardboard boxes and large envelopes used for filing. Even pen nibs, paper clips, pins and india rubbers were so scarce that in some circles they almost became legal tender. Record and account books had all been destroyed and customers had to be written to, asking 'What do we owe you or what had you ordered?', until some time towards the end of 1942 the office was moved to Staple Hall, Houndsditch and 'things became civilised again'. Other seedhouses who suffered similarly have told me that 'We had to write to our customers just like that. You know the nice thing was that no-one was ever taken advantage of. If anything it was the customer who 'forgot' to charge'. Every night, however, there were still members of staff firewatching on the roof amidst the bombs and barrage balloons and at the end of each day account books and suchlike were neatly stowed in the air raid shelter.

So, Hurst's came through the Second World War, their vast wholesale trade in grass, clover, root, vegetable and flower seeds still being carried on. They still had a branch at Lurgan, in Ireland, and another in Boston, Lincolnshire, together with their London premises in Houndsditch and Brune Street, Spitalfields, as well as seed farms and experimental grounds at Kelvedon in Essex. Nevertheless, there had been and still were grave financial and management difficulties taking place within the structure of this firm.

Hurst and Son Ltd. 1944-54

On 16 September 1944, Hurst and Son became a private limited company. The subscribers were William H. C. Sherwood and Vernon Leslie Roscoe, and it appears that Mr. Roscoe then became or was acting as Managing Director of Hurst's.

When William Sherwood died on 3 April 1945, the firm faced a considerable loss of capital through death duties. This was followed by a split up of the family and a consequent withdrawal of capital which the Sherwoods had previously invested in the firm. Mr. Roscoe was pitched headlong into this management imbroglio. His problems were further increased when, in the late 1940s, there was a run of particularly good seed-producing years. For onions, in two successive years, the yields were phenomenal and seed merchants were not only over-supplied but had, of course, already agreed onion seed contracts with their growers for the following year. Since everybody was over stocked there was no sale for this seed and consequently no money to pay the growers. Several tons were actually sold for bird seed at 1d. a pound. Then, before Hurst's (who eventually paid out their growers in full) had recovered, the Government, in 1955, lifted its import ban on foreign seeds which then flowed into this country at much reduced prices.

Each seed firm met these problems in its own way and some, by anticipating the difficulties that were likely to arise, were able, to some extent, to mitigate them and so came through. Nevertheless, it was at this time that many firms, particularly those with little reserve of capital, were either bankrupted or absorbed into one or other of the larger seed businesses.

For many years Hurst's had traded with the Gunsons of New Zealand and, at a time when that country's farmers required large galvanised iron water tanks for their livestock, Hurst's sent seed of rape, turnip and swede packed into tanks instead of into the more usual wooden boxes. These tanks provided better protection against vermin and so long as the instruction 'Stow away from boilers' was followed, the seed generally travelled very well, even through the tropics.

After the above crises and most probably in 1952, Hurst's were forced to compound with their creditors. For about two years this firm was in the hands of a bank and a receiver. However, when the firm of Gunson (New Zealand) found that they were the largest creditors and were liable to be paid little or nothing for a considerable tonnage of peas, they decided to put money into Hurst's. Their object was to keep the company afloat and so to have some hope of eventually recouping their own financial loss. This act saved Hurst's, for the

Gunsons had had practical experience of both seed growing and merchanting. It appears that at that time the control of Hurst's passed to them and that the firm continued under the name of Hurst Gunson from 1954 to 1962.

There is sometimes confusion between the two firms of Gunson. It is W. Gunson who left Hungary to farm and become a seed merchant in New Zealand. R. W. Gunson was his son who, to begin with, worked with his father in New Zealand but who, in 1920, came to England to found his own business which became known as R. W. Gunson (Seeds) Ltd. It was this firm that, in 1938, merged with that founded by Beno Balint in 1898.

PART III — HURST, GUNSON, COOPER TABER LIMITED TO BOOKER McCONNELL PLC

Hurst Gunson Cooper Taber Ltd. 1962-86

The family tree of Hurst Gunson Cooper Taber Ltd. reveals that, by 1948, some thirty or forty old-established seed houses had merged into five wholesaling companies namely, Hurst and Son Ltd., Cooper Taber and Company Ltd., C. W. Le May and Company Ltd., R. W. Gunson (Seeds) Ltd., and Peter Cassidy Seed Company Ltd.[15]

In 1962, the firm of Cooper Taber made decisions to ally themselves with Hurst Gunson, to join the other companies mentioned above under the umbrella of the Agricultural Holdings Company Ltd., and to form a central wholesaling company to be know as Hurst Gunson Cooper Taber Ltd., from henceforward referred to as Hurst. Very briefly, the Agricultural Holdings Company is one of the 50 largest private companies in the United Kingdom and it operates from both a seeds and an industrial division.[16]

The immediate effect of Cooper Taber's alliance with Hurst Gunson was that members from Hurst Gunson's staff were transferred to Cooper Taber's offices at Witham and there was a consolidation of plant breeding resources and trials. Very soon large warehouses and office accommodation were seen to be being built on a part of Taber's trial grounds (on field at O.S. number 320 (8,879 acres) on 25 in. O.S. map, xlvi (1922 ed.)). In 1964, the whole new office and warehouse block was populated by a large injection of Hurst Gunson's London staff who were now having to commute to Witham.

As breeders, growers, exporters and importers of all types of seed for agricultural, horticultural and industrial purposes, by 1978 Hurst's commercial interest covered the whole of Great Britain and penetrated every continent. Their seed is exported to some eighty-five countries and the search for new markets continues. Today, most of the seed produced for the company is grown in Africa, Australia, Canada, Central Europe, France, Germany, New Zealand, and the United States of America, and much of this production comes back to England to be properly cleaned and dressed, checked for quality, and re-evaluated in trials. Even then, so as to maintain the highest possible standard before being sent out to the retailers, these seeds are sealed into airtight cans or pockets under controlled environmental conditions. This ensures that they remain fresh and viable for an extended period and can withstand such adverse conditions as a sunny shop window or dampness permeating through a wall or floor.

Since 1983, much rationalisation has taken place in the seed trading activities of the Agricultural Holdings Company. In fact, the other companies within this group, namely Finney Lock Seeds, Gartons Gro Plan, Alexander Cross Seeds and John J. Inglis, have been incorporated into the Hurst operating company.

In October 1984, Agricultural Holdings was approaching by Booker McConnell plc to acquire the then formed division known as Agrisort, of which Hurst Gunson Cooper Taber was a part. In December 1984 this transaction became unconditional, and from that date Hurst has operated as one of the new separate operating companies within the Agribusiness

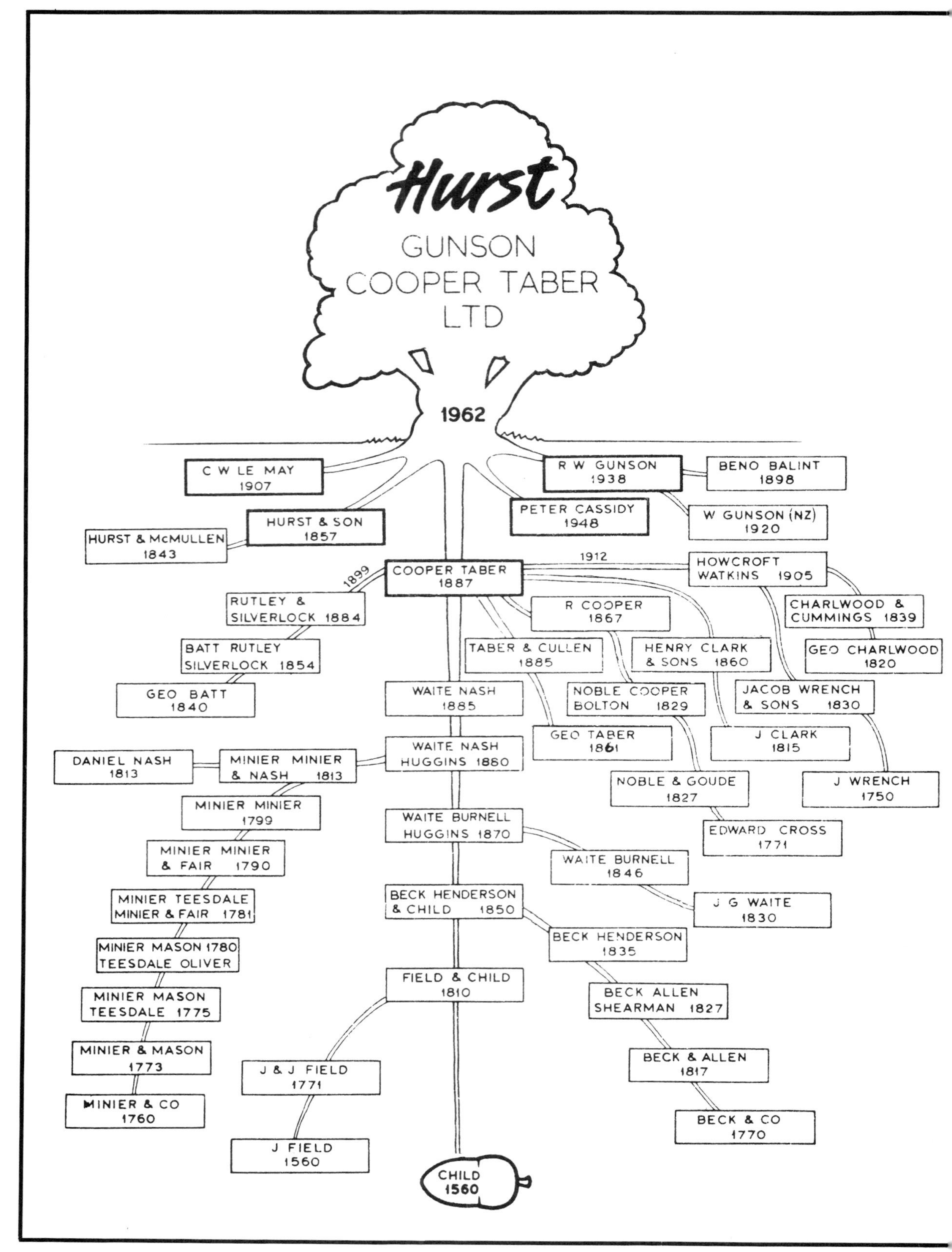

48. Hurst Gunson Cooper Taber Ltd. family tree.

49. Cooper Taber's trial ground before the alliance with Hurst Gunson, after which large warehouses and an office block were built on this site.

Division of Booker McConnell plc. Even further consolidation of their position, in both United Kingdom and international seed markets, took place when the well-known Lincolnshire seed company of Charles Sharpe plc was acquired by Booker McConnell and entered their Agribusiness Division in October 1985.

Finally, because research and development play such a vital part, it is fitting to end the history of this firm with a brief description of their research unit, some notes on former apprentices and their training, and on one of their most successful plant breeders.

The Hurst Crop Research and Development Unit, Great Domsey Farm, Marks Tey

Great Domsey Farm was purchased by Hurst in 1942 and, in 1948, Broom's Farm, Marks Tey was added to what, by the time it was opened in July 1978, had become known as 'The Domsey Complex'.

Today the whole of this company's research and development work for its entire Seeds Division is centred on these approximately 400 hectares of land. Housed within the new unit are Hurst's six plant breeders and their supporting staff. There is an office and administrative block which includes laboratories, a conference room, a library, and a barn in which to thrash, dry, clean, prepare and store the seeds.

In the glasshouse section there are 1,900 square metres of glass which is divided into four major isolation and environmental zones. There is an artificially-lighted glasshouse for winter breeding work on photo-sensitive crops. Irrigation is semi-automatic, heating automatic and oil-fired, and ventilation is not only automatically controlled but there is a safety over-ride system to cope with storm conditions. Insects are excluded from early generation seed production experiments by the use of poly-tunnels and there are alarms, linked to the public telephone system, which warn key workers of any out-of-hours problems that might upset the critical work in progress.

Twenty-five hectares of rabbit-proofed land, irrigated from a seven-million-litre reservoir, are reserved for the more demanding of the crops under research, and the remaining hectares are cropped commercially in a pattern that allows work on cereals and variety maintenance to proceed within the rotation.

Gardeners in the United Kingdom have a choice of over 600 varieties of seeds marketed in this firm's attractive 'Garden Pride' packets and there is now the 'Gourmet Vegetable Collection'. This was produced after painstaking research carried out from enquiries to their stand at an Ideal Homes Exhibition, when every vegetable seed which they could not immediately supply was carefully recorded and considered for future stock. It is also of note that in 1982, to help repair the war damage in the Falklands, Hurst's re-stocked these islands with seeds, free of charge.[17]

Each year their trial grounds are opened to the public and it is well worth contacting Hurst's to find out which weekend this is going to be. In greenhouses and on each section of the trial plots there are knowledgeable people in attendance who will help visitors with horticultural or agricultural problems and, even if one knows little or nothing about either subject, a walk round the flower plots on a sunny afternoon is a memorable experience. (Since this was written, and from 1984, when Hurst's became part of Booker McConnell plc, changes have been made in this unit.)

Some former apprentices

Every firm of any size has its apprentices. It is also the custom that seed-growing families send their sons to be trained away from home. Often they do a spell with the firm of a friendly rival of good repute, and those with real ambition and opportunity go on to one of the continental firms, where they not only learn new ways but also, if they are diligent, a second language. Hurst's has always received a number of such pupils, many of whom have become well-known in the seed world. They usually came for the period May to the end of August, and were lodged in Kelvedon and Feering, with a regular bunch of landladies, often widow women who looked forward to earning this extra cash during the summer. Tom Clucas was with them in 1925, and afterwards went on to Vilmorin Andrieux et Cie, Paris, before returning to his family firm in Lancashire; Don Clayton, who married one of Edwin Cranmer's girls, stayed on with Hurst's until he retired in 1982, after a lifetime spent on the trial grounds and inspecting crops in this country and abroad; L. J. (George) Bevan, who is now in a senior position with this firm, has become well-known for this production of 'Greenshaft', 'Beagle' and 'Canice' peas as well as several of Hurst's brassicae. John Keeling, late head of Elsom's Seeds, started as an apprentice under the overall charge of Harry Plumley, who was then in charge of Hurst's trial grounds. Three generations of Plumleys worked for this firm. Harry came after a time with Pennell's of Lincolnshire during the First World War. He is particularly remembered as having bred the godetia 'Sybil Sherwood' which was named after Edward Sherwood's wife, and for keeping his apprentices and the 'pupils' hard at work except on Friday afternoons when they were expected to parade, to be taken round the trials for tuition by 'the Boss'![18] However, as far as peas and beans were concerned work experience and instruction was under the all-seeing eye of Mr. Arthur Newby, who came down to the trials at Feering, once or twice a week from the London office in Houndsditch. Harry Plumley's son Bryan took advantage of the Ex-Service Trainee Scheme to take a Higher National Diploma Course at Harper Adams Agricultural College in 1947-49. From here he came to Hurst's and to live at Great Domsey Farm as Farms Manager from 1950 to 1954, after which he left to farm on his own. However, after graduating, his son Bryan worked for Hurst's for several years before joining the National Seed Development Organisation.

Ralph Gould

One of the best known of Hurst's plant breeders was Ralph Gould who was with the firm for half a century.

Great-grandfather James Gould (b. 1797) is remembered as 'the one who started it all'. Certainly, he grew herb seeds which were exported to Germany, and the fennel which grows wild around Kelvedon may well be some of his stock which, over the years, has become naturalised. James was one of a family of eight, and on Boxing Day 1817 he married a girl called Sarah. This couple produced a family of eight boys and one girl. The youngest, a boy named Joseph (b. 1841), became a seed-grower and married Zillah Overett from Billericay, whose forebears were refugee Huguenot silk weavers who had settled in Halstead during the 16th century. It is well known that many of the Huguenots were noted horticulturists and so it may be said that from both sides of his family the present Ralph Gould could have inherited his extraordinary talent for spotting, amongst hundreds of its kind, the one plant that is different, is likely to breed true or to make a good cross, and which also has popularity potential.

Joseph and Zillah had a family of eight boys and three girls. The eighth child, Frank, was the only one of that generation to be a seed-grower. The tenth child, Charles Overett Gould, became a builder in Kelvedon and married into the Goodwin family who were farmer/seed-growers in Great Braxted. In 1913 this couple had a son, Ralph, who was destined to become the seed breeder at Hurst's. Had it not been for a slump in the building trade before 1929, Ralph's talent might never have been discovered and he could still have been in his father's firm, building houses instead of brightening up their gardens with one 'Monarch' strain of flower after another. However, because of the lack of prospects in the building trade, his father advised him to look for other work, and so Ralph applied to Hurst's for a job on their trial grounds at Feering and, in 1929, joined this firm and remained with it until his retirement in 1981.

To begin with, he was put mainly on the vegetable and flower seed side of the business which, he remembers, entailed long hours on the trial grounds. When the Second World War came, vegetable seeds became more important and, in fact, flower seed production was ordered to be cut to a mere 10 per cent of former production. Nevertheless, by the time the war ended, someone in Hurst's had realised that this unassuming and quiet young man had potential on the flower seed side, and he was promoted to take charge of the firm's particular strains of flower seeds, and to be responsible for the flower breeding programme.

During this period Ralph wafted all over Europe and the United States of America inspecting crops being grown for Hurst's in other countries, visiting the great Continental seed-houses and meeting those from other firms who were similarly engaged. These foreign trips were by no means without incident. There was the time when, after an evening with some friends in the bar of a small country hotel, he was awakened well after midnight by the local gendarmes, demanding a search of his room. It transpired that 'a little old lady who had also been drinking in the bar' could not find her umbrella when she started for home and at once convinced herself that it had been stolen 'by one of those foreigners' and had promptly raised the alarm!

By about 1956 Ralph had become firmly convinced that Hurst's should concentrate on providing seeds for plants suitable for the small compact gardens which were attached to the houses of the age. He also bore in mind that people were conservative and so would still want to grow the same kinds of flowers, but the actual plants needed to be shorter, to have no tendency to lush or straggly growth, and, at the same time, the blooms must be as

50. Ralph Gould in a trial plot of Rudbeckia at Great Domsey Farm. He won a bronze medal in the All Britain Trials for his breeding of this variety.

big and bright as ever. So, wherever he went, he started to look for shorter plants with blooms that stood up above their foliage looking straight at you with no drooping heads. Having found something promising, it had to be crossed with a suitable parent plant and the results in the F1 generation noted. It might take six or seven years before something like the 'Roulette' nasturtium was ready to be brought out.

Like all others Ralph has had his set-backs. His wife tells of how she was once the cause. They were newly married and Ralph had gone off that morning muttering that if his row of statice plants were not soon harvested all the seed would drop out. It was a nice sunny morning and so when he had gone Molly left her housework and went out into the garden, picked the statice and because they were indeed so very dry and ready, was able to shake all the seed out into a bag. What she did not know was that Ralph had intended keeping the seed from each plant separate, and that her 'helpfulness' had set back the selection programme by several years. What he said is not recorded, but they are still happily together.

During his 52 years with Hurst's, Ralph Gould received many awards and appointments in recognition of his prodigious achievements. From 1966 to 1971 he served as an All Britain Trial judge and in 1971 was appointed a Fleuroselect judge which he has remained ever since. In the same year he was awarded the R.H.S. Associate of Honour, became one of their judges and served on their Floral A Committee. In 1976 he was awarded the Veitch Memorial Gold Medal for his achievements in horticulture and three years later received an All American Silver Medal for his successes in horticultural breeding — the only such medal yet awarded to anyone from the United Kingdom. Most recently he has received the Royal Horticultural Society's silver Medal of Honour.

Over the years he has bred for Hurst's at least 116 'Flower Seed Novelties', only 14 of which have yet become discontinued lines.

In retirement Ralph Gould is as busy and well-known as ever, constantly on the move between one conference, meeting or flower-judging session and the next. Even when at home he is fully occupied trying to meet one deadline or another for a technical article or the next chapter of a book.

Royal Horticultural Society and 'Fleuroselect' Variety Trials

Since Hurst's have on offer many hundreds of different varieties of flower and vegetable seeds, all of which undergo trials of one kind or another, this seems an appropriate point at which to write something of national and international variety trials in which seedsmen may compete.

One of the ways in which the public are safeguarded from purchasing poor supplies of seeds, and particularly poor varietal strains of flowers and vegetables, is by the annually held trials of such organisations as the Royal Horticultural Society and of the 'All Britain Trials' (which were renamed 'Fleuroselect' in 1975 when we entered the Common Market).

For some years the R.H.S. has held delphinium and sweet pea trials of the varieties produced by breeders and seedsmen. Their committee also decides upon a programme for those flowers and vegetables which they consider should be looked at in trials for several years ahead. This is a quality control trial and in the appropriate year the committee invites seedsmen and breeders to send seeds from whichever of their varieties are considered as suitable material for comparison with others in the trials of that year.

The awards to be won are the much esteemed R.H.S. First Class Certificate, the R.H.S. Award of Merit, and a Highly Commended Certificate.

After some enthusiastic members of the Horticultural Trade, and the Seed Trade, Associations realised the value of the United States of America's 'All America Selections Trials', similar trials were started in Britain in 1966. This was the beginning of the 'All Britain Trials'.

These trials are held to test new varieties of flower seed before it is put on sale to the general public. Only entirely new varieties are accepted for their evaluation of usefulness to the general public and each year the results provide a guide as to which of the many new introductions are either worthwhile or outstanding.

The trials are duplicated at a number of centres in Western Europe, each of which has been chosen so as to provide a wide variety of climatic and soil conditions. At each centre a resident judge is responsible for the fair conduct of the trials and for the evaluation of each entry, the identity of which is kept secret. At the end of the season the points awarded to each variety by the various trial centres are assessed by a panel of judges. Those gaining the highest number of points receive a gold, silver or bronze medal according to their rating.

Leading flower-seed breeders from all over the world are eligible to compete. The entries are sent for trial two years before the expected date of introduction to the public; thus winning entries in this year's trials will not be offered in seed catalogues until two years hence. This enables the seedsman to make sure that adequate supplies of seed are available.

There are two Fleuroselect Trial Grounds in Essex, one at Hurst's Trial Grounds at Feering, and the other at the By-Pass Nurseries, Ipswich Road, Colchester.

Chapter Six

Thomas Cullen and Sons, Witham

In 1803 there was born in Low Ham, Somerset, the John Cullen who was destined to be father of the founder of Thomas Cullen and Sons, Seedsmen, Witham, Essex. When he married Ann Stacey they lived in the nearby village of Huish Episcopi, and there in 1870 he died.

A surviving photograph of Ann gives the impression of a woman of courage and character and her youngest son, Thomas (b. 1846), it seems, had an early flair for commerce, for by 1858 he had already started his own donkey transport business. This operated to and from Langport, which was their nearest railway station, and functioned after school hours. It must have been a success for in time the donkey was replaced by a pony which lived to the ripe old age of forty-two.

On leaving school, Thomas was apprenticed to his brother-in-law, Mr. Gillard, who was a vehicle builder in Drayton, a few miles away. Apparently he did not like the work and soon joined Hill and Company, Seedsmen, of Langport. But London was then the place where ambitious young seedsmen should be, so in 1864 Thomas Cullen joined the firm of Frazer, Goad and Ratcliff, wholesale seed merchants of Bishopsgate-Without, and by 1872 he had attained a managerial position within this firm. In 1873, he left it to become Seed-growers's Assistant with the developing firm of George Taber, Rivenhall, and brought his young wife and daughter to live at the nearby Rose Cottage.

The move from London was a wise one, for when young Goad took over his father's company it was very soon in financial difficulties, whereas on 20 September 1881 Thomas became a partner of George Taber with a one-third share in the business. (The original Account Book of Geo. Taber and the partnership agreement, together with a letter sent to all customers at the time, are in the Essex Record Office (D/F 90).)

This business now became known as Taber and Cullen, Seedsmen, Rivenhall, Essex, for which there exists a 'List of Selected Seeds' which was issued to customers in 1886 (Essex Record Office (D/F 90)). The present A. L. Cullen tells me that in the early 1880s George Taber thought up a splendid sales gimmick for his firm by offering:

Turnip Seed dressed against the Fly — NO PLANT. NO PAY.

The dressing was a fearsome concoction of lime, soot, turpentine, paraffin and another ingredient which George Taber would not identify to anyone!

It seems that in 1884, Taber and Cullen required a correspondence clerk for it was in this year that Albert Wallis, a solicitor's clerk from Langport, was asked by Tom Cullen to join the firm. (He was Tom's sister Ann's stepbrother-in-law.) Later Albert Wallis became manager of Cooper Taber's at Witham, as did his son Arthur after him.

When in 1887 George Taber proposed an amalgamation with the firm of Robert Cooper, the ever-independently-spirited Thomas felt there was little in this for his family and resolved that, when convenient, he would set up on his own. At the time seed-growing was booming and there was room for another firm in the area. But it was not to be for another seven years that he was finally in a position to sever his connection for, in the meantime, his bank in the City failed and was able to pay but one farthing in the pound. Nevertheless, by 1894 he was living in Bramstons House, from which he could walk through the garden to his own seed premises in the Braintree Road, Witham, and his son Frank was soon made a director of the firm which was then known as Thomas Cullen and Son.

Certain impressions come clearly out of the Cullen records. These were men of the West Country, not the east, much more inclined to be scholarly farmers than business men, but hard-headed enough to be successful merchants if the need arose. Their first love was the land and, although capable of their share of hard work, they made time for other interests and had a great capacity for enjoyment. Knowing what they wanted out of life they did not hesitate to change course if by doing so they came nearer to achieving their aims. Two very different pictures of Frank Cullen (Pls. 51 and 52) clearly illustrate the two sides of this family's character. It also comes through from a generosity of judgment in Frank Cullen's writing, of which the following is a relevant example and gives an insight into a young seedsman's life in Victorian days.

YOUTHFUL MEMORIES by Frank Cullen

Although it was only a holiday occupation and my real initiation was to come some years later, I pocketed my first earnings at Christmas 1885 when Taber and Cullen's head clerk, Albert Wallis, unlocked the safe in the office at Rivenhall and took therefrom a golden sovereign which he solemnly handed to me with thanks for services rendered. I had, I think, expectation of a rather larger reward but hope I received that proffered with due appreciation, for after all a sovereign was a very useful coin in those days, and with careful handling would go quite a long way.

Movement began early in those days and strange as it may seem today the partners met in their office at six o'clock in the summer, and at seven in the dark days, opened their letters and made plans for the day before going to breakfast at eight. The hours for all workers, both inside and out, were 6 a.m. to 5.30 p.m. with an hour each for breakfast and dinner. They may seem a little long, but as I remember them they were days of contentment and cheerfulness although the work was harder than now, for there was very little labour-saving machinery and much loading and unloading without the help of hoists. All our employees were well housed close to their work and were able to go home for both breakfast and dinner. But it wasn't hard work all the time at Rivenhall for the firm's employees had their cricket club and played neighbouring villages, the losers paying for a barrel of beer, which was consumed on the spot, and there was also a new ball to the winners. Also there was the quoits club, a game hardly seen played nowadays. Their greatest achievement however, was the formation of the Rivenhall brass band of 12 instrumentalists, all employees of the firm, excepting the conductor, which performed at local fetes and flower shows, but after a few years, sad to say, interest declined partly for the reason that Fraser Cook's trombone drowned all the others.

Man's ever faithful friend, the horse, had not then been displaced, and the men were as much engrossed in the care of them as they now are in cars and lorries. Journeys of course, took longer but any one of the four nags in the stable was good for 40 miles a day and road journeys could be extended to 60 or 70 by hiring for part of the way when on crop inspection in distant parts of the county. Of course this entailed long driving hours but the roads then were open roads and the sagacious animal could always find his way home even if the driver nodded.

One of my first jobs and perhaps the most exciting one of the day was mounting the roan pony before six in the morning and jogging off to Witham post office two miles away to collect the post bag. The return journey was anything but a jog, for, with the pony's head towards his stable, we came in John Gilpin style with the post bag flapping my back . . .

. . . My school days ended in October 1890 and then followed four years London experience when I was privileged to meet some of the leading members of the trade.

There were Giants in the land in those, my early days in London, or so I thought them. N. N. Sherwood was an outstanding leader and looked up to by all; there was generally a queue of members waiting to speak to him at his stand on Mark Lane. I remember going with him in 1898, after he had retired to live at Prested Hall, in his new Daimler phaeton visiting Swede crops in the Essex marshes and I remember too the dust we raised!

H. T. Huggins, who came of a London brewing family, was a brisk and energetic worker with a good knowledge of the trade. He was previously a partner in Waite Nash & Co., which had been taken over by the recently founded Cooper Taber & Co.

51. & 52. Two very different photographs of Frank Cullen in 1954.

53. Thomas Cullen (b.1846), 'the founder of the firm'.

54. Antony Cullen (b.1915).

The brothers Henry and William Nutting were a fine old-fashioned pair; and William was the first to introduce me to a Mark Lane cellar for a glass of port from his special bin.

Alfred Watkins who had acquired a great knowledge of the trade was said to be of choleric disposition but I always found him agreeable enough.

Fred Howcroft of Howcroft and Watkins, of Covent Garden, interested in theatrical production, was also easily put out but he did not have the best of health.

Alfred Legerton of Aldgate came of an Essex farming family and was a typical and somewhat pompous Victorian and said to be an aggressive salesman.

But to me Rutley and Silverlock in their Savoy cellar belonged to an even earlier period and I can to this day see the truly named Silverlock dusting sand on the cheque he had written for me.

Other London houses with which I came in contact were Hooper of Covent Garden, Jacob Wrench of London Bridge, Thomas Gibbs & Co., of Half Moon Street, and the newly arrived G. A. Bunting.

The Lincolnshire brothers Charles Sharpe of Sleaford and John Sharpe of Bardney came to town in their broad brimmed top hats and skirted coats and were familiar figures on Mark Lane.

Alfred Johnson, in spite of his handicap through illness, was keenness itself and my invitation as long ago as 1898 to see his trials of new peas and the hospitality of Burton Hall are well remembered.

London hours were long and I seldom got back to my lodgings before a quarter to nine during the winter or even later if things were extra busy. My pay of 10s. a week was mostly spending money for fortunately my father gave me a small allowance which covered my lodgings at 12s. a week and certain other necessary expenses. Even so money could get short towards the end of the week and then lunch would be in Mr. William Harris's sausage shop where two hot sausages, bread and butter, a cup of tea and a penny for the waitress cost sevenpence.

In spite of the long hours there was time on a Saturday to spend sixpence for the pleasure of climbing the stone steps to the gallery of the Gaiety Theatre to see Bessie Bellwood and Arthur Roberts, while an occasion to be remembered was splashing 2s. on a good seat at the Savoy Theatre to see one of the first performances of Gilbert & Sullivan's *Gondoliers*.

The early nineties especially 1891 and 1895 were mostly long and severe winters and well I remember my morning and evening walks over London Bridge and the deafening roar as the dislodged ice floes surged against the groynes and girders of the bridge. Our own rivers Blackwater and Chelmer were completely frozen too and my two brothers skated from Witham to Chelmsford via Maldon.

'After these four somewhat hectic years in London', in 1894 Frank joined his father's business and in 1909, Thomas Cullen took his second son, Thomas William, into the partnership. The firm then became known as Thomas Cullen and Sons, and Frank took his father's place on their stand at Mark Lane Corn Exchange in London, and Thomas William took Frank's place in the enlarging Witham Office.

This country's trade with the Americas and Canada was by now well under way and Frank was sent to look for possibilities of trade for their firm in the United States and to make himself known to those American seedsmen with whom they had already done business. With him went his friend, Mr. E. W. King, Seedsman, of Coggeshall. Evidently these young men took time off to visit the Cawston Ostrich Farm in California. It seems they also had rides on the ostriches for Frank sent to his niece a postcard photograph of himself astride one of the birds with the message that it was 'an admirable steed in the sandy desert and its name was George Washington'.

While in America, Frank heard that the English turnip-seed crop had failed and at once obtained a supply of American seed for his father. The return journey of these two travellers was enlivened by an incident recalled in the *Gardener's Chronicle* on 5 April 1958, which says,

The despatch departments of seed firms are noted for enterprise . . .

and continues that they were 'on the ball in 1911' when a noted Philadelphia seedsman, Mr. W. Atlee Burpee, wished to take a consignment of seeds to England and ordered it to be delivered aboard the White Star liner *Olympic* before she sailed. The seed store missed the boat but he resourcefully 'chartered a plane which was piloted by an English airman, Mr. Thomas Sopwith, who took Mr. P. R. Sinclair, secretary of the local flying club, on his flight. Mr. Sinclair duly dropped the package of seeds from the plane, but alas the package fell into the sea and not on the deck of the liner'. (Frank Cullen's nephew, Antony L. Cullen, now tells me that the whole affair was a publicity stunt arranged by Atlee Burpee.)

In the First World War, key seed experts were exempted from military service, so Frank Cullen remained at home to produce seeds for the nation while Thomas William went into the army and to France to fight for it. When the war ended Tom came home declaring that there were three things he would not have in his house — a piano, a wife, or children. The following story,[1] told by his wife and as far as possible in her own words, shows how wrong one can be for he ended by having all three.

An unpromising courtship that turned out well

In 1918 after two years as a Red Cross nurse in Northamptonshire, Violet Grout of Stock Hall, Ulting, in Essex, returned home to help her parents as her sister was soon to be married. She was a girl of spirit who had tasted a measure of independence. On coming home she said to her mother, 'If I come home you will have to pay me something'. Her mother was outraged, but Violet stuck to her guns saying, 'It's no good, mother, I've got used to having some money of my own'. Resentfully a weekly wage of 8s. was agreed; it was always paid grudgingly and often forgotten. But, Violet says, 'she was not allowed to forget for long'. Today's daughters can have little idea what courage this must have required.

About the same time Thomas William Cullen returned from the War. His father set him up in a farm with a man and his wife to look after him. The farm was the Elms, Ulting, which had a beautiful walled garden.

Violet remembers one of her friends saying 'You should meet Mr. Cullen's son Tom. He's a little older than you. Lives alone and needs a wife'. 'How do you imagine that I can meet him?' was her reply. However one day in 1919 she accompanied her father, in a four-wheeler, to the *White Hart*, Witham. She was left outside as 'girls did not go into public houses as they do now'. When he came out there were two gentlemen with her father. One, Mr. Stewart Richardson, she knew, the other was introduced as 'Tom Cullen, your neighbour'. So this was the man that they thought would do for her. He was not much to look at, but he took off his hat and bowed politely enough, so she returned the bow. Some weeks later her father announced that he had a brace of partridge that he would like her to take over to Mr. Cullen. So she put on her better hat, got on her bicycle and set off for the Elms.

Once there she was shown the garden and on leaving Tom Cullen said to her, 'If you should ever need any flowers for the Church you can always come over here and help yourself'. This was duly reported to her mother who said, 'Well, yes, but you must not do it too often'.

More weeks elapsed, until flowers were required. Then she and her sister called at the Elms and Tom accompanied them round the garden. This happened on several occasions until Tom, no doubt exasperated by the ever-present sister, said 'Do we have to have a chaperone?' and received the unhelpful reply, 'I don't know what you mean'. But once started he was a man of persistence, and so said plainly, 'Does your sister always have to be with you?' At this she says she looked at him straight and reflecting that she was 36 and should be able to look after herself, dispatched her sister to get flowers from the other side of the wall. This done the conversation continued: 'I should like you to come to dinner one evening'. 'I should like that. Thank you'.

The dinner party was arranged and apparently went well, for around the coffee stage

Tom said, 'You and I seem to get along together quite well. I think we should get married'. There was a pause while Violet reflected that he was not drunk, but he had drink taken. It must have gone to his head and he would regret this in the morning. So she said simply. 'Yes, we get along all right', and that for the time being was that.

At their next meeting, curiosity getting the better of her, she asked, 'Do you remember what you said to me after dinner on Sunday?' to which he replied that he did, and that what he said then he still meant today. So she agreed to think about it. When she got home, apparently having already made up her mind, she hurriedly wrote to a friend in London and, swearing her to secrecy, asked her to buy and send a silk nightdress and a becoming dressing gown.

Weeks later the following 'romantic conversation might have been heard between the couple: 'Well, have you thought about it?' 'Yes.' 'Well?' 'I'll do it.' 'We don't want any fuss. We'll have a special licence and get married at Maldon Registry Office. You see to it.'

She wanted no fuss either. She was older than her sister and anyway her parents would not want the expense of two weddings in one year (there were 15 in the family). So telling no-one she cycled to Maldon on the pretext of having a dress fitted, explained all to the Registrar, and he advised putting the necessary three-day notice in his window on the Friday, since no-one was likely to see it over the weekend.

On Monday 6 May 1924, Violet Grout, having picked a sprig of pear blossom as a bouquet, cycled to Maldon ostensibly to have a second dress fitting. She had persuaded her brother to come on the train from Langford and to meet her there, and Tom Cullen arrived in his Belsize car from Witham. After the ceremony her husband and her brother returned to Witham where Tom went to the office of Thomas Cullen and Sons to tell his father. Violet cycled back to Ulting. She told the Vicar on her way home, so that he would not hear of her marriage from anyone else first; then on to break the news to her parents. Her mother cried, but her father, once having found out whom she had married, said, 'There is a bottle of champagne in the sideboard cupboard. I think that you should fetch it'. After drinks they all sat down to a 'wedding breakfast' of stew and rice pudding. The honeymoon was not to come until years later, when she was taken to Somerset for three days to meet Tom's relations.

History does not relate exactly when the couple got into the same house but when they did the following morning her husband went to his father saying, 'I'm in some difficulty, father — there are two single beds in two different rooms, and that's a little awkward'. 'We can't have that. I'll send you a double bed round'. Mrs. Cullen remembers that it was a lovely brass bedstead and that the farm men who delivered and set it up never did stop laughing about it — but *not* in front of her.

After such a beginning one cannot but wonder how the marriage turned out. Perhaps the following episode will give some idea.

Every Sunday the local golfing husbands could be found at Maldon Golf Course, having left their wives at home to cook the dinner. Such a one was Tom Cullen. This arrangement did not suit Violet, nor did being allowed to go along and watch admiringly from the side pacify her. One day in the club-house she announced her intention of putting up for membership. Tom said, 'You can't do that, I shall blackball you'. But some of his friends egged her on saying, 'You do, Mrs. Tom. We'll support you'. In due course she put her name forward and was elected. Going home in the car nothing was said; but still, at the age of 95 years, her eyes twinkle at the memory as she asks, 'Do you know what I found that he had done when we got inside the house? — he'd bought me a new set of clubs'.[2]

It was a very satisfactory marriage.

*****

The Minutes of a meeting of the Agricultural Seed Trade Association (A.S.T.A.) held in the Cambridge Rooms of the *Great Eastern Hotel*, Liverpool Street, London E.C. on 9 December 1918, give some indication of what was on seed-growers' minds at the time. For instance, although declaring themselves grateful to the Government for allowing the trade some exemptions from war service, it was pointed out that the increased need for seeds to be grown in this country, and not imported from abroad, had caused many difficulties both for merchant and grower who had been called upon to learn new skills at short notice, and with a much depleted workforce. During the war years business between railways had been pooled so that different companies were no longer competing with one another. Now that war had ceased there was talk of the railways being nationalised and the individual companies, who had previously been willing to pick up goods for transit free of charge, were no longer prepared to offer this service without a considerable charge being made.

There was lengthy discussion on Seed Testing Stations. This covered points such as a need for a uniform world standard of testing. The trade was asking for a licence to do their own purity and germination tests. It was also suggested that all crop inspectors and other experts should be trained, be required to qualify for a certificate of proficiency, and that this training might be part of the work of the proposed National Institute of Agricultural Botany. The A.S.T.A. had already contributed £15,000 to the formation of this institution which was matched pound for pound by a grant from the Government. Further, there were to be two members of A.S.T.A. on the governing body.

Pasture plants were rising in importance. It was recognised that there was much work to be done in this neglected sphere and a plea was made for the improvement of our indigenous species.

Finally, some members had grave doubts as to the competence of the newly-appointed seed testers at Government seed testing stations since it was affirmed that it took at least six years to train a competent tester.

Hugh Dickson's family had been friends of the Cullens for a number of years and so, when his involvement with the Carson faction in the 'Troubles' made life too dangerous for either him or his young family to remain in Ireland, he left Alex Dickson and Sons, Newtownards, Co. Down, and in 1921 came to England in the hope of a possible opening.

At this time the Cullen firm was expanding and in need of more capital and of expertise in flower seeds. Hugh Dickson had both and consequently joined this firm where he particularly concentrated on the development of sweet peas. Between the wars he bred many well-known varieties, finishing with 'Air Warden' in 1938. The sweet pea was so named because Hugh Dickson was a very early recruit of the Auxiliary Air Service. When he retired, in 1945, this tall, spare, keen-witted and colourful character, with his sardonic sense of humour and fund of Irish stories, left behind expressions which lived on for many years. One, still in use in 1982 to mean rather a long time, is 'for the best part of some considerable time'. His son, Norman Dickson, started the firm's seed testing station under the 1921 Act. It was one of the earliest to be set up in the country and was run by him until 1945.

To give some idea of a young seedsman's life and progress in the family firm in the early 1930s, I will give here, often verbatim, the copious notes, together with much other material, which Mr. A. L. Cullen has so kindly taken the trouble to prepare and lend me.

On leaving Felsted School in 1932, Antony L. Cullen at once went into the family firm. He had already worked on the trial grounds and as a roguer during school holidays. For this work he had received 5s. a week pocket money but when he became a regular employee this sum was raised to 'the munificent wage of 10s. a week of forty-eight hours, plus unpaid overtime when necessary'.

Mr. Cullen particularly remembers a stint in the warehouse learning to fill hoppers and tie sacks under the eagle eye of the foreman, 'Nipsey' Cranmer. Before this A. L. C. had thought he was fit, but 'when you have not yet got the knack, hoisting a $2\frac{1}{2}$ cwt sack of beans on to your back, then having to climb a ladder and heave it on to the top of a high pile is no easy matter'. It was almost too much for him and he still remembers his shame on having to be shown the knack by 'Nipsey', then almost 70, 'who shouldered the beans, climbed the ladder and twitched the sack off his shoulders as easily as if it were full of feathers'.

Again Mr. Cullen remembers that 'Roguing crops often meant bicycling for miles with two or three others, lunch boxes strapped on the carrier, to D'Arcy or Tollesbury, spending the day in the fields of cabbages or kale and riding home again at night — worn out'.

Distant crops meant putting the bikes on the train, in the guard's van, and riding off from Chelmsford, Colchester or Ipswich to the often far-off farms.

> Sometimes luxurious travel was at hand in the shape of the pillion seat on Gordon Keeble's motor bike (sometimes even in the sidecar) as he slowly and majestically chugged through the winding lanes of Tiptree and the Tothams where many acres of vegetable and flower seed crops were grown.

After a year of this his weekly wage was doubled to £1. Saving hard for some months he at last had sufficient to buy a used Austin Seven Chummy car for £10. The licence and a tankful of petrol reduced his savings to nil but, 'It meant easier and quicker crop inspecting and a mileage allowance of 1d. a mile helped no end'.

The new recruit was then taken into the office where he was allowed to hand-write the orders into a large bound order book and then re-copy them on a typewriter onto a warehouse order sheet. He soon devised a more labour-saving and efficient method. However, new ideas were not always popular, as when Antony had great ideas on advertising and explained them to Grandfather who listened attentively and, at the end, said, 'Well, you may be right young man, you *may* be right, but in my day good seeds sold themselves'. They were both right.

On 23 March 1935, the founder of the firm, Thomas Cullen, died at his home, Bramstons, Chipping Hill, Witham, aged 89 years. The *Braintree and Witham Times* said of him:

> The business, now of world-wide repute, has been built up greatly on its founder's sterling business qualities in selecting and improving stocks and introducing new varieties.
>
> Mr. Cullen's wonderful personality endeared him to all with whom he came in contact. Many will remember his readiness to give advice and to extend help to all who asked. He had always been held in affectionate regard by all his staff and workmen, many of whom had been in his employ from boyhood.

The next progression for A. L. C. was to be appointed personal private secretary to his uncle Frank, who, entering his office at 9 o'clock sharp, expected all mail to have been opened, sorted and put ready on his desk. Every letter having been read and placed face downwards on the side of his desk he then summoned his secretary, gave him the pile of mail and asked him to call out the name on each letter in turn. Uncle Frank's memory was phenomenal. On being given the name he could recall every point in each letter and at once proceeded to dictate a reply at considerable speed, acknowledging an order to one, quoting prices for Brussels sprout or Marrow Stem kale to another, and when his distraught personal private secretary, scribbling frantically, was unable to keep up, he would mutter irritably, 'What do you want to write it down for — can't you remember it?'.

By 1936 promotion had reached the stage of allowing him to attend Mark Lane Corn Exchange every Monday. 'Dark suit, bowler hat, rolled umbrella and gloves were *de rigeur* and travel to Liverpool Street was first class, with a scarlet Trader's ticket with one's name stamped on it gold letters — this was issued because thefirm then used rail transport, almost exclusively, for all seeds.'

On their trial grounds the Cullens both bred new varieties and selected and improved other stocks. Much work was done with garden peas; they are remembered for such varieties as Early Bird, British Lion and Blue Bird. Their sweet peas include the well-known variety Winston Churchill, and in the *Horticultural Advertiser* of 28 September 1939 there is a write-up of trials carried out by the wholesale seed trade which states that Thomas Cullen had produced 'a new cabbage' and 'splendid Sweet Peas'. This cabbage was named 'Leader'; in 1937 it had received a Wisley Award of Merit and was 'of good flavour unlike most market cabbage, which are only fit for a goat to eat'.

One of the compensations for low wages in the seed trade was the chance of foreign travel, for, even in the 1930s, to go abroad was not usual for the working man. Every year A. L. C. had the pleasure of going to Hungary to inspect crops of pea, lettuce and sweet pea seed being grown on contract for his firm; to Quedlinburg and Erfurt in Germany for flower seeds and to France to see crops with Vilmorin; Tezier; and Clause; or to Holland where many companies grew for them seeds of cauliflower, spinach, radish and many flowers. A. L. C.'s younger brother Michael joined the firm from school in 1936. After serving the apprenticeship in various departments, this young man was sent to the Official Seed Testing Station at Cambridge to qualify as a seeds analyst.

As war approached, both brothers joined the Territorial Army, as did many others from the different departments, so that on 1 September 1939 about one third of the staff of this firm suddenly left for the duration of the war.

This left Frank Cullen, now 65 years old, and Hugh Dickson, even a few years older, unable to retire and having to soldier on with more responsibility than ever as well as having to face the problems of seed shortages. The whole European production was now cut off and there were the additional worries of air raids, fire-watching and so on.

A. L. Cullen, commissioned in the 2/5th Battalion of the Essex Regiment, served in France and West Africa, Iraq, and the Western Desert where he was taken prisoner when, at the battle of Deir-el-Shein, the whole brigade was decimated while stopping Rommel's advance to the Delta in July 1942. For his part in this engagement he was awarded the Military Cross, and was later honoured with the Territorial Decoration. Michael, also commissioned in the Essex Regiment, served in North Africa and the Italian campaigns with the 2nd Hampshires, tragically to be killed at the crossing of the River Arno in 1944. In 1946 their cousin, Walter Thomas Cullen, also died just as he was about to come home on leave from National Service.

For the seed trade, as well as for returning soldiers, post-war re-adjustment had its problems, which included a search for new areas of production and for new markets. Trade with the United States of America, which before the war had provided United Kingdom seeds with a good market, was now reversed, for the Americans had learnt new methods of production.

Thomas Cullen's daughter, Ella, married a Mr. F. H. Fairweather and their eldest son, first a fruit farmer, joined the firm in about 1950. He was a grandson of the firm's founder and became a partner in charge of seeds testing and seed production. He retired, very ill, in 1976 and died in 1981.

In the mid-1960s, as the firm expanded, it became necessary for the partnership to be turned into a limited company (19 May 1964). At the same time Lionel Stoneham, the office and financial manager, and Sidney Saunders, the sales manager, were made directors. Also during these years Mr. Antony Cullen felt that he could beat serve his company and the seed trade generally by taking an active part in seed trade association affairs. For many years he was a council member of S.T.A.U.K. and Chairman of its Vegetable and Root Seeds Committee.

In the mid-1970s there were great developments in plant breeding, for by this time hybrid vigour was really being exploited and had come to the fore. Development and expansion costs were increasing and Cullen's were in need of more capital as well as greater technical expertise. This led to an approach being made to Amalgamated Seed Merchants (Wholesale) Ltd. of Leicester, the most progressive group of seed companies in the country. It already included Harrison and Sons Ltd. of Leicester, Clucas of Ormskirk, Yates of Cheltenham, Deal of Kelvedon and Watkins and Simpson Ltd. In 1974 Thomas Cullen and Sons Ltd. joined this group of companies and, at the same time, merged with the other local wholesale company in the group, W. Deal and Sons Ltd. of Kelvedon, to become Deal Cullen Seeds Ltd. The existing directors were appointed directors of the new company and Antony Cullen also joined the board of the holding company, Amalgamated Seed Merchants (Wholesale) Ltd., from which he retired and, in 1977, went off to farm some 720 acres in Devon, together with a similar acreage still retained at Cressing Temple. Thus ended this family of Cullen as directors in the seed trade.

When T. Cullen and Sons Ltd. amalgamated with W. Deal and Sons Ltd., in 1974, the joint managing directors were A. L. Cullen and L. A. W. Prior. For a time the offices were retained at Park Farm, Inworth, but in 1975 were transferred to Deal Cullen Ltd. at Witham. In 1982, L. A. W. Prior retired and at the same time he became one of only 15 others in the world to hold an honorary life-membership of the International Seed Trade Association. In 1983, the Witham Offices of Thomas Cullen & Sons Ltd. were transferred to the A.S.M.E.R. headquarters in Leicester.

'Len' Prior is another seedsman who has no intention of rusting away in retirement. In 1986 he was proud to have been made a Vice-President of the N.I.A.B., to have been appointed a member of their Vegetable Trials Advisory Committee, and still to be serving on their Brussel Sprouts and Cabbage panels. Furthermore, as a consultant to two seed firms (Unwin's and Nutting and Speed) he travels to oversee their trials, both in this country and abroad.

Chapter Seven

Some Kelvedon and District Seedgrowers

A hook, a hank and a backache, and you have started seedgrowing
T. A. Glover, retired seed grower

PART I

Although in the 18th century there was a known seed grower, Thomas Moss, in Feering (see Chapter 3), the Kelvedon district as a seed-growing area is not well documented until the 19th century.

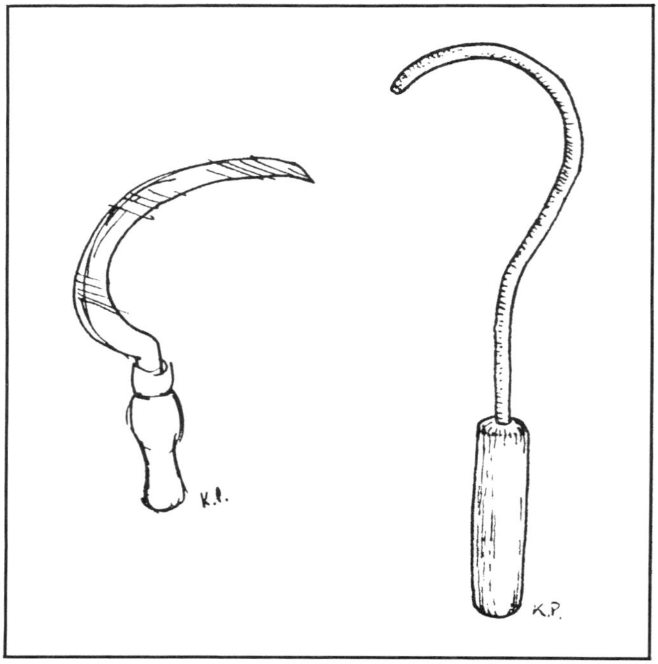

From 1800 onwards many farmers, as well as horticulturists, who lived in areas suitable for seed-growing were including such crops in their rotation. It happened around Coggeshall, Kelvedon and Tiptree with pockets on suitable soils around Colchester, Finchingfield and Saffron Walden. In a more southerly direction there was development in St Osyth, Alresford and on Mersea Island with many cereal vegetable and root seed crops, later to be followed by herbage seeds on the north bank of the River Blackwater and up through the Teys, on the Dengie marshes, Foulness Island, in the Rochford district and a scattering of fields elsewhere. Today, with the renewed interest in medicinal herbs, one may chance upon fields of evening primrose and perhaps the most enchanting crop of all, the blue petalled borage with its carmine stems and covering of silver-grey hairs.

55. A hook and a hank.

It was usual for one or more of these seed growers to become the locally-recognised person to be approached if one wished to obtain a seed contract from one or other of the big firms or to ask advice on the growing of a particular crop. Indeed, some became skilled in roguing and in the selection of plants for possible new strains and a very few developed into seed merchants who produced a catalogue and were recognised by the established trade. However, most remained as middle-men who perhaps did a small amount of local trading but who, strictly speaking, were agents for the large wholesale establishments, at whose premises parcels of seeds were collected, perhaps cleaned or dried, and then passed on to 'the trade'.

Edwin J. Cranmer, Bridgefoot, Kelvedon

The Cranmers grew seeds and are reputed to have developed 'a nice little business' but it is thought that they did not progress to the stage of issuing a catalogue — although there was almost certainly a Seed Trade List. It is said that they never became members of Mark Lane, but Edwin's son Edward frequently attended this market in company with his seedsmen friends. His daughter remembers that on most Mondays her father, dressed in his pin-stripes, black bowler and gloves, set off from East Gores Farm, Great Tey, to catch the 9.10 a.m. Liverpool Street train from Kelvedon, and that he always took with him a leather bag and black rolled umbrella.

A footpath ran right through Bridgefoot Farm and many a former Kelvedon schoolchild still recalls the blaze of colour on either side as they passed through during the flowering season. Sometimes after much rain, this footpath flooded and then they had to walk through the garden of the house. On these occasions they would be watched to see that they did no damage by Mrs. Cranmer, a rather frightening figure who strongly resembled the late Queen Mary.

Edwin Cranmer died in about 1940 leaving two sons, William and Edward. William lived in Kelvedon, first in a house called Marlers and then at Barnfield. a house built for him on Bridgefoot land (some 90 acres). The brothers were in partnership, but latterly it was Edward who took most of the responsibility for the business. After Edward died his manager carried on, seemingly just to wind up affairs, for in 1950 the Cranmer's business had ceased to exist.

J. Ottwell Polley & Son

'Joe' Polley, a builder at Kelvedon, had a son, Joseph Ottwell Polley, who first lived at Highfields Farm, Kelvedon, and is also remembered as having farmed Watering Farm, Kelvedon, and Breast End, Bradwell.

The story of 'Ott's' son is a sad one. Like many another he had gone to fight for his country in 1914 and, after experiencing the horror of the Dardanelles, where he survived being actually blown up, he came home to grow seeds and live at The Moorings, Kelvedon. Not very surprisingly he took to drink and Tony Bonner of Threshelford's, when still a schoolboy, remembers crossing a field with his father and encountering 'Ott's' son who said to him most seriously, 'NEVER START to drink, Boy', which then struck Tony as odd, because he knew that this man was frequently intoxicated and that if there was a car in the ditch anywhere between Coggeshall and Kelvedon, no-one ever bothered to ask whose it was, for, as was said in the village, 'Joe never could seem to get round a corner — he just kep' right on agoin' straight'.

At some time 'Ott' Polley moved from Highfields to Ormond Lodge, which is opposite the Conservative Club in Kelvedon High Street. It was here that the 17-year old L. A. W. Prior, then a Crop Inspector for Nutting and Sons, first saw a grand piano. Ottwell, seeing that this youth was gazing at the piano, observed pleasantly, 'That's my parsnip piano, boy', and then proceeded to tell the story. One year, during the First World War, when there was a good trade for parsnip seed, Ottwell, who happened to have a one hundredweight sack of it, decided to send this to his merchant. So, hoisting it onto his shoulder, he 'humped it down to the station to catch the next train'. To his great satisfaction the seed made £1 a pound and, somewhat astonishingly, he spent the lot on a grand piano. One can imagine the added status that this must have given to Mrs. Polley's front room. Nearby, in

56. Mr. Polley, a relative of Ottwell Polley, supervising the cutting of a seed crop at Springholds Farm, Rivenhall.

Rolley Lane, was 'Ott's' two-storeyed warehouse in which he stored and cleaned seeds. Interestingly, this warehouse is still there today and has been converted to housing.

James Parrish & Sons Ltd., Grange Farm, Coggeshall

The Parrish family was formerly connected with mining in Northumberland and, like many another, it had its ups and downs. For the present purpose, the 'up' was when grandfather James Parrish, having struggled through the depression after the Napoleonic wars, moved down to Essex and began to grow seed crops on contract to the merchants. As has already been mentioned, this was the time to 'get into seeds' and so it was not long before his farming enterprise expanded to become James Parrish and Sons with their main office at Grange Farm. There were four sons, Sid, Ernie, Jim and William, and one can imagine that they were kept busy, for the business prospered and they gradually became the owners or the tenants of eight farms, namely:

In Coggeshall	Grange Farm, Scrips, Curd Hall and Coggeshall Hall
On the Tey Road	Markdowns
In Earls Colne	Hungry Hall
In Kelvedon	Leapingwells
In Messing	Stubbers Farm

Before 1914 this family was growing flower seeds, many acres of root and brassica seeds and also seed corn. They grew for Cooper Taber's, for Hurst's and for Carter's. Also for many years they held regular contracts to grow several varieties of Spring Heading Broccoli (now called Winter cauliflower) for E. W. King and Company.

With this firm, William Wilberforce Moles once more enters the picture. In 1882 he had followed Ezekiel Deal as an apprentice with John Moss (see p.31) and, having gained sufficient experience, he then left Mr. Moss to take charge of seed production and cleaning for James Parrish, at Grange Farm.

Grandfather James Parrish had for many years attended Mark Lane clad in his frock coat and topper but, when in 1920 or 1921 he arrived at Kelvedon Station in his own chauffeur-driven Daimler, it caused something of a stir. He was immensely proud of this car but could never be bothered to learn to drive it. Perhaps it was really purchased as a fitting vehicle for an aspiring Parliamentary candidate, for he ran as a Liberal during this period for the Maldon division of Essex.

As well as their extensive farming and seed-growing activities the Parrishes set up as contractors for steam ploughing and other agricultural work, and by the time that war broke out in 1939 they were well equipped to assist those who had been ordered to break up their grassland in order to plant corn for the nation. Similar to the Moss family, it was the grandsons in the business who took to the mechanical side. Certainly they were delighted when the new steam ploughing tackle was delivered to Kelvedon station and driven away straight to its first job at Coggeshall Hall, with no adjustments having to be made.

Jim Parrish, now more or less retired and well over retirement age, was farm manager for the Doughtons, of Park Farm, Kelvedon, for 32 years. They owned the first Class Combine in this area, and this was superceded by a little Allis Chalmers '60', Olivers and some John Deeres. There was also a Minneapolis Molline and a big self-propelled Allis Chalmers Gleaner. The Allis Chalmers '60' is remembered as having its iron beaters and concave encased in rubber. This, together with a drum speed which could be adjusted down so that it was possible to see the drum actually going round, is said to have made it the only combine capable of thrashing runner beans without cracking them in half. The present Jim Parrish recollects that before his family's fortunes fell (after the Second World War) he and his brothers and sisters led a lovely life, shooting, playing tennis and generally enjoying themselves between working on the farms or with the machinery. Apparently, as tennis players, they travelled far and wide to tournaments, and, teamed with their friends, were practically unbeatable.

Another glimpse of the Parrish family comes from a letter[1] written in 1976 by Mrs. Field of Tiptree. Recalling her childhood she wrote:

> My first job was helping my mother — I was the eldest of nine children, and when I was just a little girl I peeled potatoes and all sorts of things. I ran all the errands for her and my grandparents, and walked to the shops four or five miles away at Kelvedon. I used to help my mother glean the corn — my father ground this at the mill for us to use at home.
>
> I went fruit picking, stone picking and blackberrying. I sold the fruit to Tiptree Jam Factory — I lived at Withickers Rookery near Tiptree Mill. I went out to work when I was nine, working for Mr. Parrish — a seed grower. In winter we worked inside a shed cleaning out peas and beans and getting pips from marrows and cucumbers. In summer we collected carrot and parsnip seeds and everything you can think of — it was at Tiptree but I have forgotten the name of the road, it was on a hill just outside Tiptree. The very special thing we did was picking up Canary Creeper seeds from rows. It was the first that had been grown and very precious — Mr. Parrish used to come behind us with a stick in case we dropped any — they were funny little black things — and we had to go back and pick them up. I earned 3s. a week and I gave it all to my mother for my father was ill and could not work and he died when I was twenty-one. I used to pick water-cress growing wild and had to go right into the pond to get it, I bunched it up and sold it and once I got enough to buy my father a

> tin of crab — he liked that better than anything as he couldn't eat much. We used to go to Totham, a long ride with Mr. Parrish in a wagon, doing all sorts of jobs in the fields — mostly 'twitching' — we walked behind the ploughs and picked up every little bit of white root and burned it. We took all our food to the fields, cold tea to drink, and bread with something homemade or a bit of cheese.
>
> I worked there until I was fourteen when I went to service with Mr. and Mrs. Webb of Brentwood.

Jim Parrish also remembers how they grew celery seed:

> Two pounds of seed/square yard of seedbed provided plenty of plants for half an acre. It was sown in March and then kept clean by hand weeding. This was necessary because celery is a slow grower and using a hoe in the early stages is liable to result in too many seedlings being hoed up. Using a garden fork, plants are taken from the plant bed in August/ September and the roots are trimmed. These plants are then set out at nine-inch row spacings and three feet between the rows according to the width of your drill — one person to deb and two to drop the plants was usual.
>
> As soon as the plants are established it is important to hoe the rows frequently to prevent competition by weeds. Celery Fly is a troublesome pest.

In order to fit in with the farm machinery, rows are usually spaced to the width of the drill. The Smythe Drill was apparently made to slightly different widths according to the customer's wants. This, Jim Parrish says, accounts for the differing size of the 'stetch' in different places.

In August the crop was cut with a rip hook — tied into bundles by hand and 'stood up four square' — the produce of two stetches (six rows) being put into one. This method left space for a wagon to go down the row between the thraves, to pick up the sheaves. It was necessary to spread a good cloth over the floor and up the sides of the wagon to catch the seed which sheds very readily at every movement. Generally the wagon took the sheaves to a prepared floor in the barn (i.e. a good layer of straw, covered with a hessian cloth) where it was stacked in one or other of the bays to be flailed out in the central space between the doors in December or January. This seed, like that of parsnip, had to be 'ryed' because the cleaning machines were not sophisticated enough to do the job properly.

An average yield was three hundredweight (or a little more) per acre. The price in the late 1940s was from 2s. 6d. to 3s. 0d. a pound.

A small Stubbs and a Gentry dressing machine were used. The Gentry had two sleeves and a blower. Nevertheless, the Stubbs was a better machine — at any rate, Jim Parrish remembers that it had more gadgets — and delivered seed straight into the sack and not into a heap on the floor.

In order to prevent mistakes being made by labels being torn from sacks, two labels were always used, one on the outside and one pushed well down inside the sack.

Thomas Harvey and Son, Scrips Farm, Coggeshall

Although the name Harvey can be found amongst the earliest records of this district I have not come across any who have been seed growers until after the First World War. In 1899, grandfather, Eli Harvey, died, aged 46 years, leaving an 11-year old son Thomas and his two brothers to help to augment the family's income and to make their own way in life. This early start probably accounts for Thomas having become a master of many country skills. It is also noteworthy that from the reports of those who knew him there emerges no sign of bitterness towards life but a picture of a hardworking, honest and kindly man, who took a pride in a job well done.

Eric Deal, of Inworth, recalls that his father once asked him to find someone to thatch their corn stacks. So, knowing that 'Thomas and his cousin up at Tiptree' did such work, Eric arranged this with them. When Eric's father heard about it he was not too pleased. He had seen none of the Harveys' work and did not want 'a couple of boys doing a job which might end in the rain getting into my corn stacks!'. However, when the work was done, to

Eric's immense relief his father said, 'You may get those Harveys in again whenever I want any more thatching done, boy'.

Thomas married Eleanor Chapman who lived on Appleford's Farm at Rivenhall, and in 1907 they lived at Brown's Cottages, Rivenhall, and it was here that their son Tom was born in 1915.

Trees and wood became a part of Thomas's life. He provided sticks for sweet peas, garden peas and runner beans; faggots for bread ovens, and thatching pegs; and he would cut the 'lop and top from a spinney' and could 'climb a tree as nimbly as any squirrel' in order to cut off a branch when, it is said, he could 'judge to a nicety just where the timber would fall'. (When a new spinney is planted the hardwood trees are initially interspaced with something that will grow quickly. The idea is not only to protect the slower growing trees but also to 'draw them up straight'. Hornbeam is often used for this purpose and before it begins to have a smothering effect it is cut down and the branches are sold as 'lop and top'.)

Together with this work was another side-line, the selling of logs for firewood. The present Thomas Harvey (hereinafter referred to as Tom) remembers that when he and his brother returned from school they were often enlisted to help father on the cross-saw. At such times, in the eerie light of a hurricane lantern, they would spend one or more hours sawing up the next day's load. To the end of his life, Thomas Harvey enjoyed nothing better than 'a bit of a deal' and no doubt the log-selling fitted in very nicely with this pursuit.

Despite setbacks, this family's history shows steady improvement. As their son Benjamin (Ben) says, 'My father was a skilled worker who preferred piece-work to being a regular farm worker and he had a wife who provided the driving force which encouraged her family to go on striving for improvement'. All her encouragement was needed, for although this was a period of increasing educational opportunity it was also one of great agricultural depression. The following extract from an article written by the Right Honourable Lord Ernle, for the 1923 Agricultural Seed List of Hunter's of Chester, shows this clearly:

> On the heels of the drought of 1921 has trodden the fall of corn prices in 1922. Arable farmers now bear the brunt. Their financial resources are melting: they are threatened with disaster. The ordinary crops of the arable farm, with the exception of well-saved barley, cannot be sold at a profit, and selling below or even at cost price spells ruin to business. If men are forced to go out of the industry, their capital loss at once materialises to its fullest extent. The depreciation in value of livestock and equipment has been heavy . . . The approximate aggregate amount of the loss cannot be put lower than forty per cent of farming capital, and it might be put higher.

To show what happened to many who ventured into farming at this time (for it was very common for ex-servicemen to put their gratuity into a piece of land after the First World War) the following story will serve as an example. In the spring of 1921 Thomas Harvey went into partnership with his two ex-service brothers-in-law. Previously, Thomas had gained some experience of seed growing while working 'odd times' for Mr. Walter Taber. This work had brought in 13s. a week and from it and his other side-lines he had managed to save the then princely sum of £100. The three of them put their combined savings into renting and equipping Dengie Farm, Witham.

The venture was launched by the purchase of a pair of horses, one in-pig sow, a few strawberry plants and two or three small contracts to grow flower seeds.

All through the hot and droughty summer of 1921 the partners tended their plants only to see them shrivel and die as one rainless day followed the next. The sow had a good litter of pigs, but when they reached the stage at which they should have sold at a profit, no buyer could be found because nobody had any food to spare to feed them. Eventually, when they were sold, the pigs only made what the sow had originally cost. This left nothing with which to pay for their food or the labour entailed. By the end of that year all Thomas's hard-won investment had been lost and it was clear that he must leave the partnership and find more remunerative work.

Not long afterwards this family obtained the tenancy of Great Braxted mill house and its adjoining three acres of land. Mr. Wallace arrived on his motorbike from Messrs. Cooper Taber and they were given contracts to grow wallflower, nasturtium, sweet william and parsley seeds. There were, of course, also some strawberries and possibly a few peas.

However, more land was needed to support the ever-increasing family, and when two rabbit-ridden fields in Braxted Park became available, Thomas took them on and also found enough money to surround them with wire netting to deter the rabbits.

By 1928, Thomas and Eleanor's third son left school. This was Tom Harvey and, since it is he who stayed at home to farm and grow seed crops with his father, it is his story which will be told. By this time they were spared the work of having to take their fruit and greengrocery to the nearest town for sale. It was collected by a lorry driver who had been commissioned by the buyers at the London markets to travel round the countryside to find them suitable produce.

In 1931 the house and 64 acres of Glebe Farm, Great Braxted fell vacant and they moved in. Eleanor Harvey's heart is said to have been very near breaking for they could not afford to rent both properties and she was loath to leave her pretty Mill House for the smaller and damp Glebe farmhouse.

In due course, Tom became restive and one day set off for London to look for a better job. This evidently jolted his father into the realisation that his son was growing up and that if he wanted him to stay on the farm, he must be offered a better position; so when Tom returned his father offered to take him into partnership. It did not amount to much, but as Tom laughingly says, 'It did no end for my morale'.

Nevertheless, in 1932, enough money was coming in to enable them to employ a man at 30s. a week. By 1933 the family's first tractor, a 1927 model Ford — together with a plough, was purchased for £27. Their mechanisation programme had begun and, in 1938, a 70-acre Essex County Council smallholding, Ford Farm, Rivenhall, was rented and, by 1940, Tom had married and was living there.

Evidently by now they were credit-worthy, for the bank allowed the partnership a loan of £535 to purchase an Allis Chalmers Crawler tractor and also to rent 190 acres of land at Bower's Hall, Silver End. The two fields in Braxted Park were now relinquished.

Not all was plain sailing. One year a dreadfully sharp and late spring frost almost wiped out all income for that year by killing the plants in the fields. Nevertheless, when T. A. Glover offered to rent Scrips Farm, Coggeshall (258 acres) to the Harveys in 1942 ('right in the middle of the war with all Land girls and P.O.W. labour') Tom Harvey did not miss the opportunity.

In 1954 the firm was made a limited company and Scrips Farm was purchased as, in 1960, were Curd's Farm and Hayward's, Coggeshall (404 acres). There was also an additional 420 acres of rented land at Kelvedon Hall. This latter has since been relinquished.

During this time and for several subsequent years, these farms grew many kinds of vegetable and farm seeds including such exotics as maize, Navy soya beans, sunflowers, and soya beans. However, when the newly-invented precision drill, which was more economical with seed, arrived at Scrips and Eric Deal and Tom were trying it out, Eric remarked prophetically, 'It's a good machine but it will be the end of our seed growing' — and so, from having been one of the biggest seed growers in the area, Tom's son William says that 1982 was the first year in which no seed crops were grown on the Harvey's land.

J. W. Ireland of Feering

Until well into the 20th century the recommended cure for tuberculosis was an outdoor life. Therefore, when John Ireland developed this disease he gave up his job as a steam engineer at Chelmsford's Power Station and started to grow seeds on an horticultural holding in Feering. He is remembered as a man who 'had a marked mechanical and electrical bent', and this he put to good use to improve his horticultural enterprise. It appears also that he readily assimilated the practical side of his business for when, after a long period of drought, a seed merchant's representative called to look at some crops,[2] he was found 'running his Planet hoe between the rows of plants — blunting blades by the dozen in the parched and unyielding soil'. Upon enquiry as to what good he thought he was doing he declared that hoeing was 'Good as a shower of rain, boy — good as a shower of rain'.

The American 'Clipper' seed-dressing machine has been described as 'the only piece of dressing equipment that, in the early 1920s, was both available and any good'. It was a hand-operated tool and John Ireland immediately set about adapting it to power, by means of a connecting belt to an electric motor with a rheostat to control the speed.

At this time the firm of Boby in Bury St Edmunds were agents for the 'Clipper' machine and when they saw John Ireland's adaptation they immediately entered into negotiations to have it incorporated into all future American 'Clipper' cleaning machines. (The prototype of this adaptation is said to have last been seen at Clive's Farm, Boxted.)

Kenneth J. Ireland, 'Saint Patrick's', Feering

A little before 1939, 'Ken' Ireland (John's son) seems to have taken control of this business. Both he and his father were men who soon found out the best way to do a job. Ken, in particular, seems to have had the ability to 'smell out an opportunity before anyone else knew that it was there'. It is even said[3] that at a time when Hurst's was in trouble, he suggested to Mr. Browning of Tey Brook, Great Tey, and to Harold Seabrook, of Garlands, Tollesbury, that they should go into partnership to take over the business. It is diverting to speculate on what might have happened to the fortunes of that firm if, in fact, these three had done so.

The Irelands grew sweet peas for Unwin's and later for Carter's Tested Seeds. The *Horticultural Trades' Journal* of 5 October 1938 reports that if Mr. K. Ireland's rows of sweet peas were laid end to end they would stretch for some 17 miles.

Pot plants were then a developing industry and with this there followed the need for the production of such seeds as calceolaria, cineraria and *Primula suriensis*. These seeds often have to be hand-pollinated which is done with the aid of a paint brush, or sometimes a rabbit or hare's tail.

Flower seeds were the main crops until, in 1939, the Government curtailed this production and, having grown annuals for Ryder's and for Elsom's, biennials for Bee's and sweet peas for Unwin's, their contracts changed to growing vegetable seeds such as celery, Cheltenham red beet, cabbages and tomatoes for the firm of Nutting and Son. After the war Ken went back to flower seeds until a disastrous harvest persuaded him that he would do better to seek some more lucrative employment. It was at this stage that he joined the Board of the agricultural firm of Williams's of Colchester. Towards the end of the 1950s, he sold his land and greenhouses to Carter's Tested Seeds and left the seed-growing scene.

The Bonner family

When I first started to write this book, B. A. Bonner very generously offered to help by writing something about his family's history for inclusion. Like Topsy, this something grew until it became a small book. It would be a shame if this informative and amusing manuscript were shortened and so it is to be published separately. Nevertheless, no book on Essex seed growers would be complete without mention of the Bonners.

It was Alfred Bonner (b. 1860) who first established this family as seed growers in the Kelvedon district and they remained multipliers of flower, vegetable and farm seeds and did not enter the field of seed merchanting. By at least the second generation they had become recognised as 'seed growers proper' and by 1986 the family had built up a seed growing and horticultural enterprise of some 600 acres. Of Alfred's three sons, Hubert, Harry and Frank, it was Frank and his boys, Tony, Derek and Barry, who built up the business and became seed growers of note. Derek left school in 1936 and in that year his father increased their holding to some 400 acres by taking the lease of Coggeshall Hall. At the same time extra equipment, which included their first two tractors (few people owned one at that time), was purchased. Both tractors were Fordsons and were fitted with spade-lug wheels and a wrist-wrenching steering wheel!

Tony was called into the Air Force in July 1939, thus leaving his father and brothers to contend with all the farm work, together with the regulations and restrictions of the war years. Frank's foresight in having bought the tractors, and a large Ransomes thrashing machine, now paid dividends.

On his return from the war Tony found that there had been great changes in farming. Lack of money was no longer the governing factor. The need for food production, good harvest weather and a seller's market had restored many a family to its feet. What was lacking, and the shortage was acute, was a supply of goods and farm machinery.

In 1950 Tony and Derek broke away from the family farm to form the independent partnership of B. A. and D. Bonner. From the late Joseph Orst, who had succeeded William Moss at Threshelford's Farm, Feering, they took over 140 acres of seed-growing land. Later, when they purchased Watering Farm, Kelvedon, their holding was increased to just over 200 acres. By the time Frank Bonner died, in 1961, his youngest son Barry was farming with him, had married and was settled into Hole Farm, Rivenhall. Frank left his estate between his three sons and so they formed a partnership which currently goes under the name of Bonner Brothers.

The Bonners are innovators who make sure that they are up-to-date with new developments as they take place. Since B. A. Bonner moved into Threshelford's, the vegetable and flower seed crops have been concentrated on this farm and are under his management. Tony has always been quick to alter his cultural methods to suit the constraints of the times and consequently, although contracts for these crops have become increasingly scarce and many growers have abandoned them as uneconomic, he has been able to maintain the tradition of growing these crops on this farm. It is a tradition that can be traced back for at least a hundred years.

After the Second World War, even if skilled labour had been available, wages had outstripped returns to the extent that farmers were no longer able to maintain a large labour force. Furthermore, most of the former 'seasonal labour' had retired or found other jobs and the available 'casual labour', which came chiefly from new housing estates in nearby towns was, even if willing, almost totally unskilled. Clearly reductions had to be made in the labour requirements of all crops, and particularly in the labour-intensive vegetable and flower seeds.

The idea of a standard, rather than an optimum, row width for their crops was attractive as it would save both time and energy by removing the need to adjust implements between different crops. Trials proved that what was lost in yield was more than compensated for by a saving of time and labour and so, on the Bonners' farms, everything was very soon geared to the width of their Smythe drill (7ft. 3ins.) and usually at three rows to the stetch.

Perhaps their most spectacular saving of labour occurred in the extraction of marrow

57. Threshelford's Farm from the air in the 1980s: 'fields striped with crops of many colours'.

seeds from the shell. Hitherto the ripe marrows had been carted home from the field to a cart-lodge, here to await hand-splitting and seed removal by a gang of women. An aged Allis Chalmers model A combine was, after much trial and error, successfully adapted to do this job in the field. As the machine slowly coughed and choked its way up and down it became known as the 'Marrow Basher'. Locally it was a nine days' wonder and made headlines in the press. By using this kiltered-up contraption an operation which had hitherto taken a week was reduced to a single day.

It was not to make wine, but to begin the separation of seeds from the fruit that wellington-booted farm hands once trod around in tubs of ripe tomatoes. The process was messy, laborious and time-consuming but was much improved when one of the Bonners adapted a disused cattle-cake crusher to squash the fruit. The resulting slush of seeds and pulp had formerly been left for three or four days to allow fermentation to release the seeds from their protective surrounding jelly. However, when it was realised that it was the acid formed during fermentation that released the seeds, this process was accelerated by adding hydrochloric acid to the plastic containers of washed, but still slimy seed. Separation then took approximately 20 minutes and germination was unaffected provided that the seed was washed free from acid at once and then dried immediately.

58. B. A. and D. Bonner washing and sieving marrow seed in a 'kiltered up home-made machine', 1965. Marrow seed needed to be washed free of acid and slime.

59. Sieving marrow seeds.

A visit to the Bonners is always stimulating. They have many interests and their conversation, punctuated with keen humour, is likely to range crazily from the use of photo-destructable plastic film, archaeological digs in remote parts of the world, the best obtainable straw for corn dollies and former seed-growing techniques, to what has been revealed in some ancient family photographs that have recently been blown up. They once tried to prevent, or at least deter, crops of parsley and helichrysum from shedding their seeds by spraying the heads with plastic glue. This had been reported as successful on crops of lettuce seed in Australia. Unfortunately, in our climate, the result was inconclusive.

When hand or machine hoeing can no longer cope, weeds are controlled by chemical sprays. They use knapsack sprayers and chemically-impregnated glove 'Weed Wipers' for spot treatment and in small plots. When, as sometimes happens, weeds overtop a crop the situation is restored by the use of a tractor-mounted bar which carries a strip of felt which is constantly impregnated with a stream of weed-killer and this wipes off onto the weeds, leaving the shorter crop unharmed.

60. B. A. 'Tony' Bonner, *c.*1987.

When they heard that the crops of glasshouse tomato growers were being induced to ripen earlier by spraying them with Ethrel 'E', they tried out this technique under field conditions. It is supposed that cold night temperature prevented success. One thing that did succeed, at least under dry conditions, was their attempt to prevent bird damage to seeds of godetia and summer chrysanthemums as these matured in the swathe. The simple preventative was a light film of straw to cover the swathe.

Sometimes a seedsman has a new and unfamiliar seed and he may have little knowledge of its cultivation. This seed will very likely find its way to Tony Bonner to be multiplied because he, like the James Gordon who was gardener to the eighth Lord Petre, by just examining an unfamiliar seed, has a rare instinct for knowing just what treatment it will require in order to grow happily.

T. A. Glover, The Leat, Mill Farm, Thorrington, Essex

T. F. Glover, in partnership with his brothers, started a motor and cycle business in Witham in 1896. Later he left the partnership to start a similar business on his own in Kelvedon Street (now known as the High Street). Mr. L. A. W. Prior remembers this shop as the place from where he hired a bike for 2s. 6d. a week, every year that he came to Essex to rogue and inspect crops for Nutting and Sons. On these occasions he also stayed in digs provided by 'a dear old soul who fed me well for the sum of 21s. per week for bed, breakfast and an evening meal'.

T. F. Glover's son, T. A. (Tom) Glover (b. 1906) returned to the pursuit of his ancestors, some of whom had farmed in Pembrokeshire and others in Great Leighs, Essex. On leaving school and after three years of practical training, following by his attendance at the 1923/4 Winter Course arranged by the East Anglian Institute of Agriculture, Tom in 1925 began farming on his own at Great Domsey Farm, Marks Tey.

It was a time of farming depression with wheat selling for only 18s. a quarter (4s. 6d. a bushel) and it soon became necessary for him to look for more paying crops. At this juncture James Carter and Company offered him some seed contracts. This led to a mutually useful association which continued until Carter's became part of a large complex of seed businesses.

On Great Domsey's fields were grown seed crops of vegetables, flowers and corn. Then, when Carter's required seed from their single plant selections of cereals, Tom Glover was entrusted with these. In fact, it became an annual event for Carter's to arrange for a party of their representatives, staff and growers, to visit Great Domsey to see these crops being grown. It was in 1939 that Cockerill's Farm, Feering, was bought and farmed together with Great Domsey until, in 1942, this latter was sold to Hurst and Son to become part of their trial grounds and a major centre for plant breeding.

When Cockerill's was sold in 1956, Tom moved to Thorrington. Here, on the Mill farmland with its favourable slope towards the Tide-mill (now preserved as an ancient monument and open, by appointment, to the public), he proceeded to grow 'a sea of flowers' for seed, first for Carter's and afterwards for Sutton's.

Here also he has retired from farming and built a house named The Leat. It overlooks Alresford Creek and today his son, another Tom, lives in the Mill House and farms the land upon which there are no longer any crops of vegetable or flower seeds. Now in summer, instead of the endless work in his seed crops, when tide and weather are right, Tom can go off in his boat, down the winding creek to the river Colne and beyond and in winter he can watch comfortably from the windows of his house as swans, mallard and many other water fowl come down on to the mere and reed-bed immediately upstream of the ancient mill.

Carter's Tested Seeds Ltd.

Although Carter's did not move their headquarters into Essex, for many years they owned farms and trial grounds here, and much of their seed multiplication took place in the county. This is an example of an apothecary who became a seedsman.

In the days of the Prince Regent (1762-1820) there was in Drury Lane a shop which proclaimed itself to be the establishment of James Carter, Apothecary and Herbalist. At this time also, flower seed firms in Germany were paying particular attention to the improvement of asters and were offering new 'Aster Collections and Novelties' in their seed lists. On one of his visits to the continent James Carter had the idea of obtaining some of these choice seeds to be put up into little packets as a complimentary spring gift for favoured customers. He received so many flattering letters as a result that he decided to sell the seed on a commercial basis. From then on the apothecary and herbalist side of the business dwindled and by the end of the 19th century a small horticultural empire had developed, supplying large quantities of seeds to customers all over the world.

The *London Directory* of 1804 lists the business as 'James Carter and Company' and, as in 1835 he is said to have been simply the London agent for German seed exporters,[4] perhaps

61. ‘On Great Domsey’s fields he grew seed crops of vegetables, flowers and corn.’

62. Carter’s representatives visiting Great Domsey.

we may assume that the 'and Company' referred to the interest that a Mr. Dunnett, of Dedham in Essex, was given in this firm in place of payment for his crop. James Carter is said to have been a good linguist and to have had literary ability — qualities which no doubt stood him in good stead when it came to the compilation of at first a broadsheet (one of which, still in the Company's possession starts with an elaborate explanation of the Linnaean and Natural systems of plant classification) and then an annual catalogue. At any rate it has been stated[5] that 'his annual catalogues were for many years the index of educated horticultural taste'. The Company's Blue Book at one time offered as many as 2,000 varieties of flower and 500 vegetable seeds.

On the cover of the 1837 catalogue the firm is entitled 'James Carter, Seedsman and Florist'. (In 1837 the meaning of 'florist' signified a grower of flowering plants, and flower seeds, rather than a seller of cut blooms.) This seems to indicate that by now he was on his own and arranging for seeds to be grown for him in this country. Certainly he had moved to a pretty little bow-windowed shop, No. 238 High Holborn. James Carter probably died sometime around 1840, and no more Carters followed on in the firm. By 1857, the catalogue proclaims James Carter and Company to be Fellows of both the Horticultural Society of London and the Agricultural Society of England. It is probable that about this time, when the business was increasing and money was required for expansion, the Beales joined the firm. That the business did increase is evident, for there were now offices and seed warehouses at Nos. 237, 238 and 261 High Holborn, and the firm was styled as Seed Merchant and Nurseryman. Listed also were two seed farms, namely East House Farm, Dedham, and The Seed Farm, St Osyth, Essex, comprising some twelve hundred acres in all.

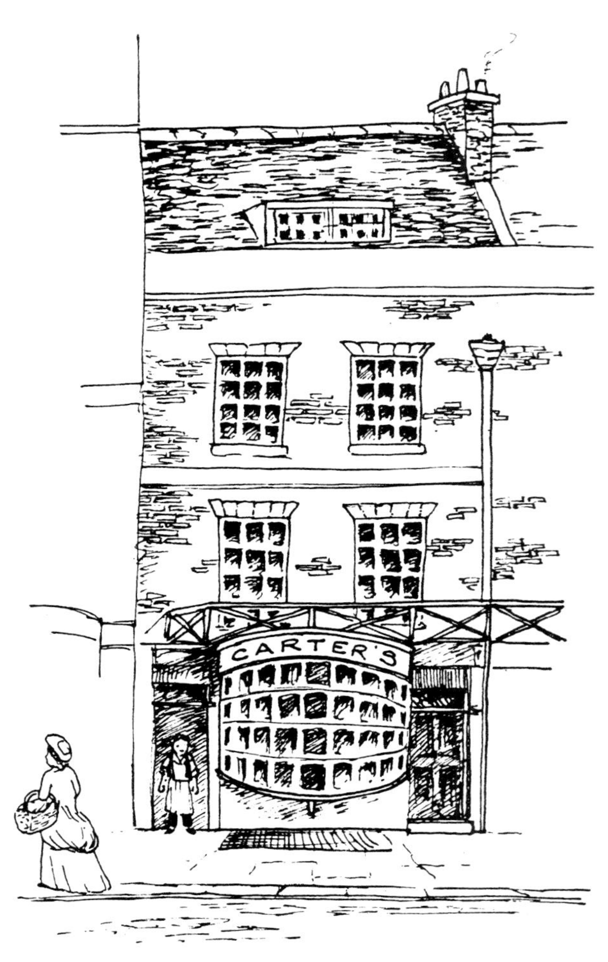

63. Carter's shop at No. 238 High Holborn.

It was not until 1860 that H. N. Dunnett, who is thought to have farmed at East House, Dedham, was made a partner in the business, of which there were, by then, two distinct sides: the wholesale, known as Carter, Dunnett and Beale, and the retail, which became Carter's Tested Seeds Ltd.

Mr. H. N. Dunnett's wife and family, Norman, Jack and Daisy, are said to have sat round their kitchen table busily sorting and putting seeds into packets with the aid of a small thimble, used as a measure. Jack Dunnett, who later lived in some style at a large red brick residence known as Stour House, Dedham, is still spoken of as a great sprinter. On one occasion, when he is reputed to have won a gold medal, a small boy was seen running up the street shouting 'Dunnett done it! Dunnett done it!'

The Beale family is said to have originated in St Osyth and to have moved to London, where they are thought to have become millionaires. Three Mr. Beales are known to have been in the firm, Gilbert, Reginald and Harold, all of whom are reputed to have been a little eccentric. Gilbert Charles Beale held a higher position than the other two. It was he who bred peacocks and owned a Rolls Royce which, legend remembers, he drove with more faith than skill! The grounds of his house in Pangbourne sloped down to the River Thames in which he owned an island with a tea room. There were also boats — one a barge — on which he liked to take parties of friends and of children for a sail and to bring them back for tea on the island. There was also what is remembered as a 'Temple Folly', but which was, in fact, a mausoleum built to the memory of his parents. Once, after a good luncheon, when Gilbert, then aged around ninety years, was driving his guests down to the barge, he mistakenly put his foot on the accelerator instead of the brake and charged across the barge deck and straight into the river. Fortunately all survived the ducking and Gilbert lived until his ninety-second year.

64. Children's thimbles used as a measure for seeds.

Carter's obtained a Royal Warrant of appointment to the monarch in 1886, and it has been renewed without a break ever since. Harold Beale was the grass seed expert and, as demand for these seeds rose, this firm also played its part. Indeed it claimed to be able to produce

> a turf of finest quality, strong and fibrous, with every appearance of great age, in just over nine months,

and substantiated the claim by growing an acceptable turf for Walton Heath Golf Club between September 1903 and May 1904. Many other golf courses have been laid with the aid of Carter's seeds, and at one time they supplied the Lawn Tennis Association with seeds for the grass courts at Wimbledon.

The vast volume of trade once carried on by such seed houses is reflected in their continual renting and building of additional premises. Carter's in 1878 purchased another 5,000 square feet of ground at High Holborn, where they erected a six-storeyed warehouse together with other offices. Yet again, in 1887, another substantial block of buildings, No. 97 High Holborn, was acquired. Then in 1911 the main business was moved to Raynes Park, London SW20. Here, after harvest and through to spring, seeds arrived at their warehouses from many an Essex farm and smallholding. All had to be cleaned and-dressed, perhaps dried, stored, and then tested for germination and purity before finally being put into sacks or packets for sale. The packeting was done by a bevy of women who are reputed to have been quicker than any machine.

Also at Raynes Park was a 25-acre trial ground with greenhouses and many other necessary buildings. Naturally, among the machinery requirements was a quantity of different types and sizes of sieve. So estimates for sieves were asked for and the contract was finally given to the small but well-known firm of Isaac Brazier and Sons, High Street, Halstead, Essex, for their price was reasonable and their product was excellent. (See pp.222-4.)

Before leaving the 19th-century history of this firm it is worth noting that in their 1887 catalogue there are photographs of a tobacco crop which had been grown by a Mr. Bateman of Brightlingsea, and for which they had been awarded,[6]

65. Carter's six-storeyed warehouse, 1878.

the First and only prize ever won with English Grown Tobacco AND Her Majesty the Queen was graciously pleased to accept from us an ILLUSTRATED DESCRIPTION OF CARTERS TOBACCO CULTIVATION.

This booklet was, for that time, quite expensive, for it cost five shillings, and one feels that the firm deserved an additional medal for bravery, for having sent a copy to, of all people, Queen Victoria!

By 1906 this firm had progressed from the stiff, brown paper seed envelope currently in use to an illustrated seed packet. Then in 1916, in the middle of the First World War, there appeared in the dreary shops a profusion of their brightly coloured 'Pictorial Seed Packets' at a cost of 3d. each. In 1919 the price rose to 4d. and the illustrations continued to improve until, in the 1930s, they put on to the market the 'Art Series' of coloured packets; these contained supplies of the more rare and expensive kinds of seeds listed in the firm's Blue Book of Gardening, and the cost was first 1s., later raised to 1s. 6d. a packet.

Their trade was not only in garden seeds for a testimonial praising their 'Quota' wheat is to be found printed in their 1938 catalogue. It is from Joseph Smith (Fms.) Ltd., Park Gate, Rivenhall.

Meanwhile, over the years, Carter's name frequently appeared among the award winners at Shows and among seedlings entered in the National Sweet Pea Society trials. At St Osyth, on their own land and that of William Gardener who grew for them, there was for many years a profusion of summer blooms so striking that, when the author Charles Dickens visited the village, he was moved to write,

> far from the screech and crash of railroads, in such an unexpected place, a mass of brilliant-blooming flowers was to be found.

William Gardener is remembered by Mrs. Violet Hughes (the granddaughter of H. N. Dunnett) as 'a gentleman who specialised in Eschscholtzias, which he crossed and succeeded in breeding several named varieties'.

When in 1959 Ken Ireland moved to Boxted and gave up seed growing, he sold his greenhouses at the end of World's End Lane, Feering, to Carter's Tested Seeds. It then became a trials nursery for this firm under the supervision of Mr. Ireland's assistant, David Church. In 1967, Carter's sold the nursery to Hurst's who retained it as part of their farming complex and David Church transferred to their employ.

In 1966, both Carter's wholesale and retail businesses were absorbed into the R. & G. Cuthbert Group, and quite soon Raynes Park was shut down and their office moved to Llangollen. At this time the holding company, the Horticultural and Botanical Association, was producing some fifty million packets of garden seeds each year.

In 1976, R. & G. Cuthbert became a part of the giant Swedish chemical group, Kema Nobel AB. This firm's annual sales were then approaching £300 million. Therefore Carter's Tested Seeds Ltd. are now part of Europe's largest seed company. However, they retain the name and still claim the high standards of their founder.

Frank Folkard and Sons Ltd., Copford

Sheep no longer graze on what was Walnut Tree Farm, Shrub End, Colchester. Before 1900, there was a flock large enough for William Folkard to send some for sale at Colchester Cattle Market on every Saturday of the year.

William's son Frank also became a farmer and he grew seed crops of roots, vegetable, and peas. At some time around 1895, Frank's ever-increasing family necessitated a sideline which would augment his income and he started a seed business. His first warehouse was at Copford Green Farm and there is an advertisement in the first edition of the *Essex Farmers' Union Journal*, dated March 1922, which announces:

FRANK FOLKARD & SONS LTD., COPFORD, ESSEX
FARM SEEDS

Buy direct from the growers

Grass mixtures for Permanent and Temporary Leys
Mangolds, Swedes, Turnips
Marrow-Stem Kale, Kohl Rabi

All seeds for the farm

Two of Frank's four sons came into the firm. The eldest, Owen, in time took over from his father; Frank, his second son, joined the Army and served on the North-West Frontier of India; the third son was Cyril, who attended to the running of the firm's office; and the fourth son, Harold, owned a small farm. When Captain Frank T. Folkard returned home he became secretary to the Colchester branch of the National Farmers' Union and, in the Second World War, was first secretary and then the District Administrative Officer of the Lexden and Winstree District War Agricultural Executive Committee. This Frank Folkard recalls that, as a boy, he sometimes accompanied his father to markets held at Colchester, Chelmsford, Braintree and Sudbury, at all of which the firm had a stand. Sometimes he was taken to agricultural shows. The first Essex County Show that he remembers was held at Clacton and his father wore a tail coat and top hat for this occasion. Another time he accompanied his father and the famous Dr. Salter of Tolleshunt D'Arcy to a Brotherhood Show at which they were co-judges. When cutting a turnip the doctor cut his thumb — and he *swore*. This shocked young Frank; he only heard his father swear on one occasion, which was when a sheep butted him!.

It is also remembered that, all through the winter months, two old men spent their time in the barn dressing seeds; that their family used the downward-working sliverer for cleaning their mangel seed and peasmakes to harvest the peas; and that seeds were grown on their family farms as well as being contracted out to other reliable grower clients, to be used by their own firm or sold to one of the larger seed firms with whom they did business.

Frank Folkard's firm was another one which became well-known for its mangel seed and there was always a picture of a mangel on the front of their catalogue.

As this business expanded more storage space was required and a disused maltings, two cottages and use of a railway siding were acquired at Marks Tey. Peter Folkard, Owen's son, followed his father into the business and for many years all went well. However, when the plans for the A12 road to by-pass Marks Tey village showed that this new road would bisect the Folkard's warehouse, the firm chose to go into voluntary liquidation in 1967. This piece of land like the fields of Walnut Tree Farm has changed its purpose and today two rather sad-looking red brick cottages beside the road bridge which crosses the railway are all that remains of what has recently been described by another seedsman as 'a good reliable little family firm'.

Lavender

> Goodmaster, let's go to that house, for the linen looks white and smells of lavender, and I love to lie in a pair of sheets that smell so.
> Isaac Walton, 1682

Lavender for seed and for bunching was grown on a field scale in Kelvedon by the early 20th century. The crop probably moved here from the Mitcham area in Surrey soon after 1891, for at that time the Mitcham crops were suffering badly from a dieback fungal disease.[7] For seed production, Essex, with its usual dry summer and early autumn, would have favoured a plant with seed-heads which readily become sodden with water, and under such a condition rot and drop off.

Contrary to previous belief, recent research[8] has revealed that this plant was being grown in England by at least 1300. Sally Festing,[9] quoting from the 'Records with Commentary' of Merton Priory published in 1898, writes that in 1301 the Mitcham area, 'partly from the sale of lavender seed and partly from tenants' donations', raised £50 to lend to King Edward I.

Whatever the date of its introduction, lavender settled down happily and over the years gave rise to a variety which yields the unsurpassed English Lavender Oil with its non-camphoraceous, high-ester content. Originally it was grown from seed sown in March and when two inches high the little plants were transplanted into nursery beds, where they remained until planted out in the following year. Today it is more usual to propagate by root division or by cuttings. This is a more satisfactory way of maintaining a uniform 'stand' for the seed does not necessarily breed true. The young plants should be set out in the field at 18-inch intervals, with nine inches between each row. In the first year a catch crop of lettuce or parsley may be taken. Subsequently, as the bushes increase in size, alternate rows are taken out until the final stand measures three feet either way and with no intercropping. The wider planting of four feet apart and five to six feet between the rows was thought by some growers to help prevent disease.

At each twice-yearly cutting for oil, men and women armed with bagging hooks and large hessian mats repaired to the field. As they cut the flower heads these were laid inwards between the folded hessian to protect them from the sun, and when sufficient had been cut the bundles were secured by wooden skewers for immediate transport to the still room.

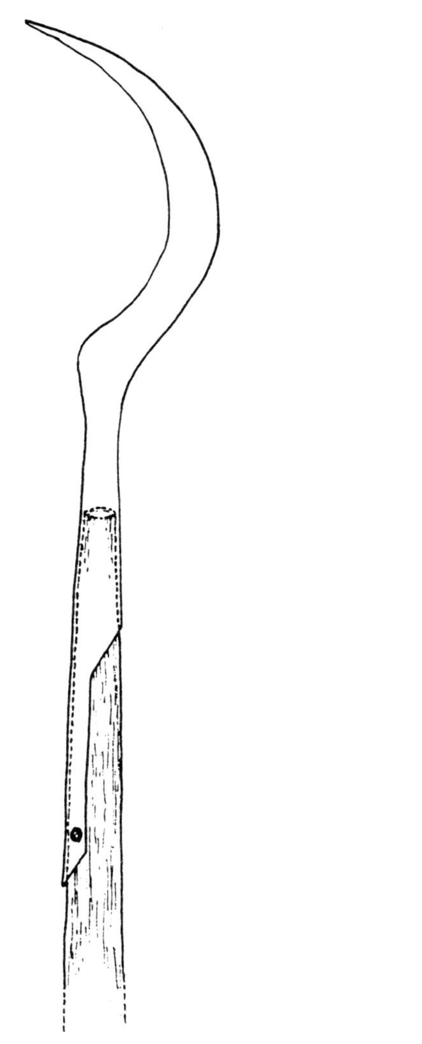

66. Peasmake.

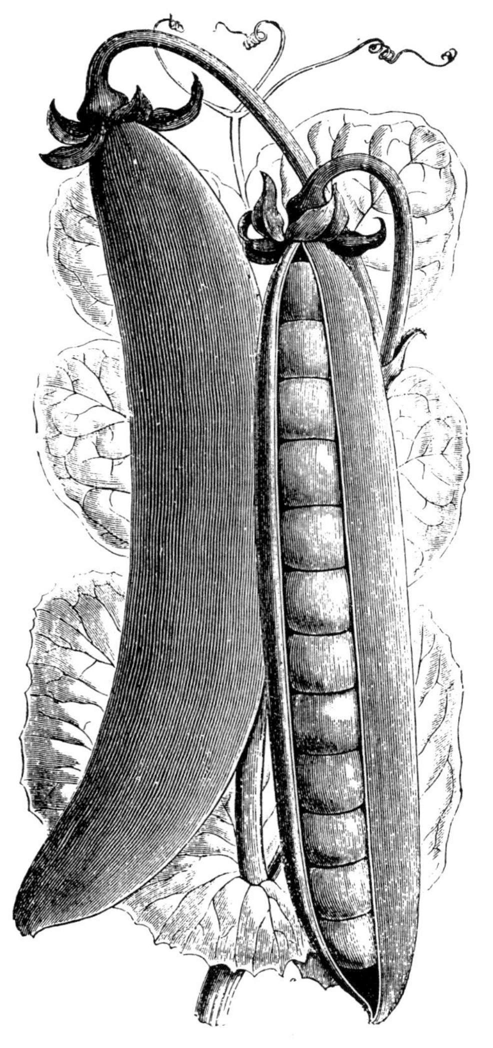

67. Peas from an early catalogue.

Here the contents of each mat was sometimes pitched into the still, stalk and all, but at other times 20 to 30 women were hired for six to seven hours to pick off the half-ton of heads needed to charge the still.[10]

In Essex, lavender seed is no longer a crop. Even E. W. King and Company Ltd. of Coggeshall harvest only small quantities from their trial plots. The remainder, for their seed packets, is now imported from France or California. When it was an Essex crop, Mr. K. R. Phillips, of E. W. King, suggests that the ripe seed heads were cut off in mid-August, dried by one means or another and then thrashed out. The second growth was unlikely to be taken for seed but would probably have been bunched for sale, to make lavender bags, to put amongst linen or to be burnt in sick rooms to sweeten the air.

PART II

William Deal and Sons, Park Farm, Inworth

For William Deal (1832-1905) the year 1873 was memorable. His first child, a son, was born, he moved house, and it was probably at this time that he began seriously to consider growing seeds on his own account. William was foreman to the much respected seed-grower

68. Mr. Orst (in boater) supervising the gang of women bunching lavender for William Deal & Son in a field at the top of Feering Hill, *c.*1900.

John Moss and Son (see p.31) and had already learnt a great deal about the practical side of this business. Then, also in 1873, when John Moss assumed the lease of Park Farm, Inworth, it must have been suggested that William should move from his cottage on Threshelford's farm to Park Farmhouse.

John Moss seems to have aided William to set up on his own account for at some time prior to 1892 William took over the lease of Park Farm and in that year he founded his business — William Deal and Sons, Park Farm, Inworth. In common with most flower seed growers of that era he became interested in the development of the sweet pea, and in 1895 it is said that there were 36 acres growing on his land — a lovely scent and sight when in full bloom. Park Farm was purchased by William in 1899 and then, possibly when his second son John married, Hill Farm, Inworth was leased to them.

William and his eldest son, also called William, seem to have worked well together and particularly on the firm's trial plots. It appears that they were constantly discussing and observing their results, improving their own selections of culinary peas and also sweet peas and trying out new varieties of potatoes. These latter were William junior's special interest and it is possibly at this stage that he started his own business at Brooklands on Feering Hill. As the following story shows, the potatoes were not always very profitable. When the ill-fated potato called 'Eldorado' came on to the market William managed to obtain one pound at a cost of £160. These tubers were brought home in triumph and put into the strong room of Kelvedon Bank until the time came for planting (just in case somebody 'took a fancy to one or two of them'). However, as the variety did not prove a success, William soon cut his losses and replaced with 'Northern Star' and 'Magnum Bonum'.

In 1901 William (senior) retired from active participation in the business and was succeeded by his second son John. The third son, Ezekiel, first apprenticed to John Moss, left Essex to seek his fortune elsewhere. In fact, by a mixture of astuteness and good luck, he was to become perhaps the most successful of them all. His obituary tells us that he became the Senior Managing Director of W. W. Johnson, Seed merchant, Boston, Lincolnshire, a J.P. for the Holland division, a well-known character on Mark Lane, a President of the Agricultural Seed Trade Association (United Kingdom) and of the Horticultural Trade Association. The fourth son, Fred, first worked for John K. King and Company and then, in 1920, moved into the office of Thomas Cullen and Sons, Witham, and remained with that firm until he died.

As with the two firms of King in Coggeshall, the two firms of William Deal in this area led to confusion. It was therefore a wise move, on his father's death, for Bertrand, son of William (junior) to change the name of his firm to Bertrand W. Deal — although this was considered in the district to have been done 'altogether too quickly'. However, by 1920 Bertrand was already trying to sell out to E. W. King of Coggeshall and before the matter was completed he had died of tuberculosis. Then after E. W. King's death this land, but not the house and buildings, became part of J. W. Ireland's horticultural holding.

John Overett Deal (1873-1927)

After his father retired John took over the management of the farms and the seed-growing. He had always shown talent on the merchanting side and until he became ill continued to increase the family's trade connections. Also, as the following story shows, he had inherited some skill in picking a winner.

In 1922 Arthur Edward Newby, who had succeeded his father as the pea expert for Hurst's, was walking round their trials with John Deal. Two of Arthur's new seedlings took John's eye and, on finding that they were not to be included in the following year's trials, but were to be discarded, he asked if he might have the seed from them. Edward Sherwood, the head of Hurst's, was consulted and agreed, provided that if either seedling proved a winner Hurst's be offered some of the first seed. One of the seedlings more than fulfilled its early promise and in 1925 was named and introduced as the still popular garden pea 'Kelvedon Wonder'. Furthermore, once it was on the market, the first half-ton of seed was purchased by Hurst's and this variety has appeared in their seed list ever since. (Arthur Newby was 'known as "Swifty" because he wasn't'. He died, still breeding new fuchsia and pelargonium varieties, on 13 February 1969, aged 91 years. His father, 'A. W.' is remembered by Hurst's apprentices as being a 'terror'.)

After his father's death in 1905, John demolished the charming but inconvenient old house at Park Farm and built the present residence in 1906. In 1911 Inworth Hall was leased for a period of seven years. This lease was not renewed and in 1918 the Deals decided to give up some 300 acres of their by then approximately 400 acres of land.

It was about this time that the runner bean, which the 16th-century plant collector John Tradescant had introduced into this country as an ornamental climbing plant for the flower garden, gained immense popularity as a vegetable. Boxes and boxes of these green beans were sent by the 2.00 a.m. train to Covent Garden and other markets from all stations along the line and so, of course, a fair acreage was also grown for seed. The green beans had to be loaded on to trucks at Kelvedon by 5.30 p.m. on the previous day and it was necessary to judge to a nicety just when to arrive at the station. No-one wished to be the first loaded because it was 'last on, first off'; on the other hand, if there was a glut and the truck had been well-filled at previous stops, there might be no room for your consignment if you had hung back for too long. This meant waiting for the next train by which time a message might well have come through that no more beans were required at the market that day. Tom Glover remembers that when he lived at Kelvedon there was a saying, 'If he has a runner bean in his pocket he must come from Kelvedon or thereabouts'. John Deal was nicknamed the 'Runner bean King' and when he was buried his workmen lined the grave with these red flowers.

In 1913, the Deals were well and truly into the culinary pea and bean trade and supplied both the green product and the seed from their farms. Some of the seed peas such as the varieties Thomas Laxton, Gradus and Telephone were even being exported to France.

Before the days when vegetables could be preserved by canning, freezing or freeze drying, and so became available to the housewife throughout the year, each one appeared in the shops only during its own season. Over the centuries, gardeners by one device or another had achieved a lengthening of this season. Rosetta Clarkson states that on 24 May 1496, the Privy Purse expenses of Henry VII show a gift or reward of three farthings for a dish of peas which, she adds, were no doubt forced with artificial heat.[11] However, had the grower known of and practised the method of the Frosts, of Parsonage Farm, Tolleshunt Major and sown them into a ploughed ley on Boxing Day, he could, in a clement season, have grown them in the open.

Between the two world wars gardens, which were once large and productive, fell derelict for want of men to tend them and also because their owners no longer had the wherewithal to pay the necessary staff for their upkeep. In towns, which were then becoming more than ever built up, it became a common practice to insert one or more smaller houses into the grounds of former palatial residences. In fact, kitchen gardens were 'out' and culinary vegetables, grown on a field scale, were 'in'. Farmers, market gardeners and seed merchants were all actively, and with more or less friendly rivalry, attempting to find either a cultural method or a strain of plant which would extend the season at one end or the other, or would particularly suit some soil or climatic conditions. This naturally led to there being a great many varietal synonyms.

As well as the runner beans, hundreds of bags of peas were sent to London on the night train for sale in the shops and to hotels. It was a Mr. Bailey who organised gangs of Irish women to shell peas at Covent Garden Market. These they separated into large, mediums and smalls for the hotel trade. The medium-sized peas made the most money as the large ones tended to be rather mealy. It must have been quite a sight and these women, who demanded extra pay for a maggoty sample, are affectionately remembered as 'good ole gals, with gardens on their hats'. By the early 1930s their services were no longer needed and they disappeared.

Mr. Eric Deal, who at one time organised the bean and pea sales of his Essex clients in Covent Garden, remembers that as soon as the peas were shelled they were sent off in oblong baskets on trolleys to the hotels and that Laxtons were the favourite variety until rivalled by the Kelvedon Wonder in 1925. Also, some shelled peas and broad beans were put up in small brown paper bags, as pint or quart lots for boarding houses and smaller establishments. Local seed firms that specialised in pea breeding and selection traded in their own named varieties. Thomas Cullen's included 'Essex Star', 'Early Bird', 'Blue Bird', 'Tip Top' and 'British Lion'. John Deal picked out the discarded pea from Hurst's trials which was subsequently introduced by Eric Deal in 1925 under the name of 'Kelvedon Wonder'. The 'Kelvedon Wonder' runner bean was multiplied up from a plant 'full of pods' which Eric Deal had seen in a crop of 'Princeps'. Later Eric bred the 'Kelvedon Marvel' runner bean, crossing 'Best of All' with 'Painted Lady Marvel'.

69. 'Good ole gals with gardens on their hats.'

The Bottled Pea

Some time before 1930 there was an attempt to preserve peas by bottling. This occurred at Edgar Brothers' bottling plant near St Botolph's, Colchester, and at Deal, in Kent. All around, crops of 'Thomas Laxton', 'Standard' and other peas were grown for this purpose and farmers and seed merchants who wished to do business with Mr. Edgar would find him at *The Cups Hotel*, in the High Street, between 6.00 and 8.00 p.m. for this hotel was then the centre of much of Colchester's commerce and particularly of that to do with agriculture. Farmers could leave their traps or motors here while they attended the market and their wives went to shop; it was a stop for the station bus which would pick up and deliver packages to or from the trains; and over a good meal, or a drink, it was a suitable establishment in which to do business or to meet one's friends and perhaps afterwards attend the theatre. Those who remember them maintain that Edgar's Bottled Peas were better than the canned ones which superceded them.

Eric William Deal (1904-85)

The late Mr. Deal came into farming and seed growing early in life for, at the age of 11, his father sent him off on his bicycle to buy runner bean seed from Fred Deeks of Lingwood's Farm, Kelvedon. Before the time when every farm of any size possessed a mechanical drill, corn and large seeds such as beans were 'debbed' in by hand. This was quite an art and there was considerable rivalry between debbers regarding their prowess. An average worker would succeed in putting in half an acre in an eight-hour day, but some were quicker. Mr. E. H. Ashby, of Sturgeon's Farm, Earls Colne, was a quick worker, but he told me wistfully, a few months before he died, that he never could quite keep up with Frank Bonner of Coggeshall Hall. Eric Deal set something of a record when, drawing precisely straight lines with his booted foot, he completed an acre a day over three successive days — and there are others such as Harry Bonner, who was even quicker than Frank, who can stake a claim.

In those days, when there was work to be done in a relatively short time, such as at seed-sowing, planting-out and harvest, it was customary for a labourer to contract to do this work for a fixed wage. It was then up to him to get the job done as promptly as possible by summoning his immediate family, any nearby relatives, and if need be, a few friends. Sometimes the payment would be shared or the work might be done on a reciprocal basis.

70. Eric William Deal.

Before his father died Eric helped on the farms and with the trial plots, placed contracts with farmers who grew for them, attended local Corn Exchanges and Agricultural shows, and handled the sale of the customers' crops in Covent Garden. Then suddenly in 1927 he became head of the family firm, a position which he had held in all but name for some time due to his father's ill health in his later years.

A story is told of how Eric dealt with the situation when a morning train to Liverpool Street Station failed to stop at Kelvedon as scheduled. On certain week-days, on all stations between Colchester and Witham, seedsmen would be awaiting the train which customarily carried them to the City for attendance at Mark Lane Corn Exchange. Many of them would be carrying a leather bag in which was a red Trader's Season Ticket and some samples of seeds. (Eric Deal still had in his possession a Trader's Season Ticket issued in 1951. It then cost £45 3s. to travel First Class for a year to and from Kelvedon and Liverpool Street. One such ticket was allowed by the railway for each firm and it was valid only for the person whose name it bore.) On this particular morning the train was sighted, bags were picked up and the groups of seedsmen and others made for their usual place along the platform. However, the train rushed through the station leaving all standing. Then amidst the protestations and consternation Eric Deal kept his head and got on the telephone to Ipswich. He told the booking clerk what had occurred and asked him to tell the driver of the next train — a through express to London and soon expected to arrive at Ipswich — to stop and pick them up. The clerk said that such a thing could not be done, so Eric demanded to speak to the Station Master, who said it was unheard of. When it was mentioned that if the express did not stop, the London North Eastern Railway — by no means a well-endowed line — would find itself in receipt of a great number of claims for the thousands of pounds worth of business which would be lost by the seedsmen, the express was ordered to stop, much to the astonished annoyance of its passengers, and Mrs. Oster of Kelvedon, who was 'something to do with films and was going up to have her hair done' that morning, told all and sundry that 'Mr. Deal was very clever, he could even stop an express'.

Another of Eric's attributes was his mastery of the art of carving a joint. In fact, so often had he been asked if he would do so at shoots and at parties, it is said that he always travelled with a ready-sharpened set of carvers in his car.

In 1925, the Essex Show was at Colchester and it was while he was having his lunch at this event that Eric heard the news of his firm's fire; the big seed warehouse at Park Farm had been burnt down.

Because Essex seed merchants were very annoyed by the treatment that their trade was receiving nationally and particularly by the sparsity of the information that came their way with regard to any proposed plans for their trade, on 29 August 1946 the Essex Provincial Seeds Trade Association was formed. Twenty-eight firms were invited to the *Angel Hotel*, Kelvedon, and 22 became members of the newly-formed association. The result was that within two years seven of its members were on the National Council of the Seed Trade Association, and from then on the 'rebels' played a leading part in determining both national policy and the conduct of affairs within the industry.

Eric Deal was made Chairman and remained so for the first 21 years and when in 1967 this association held its 'Coming of Age Dinner' Mr. Deal stoutly affirmed that 'the Common Market would prove ruinous', after which Mr. Peter Kirk M.P. is reported to have forecast that it would bring long-term profits. It is still not clear which of these two will, in the end, be proved right.

In the early 1940s L. A. W. Prior, who was then working for Nutting and Sons in the City, decided to leave and seek his fortune in the New World. He went to Canada, with little or no money but full of expectation and hope, to join the firm of Govier of Montreal. Alas Canada, even if a land of promise, did not prove to be one of fulfilment and it soon became clear that the firm which he joined was rapidly approaching bankruptcy. Very sensibly, in 1949, Len Prior returned to this country where, most fortunately, there was a place for him with the firm which in 1947 had become W. Deal and Sons Ltd. and of which he became a Director.

In 1950 this firm issued its first Trade Catalogue and in 1962, when four seed merchants got together and formed the Amalgamated Seed Merchants' Company (A.S.M.E.R.), W. Deal and Sons Ltd. was one of the four founding members. Then, when T. Cullen and Sons joined A.S.M.E.R. they also amalgamated with Deal's to become Deal Cullen Ltd., and in 1971 Eric Deal retired but continued to rent his firm's premises at Park Farm to Deal Cullen Ltd. However, in 1974, both the office and L. A. W. Prior removed to the premises of Deal Cullen at Witham, and these in their turn have now moved to Leicester.

Therefore, two more old family firms have now virtually disappeared from the Essex scene. However, when he was not out shooting and until the last few months of his life, Eric Deal was still to be found in his office every morning answering correspondence, keeping up to date with the trades journals, perhaps reflecting upon his firm's 25 or so awards for seeds submitted to the R.H.S. Trials at Wisley, and happy in the knowledge that the seedling, which his father spotted, the 'Kelvedon Wonder' — was still selling well as a quality culinary pea and had, in its time, justly claimed the largest sales of any pea on the market (hundreds and hundreds of tons) and this, despite its never having become popular in the United States of America.

The Placing of Seed Contracts and subsequent Roguing and Inspection of the crops

It has always been something in the nature of an honour to be offered a contract by a reputable seed house. Indeed, there was a time when a contract to grow seeds might by used as collateral for a bank loan and, certainly in the early days, the procedure of placing, roguing and inspecting of the seed crops was almost a ritual that was conducted in an atmosphere of great formality. The Directors of seed houses, together with the more important members of their staff, were always very conscious of their place in society and jealously guarded their own established position.

Whether the grower be a 'seed grower proper', a farmer or a smallholder, the merchant will choose someone in whom he has confidence or who has been recommended to him by a reliable agent (for example a smaller local firm or a grower who has been commissioned to place contracts). In the early days, word would be sent to the prospective grower that the merchant's senior representative, or even the merchant himself, would, on a certain day, be arriving at the nearby railway station from which he wished to visit the farm. Transport from the station would then have had to be arranged (usually a hired horse and trap), the front parlour aired, and suitable refreshment prepared for presentation on the best trays and dishes. On the day, the grower and his wife, clad in their Sunday best, anxiously awaited the arrival of a personage in top hat, tail coat and gloves. The business was all conducted in the front parlour and after being offered refreshment suitable to the time of day, the august personage would either return to the station or continue on to another farm in the district with which his firm did business. There was no inspection of the field or crops on this occasion and it was simply a matter of whether a contract would be placed or not. These early contracts and those of many years later were seldom, if ever, signed. It was considered an agreement between gentlemen and, as such, each side had complete confidence that the other would honour the bargain to the best of his ability.

In the selection of the field for the crop many points, other than soil and climate, have to be considered. It cannot be done with training and today there are both statutory and practical requirements to be met. The soil, as well as being reasonably free of all weeds, must not contain any that are likely to cross-pollinate with the seed crop or that will be difficult to remove from the seed sample. A sufficient interval of time must have elapsed since either the crop in question, or any of its near relatives, has been grown in the field; there must be a specific distance between the crop to be grown and any other with which it will cross-pollinate — private gardens and by-pass road verges can sometimes prove a problem in this respect. Soil-borne diseases and even the likelihood of pests, such as a heavy rabbit, wheat bulb fly, slug or wireworm infestation, all need to be avoided, as also do 'frost pockets', the north side of a high hill, exposure to high winds or a poorly-drained soil.

The field having been decided upon, the merchant usually supplies the seed (the cost of which is deducted from the grower's final payment for the seed grown). Fertilisers and any necessary spray may also be provided and if it is an unfamiliar crop, some cultural directions may be given.

From time to time during the growing period, and certainly at flowering, the crop is inspected by the firm's trained staff: today all crops of grasses, clovers, cereals, fodder crops and a very few vegetables, which are for 'Basic or Certified First Generation' seed, have to be inspected by the Ministry of Agriculture.

Roguing usually takes place during the flowering period and it may have to be done more than once. This is an extremely arduous and skilled operation which necessitates the 'walking' of a crop at suitable spacings, in order to remove those plants (sometimes hardly distinguishable) which are not of the right type and whose seeds must not find their way into the seed packet or sack.

In the Kelvedon district around 1910 the crop inspectors stayed at *The Star and Fleece* in Kelvedon. The landlord, Edward Frank Porter, was also a coach builder who would hire out his pony and trap for farm visiting and at the end of the season gave a splendid duck supper to the roguers, merchants and growers who had patronised his establishment.

Also to the Kelvedon district, during and just after the 1939 War, Carter's Tested Seeds Ltd. would send a team of their men down from London for four to six weeks each year. They came to rogue and inspect their crops which were being grown in the area. The team consisted of the 'roguers' who were accommodated in lodgings and the firm's representatives who, on these occasions often being Directors of the firm, stayed at the *Silver End Hotel*. From this hotel they not only oversaw the work of the roguers but also inspected the crops both before and after this was done.[12]

That formality was still maintained between firm's representatives in 1939 is demonstrated by the fact that it is still remembered, in Kelvedon, that Carter's were represented by 'Mr. Parr, who was the gentleman in charge of vegetable and flower seeds, and a Mr. Cross who looked after the corn, peas, kales and roots'. These two men had known each other for years but nobody ever heard them address, or speak of, one another by any name other than Mr. Parr or Mr. Cross.

Two seed growers who helped merchants by finding suitable places for the growing of their seed crops were the Martins and the Scotts. Both originated in the Kelvedon/Tiptree area and both left this district to go in opposite directions before starting in the contract business. There were, of course, many other growers as well as small local merchants who placed contracts for the large establishments. These two will serve as a good example of them all.

Frank Martin and Sons Ltd. of Colne Engaine

Frank Martin was born in Kelvedon in 1883. When he was about 17 he went to work for Bertrand W. Deal, the seed merchant of Brooklands, Feering Hill, Kelvedon. After four years there he left, and with the help of a loan from his brother-in-law, Will Warner, of Church Hall, Kelvedon, who was also a seed grower and placer of contracts, he took the tenancies of Lodge Farm and Millbrooks Farm, Colne Engaine. This gives an example of what was very usual in this area at the time, namely the way in which financial help was given to promising young men who wished to start in the business. In fact, it would be true to say that there are few families who, during the years of the seed-growing boom, were not helped to make a start by another established grower, relative or merchant.

In 1906 Frank went into partnership with his brother William to farm both holdings — about a hundred acres. William left in 1921 to set up on his own. The Martins were more than seed-growing sub-contractors, for they also grew and improved stocks of seed that they then sold, and even exported. From 1906 contracts began to be placed on behalf of other merchants. Peter Martin (Frank's son) says that his father would often put his bicycle on the train and travel to somewhere on the Colne Valley line near to the farms that he wished to visit that day. The bike would then be off-loaded from the guard's van and he would be off on his round, more often than not to cycle home after his visits were completed. This business also had useful contacts with continental seed houses. For instance, Frank remained a lifelong friend of a German, Frederick Herzog, who had been his fellow apprentice when he was with Bertrand Deal. Herr Herzog was connected with two large German seed firms and he required kohl rabi and other seeds, such as marrow-stemmed kale and vegetable seeds, which were exported to him by Frank Martin, both before and between the two world wars. There was a time when as much as 100 acres of red cabbage seed were grown by Frank Martin for Herzog's.[13]

The Martins also had some export links with Holland, principally with the Singer family, proprietors of the Hem Seed Company. Two generations of the Singers stayed at Colne Engaine, for fairly long periods, to learn the language and something of the English seed industry.

During the Depression around the 1930s the Martins say that they kept their heads above water, but not very high. By 1936 their export trade to Germany gave things a little boost and from 1939 to 1945, while his sons were in the army, Frank carried on the business and it was then that it really expanded to become what is claimed to have been the largest of its kind in this county. Certainly it was much larger than most people suspected. Some idea of this expansion may be seen in the record of acreages of individual crops placed from 1943 to 1949.

Frank Martin & Sons, Lodge Farm, Colne Engaine, Essex
Total acreages — by varieties

Name of seed	*1943*	*1944*	*1945*	*1946*	*1947*	*1948*	*1949*
Sugar beet	61	72	36	75	66	203	238
Garden beet	32	31	14	23	57	46	53
Brussels sprouts	19	11	12½	17	24	40	44
Broccoli sprouting	40	11	7	13	4	8	14
Broccoli heading	—	—	7	67	32	64½	42
Cabbage	49	32	46	86	95	154	123
Carrot	3	—	6½	5	7	24	28
Cress	20	5	10	12	12	19	—
Kale G.M.S.	33	10	34	10	54	36	56½
Kale thousand headed	7	—	6	10	14	37	—
Mangel	87	115	157	156	165	180	208
Mustard	—	—	—	5	14	—	—
Parsley	5	—	—	—	1	2	1
Parsnip	7	7	7	3½	6½	9½	5½
Savoy	16	26	26	40	31	50	36
Swede	7	27	70	84	100	134	155

For those unfamiliar with this trade it must be explained that it had, of necessity, always to be conducted in an atmosphere of secrecy, so that those placing contracts on individual farms and with farming companies throughout the area had to use the utmost discretion. Every possible precaution was taken to prevent a rival from knowing anything of one's trade. Employees who spoke to those from another firm were severely reprimanded or even dismissed. No two firms patronised the same public house and carts carrying seeds to the railway station or past another seed establishment were sheeted over so that no labels, disclosing the seeds' destination, would be seen.

It is even remembered that once, when two firms whose businesses were close to one another were not on friendly terms, a neutral party who had dealings with them both had to resort to quite ridiculous capers in order to buy seed from one and sell it to the other, without either knowing what had happened. In fact, lorries were hired from a contractor. The driver was suitably 'encouraged' to keep his counsel and to drive well out into the country to a reasonably remote spot, there to remove labels which identified the seed as having come from seedhouse A and to replace them with those of the neutral party. He then drove back with the seed required by seedhouse B.

Among others the Martins were putting out contracts for firms such as Clucas of Ormskirk; Cannell's of Loddon, Norfolk; Finney of Newcastle; Lawson of Edinburgh; Bee's of Liverpool; Sharpe's of Sleaford; Johnson's of Boston; Webb's of Stourbridge; H. J. Speed and Son of Evesham; Toogood's of Southampton, and Thoday of Cambridge, as well as with local firms. By 1946 there were 22 people on the payroll employed in receiving the various parcels of seed and giving them any immediate attention, such as drying or cleaning, which was necessary if they were not to suffer harm before they were moved on to their destination. In a wet season this could be more than a headache. For example, during the 1930s, without the aid of today's developments in machinery, some very odd practices had to be employed. For instance, a wet sample of beans was, on occasion, saved by obtaining some hot malt culms and mixing them with the beans, with the result that the hot dry culms took up some of the moisture and prevented the beans from sprouting. Again, there was the occasion when some hemp seed became contaminated with wheat after having been put through an improperly cleaned thrashing drum. These two seeds are very similar in size and shape and Mr. Martin could not sell the hemp until the wheat had been removed. After some thought he shut up his hens and starved them for a bit, then spread out the seed thinly on a stack cloth and released the hens. They immediately rushed to the cloth and made a good meal of all the wheat grains, after which, apart from the necessity of removing their droppings from the hemp, all was accomplished. It sold for 13s. 6d. a pound, 10s. 6d. going to the grower. Hemp seed is used in some bird seed mixtures for brightening and darkening the black colour of bullfinches' plumage, and as fish bait. The fibre from the stems is used in rope-making and the drug cannabis is obtained from parts of the plant. Until after the war, hemp was grown on a field scale. Today, because of legislation, one is liable to prosecution if found growing even one plant in a pot on the window sill.

Peter Martin recalls that those concerned with drying and conditioning seeds did not altogether welcome the coming of the combine harvester. It made necessary the provision of more space suitable for seed storage, and sufficient labour to cope with the rush of seeds coming in at harvest.

Very early in their seed business this family had every sample of seed which they handled analysed for germination at the Seed Testing Station in Cambridge. This prevented many an acrimonious argument, both with individual farmers and the trade. Again, they were early in the field with the use of hormone crop-spraying. This was not always a straightforward operation and one well-remembered occasion was when the helicopter and crew did not arrive at the time for which they were booked and then refused to do overtime to finish the job.

Clucas of Ormskirk and Cannell's of Loddon were the Martins' best customers as regards crop value. They had substantial annual requirements for suitable sites for the production of their own specialities. The brassica varieties very easily cross-pollinate and for this reason rules for their isolation are more than particularly demanding. Clucas were extremely careful in this respect and all their crops were personally inspected by their representatives more than once a year. This firm, whose name crops up in conversations on seed all over Essex, was also very early in the hybrid field.

In 1948 the Martins became a private limited company. Frank Martin died in 1955 and they have now almost given up the contracting side of seed production. However, they still have on their premises neat rows of the attractive bird seed mixtures in which they continue to trade, and recall with pride the work done on behalf of many people in past years.

H. Scott and Sons, Bovill Upland, Mayland

The branch of the Scott family that moved from Grouts Farm, Tolleshunt D'Arcy, to Mayland near Southminster still remembers that great-grandfather James Scott lived at Oxley Farm, Tolleshunt Knights, and that he married Emily Parrish from another locally well-known seed-growing family. Therefore it is not surprising that his two eldest sons, Arthur and Harry, became well-known and respected in this profession.

For about 18 years these two were partners at Grout's Farm, Tolleshunt D'Arcy. Harry, in 1919, decided as the Scott's say 'to go over the other side' (of the River Blackwater) and to set up on his own at Bovill Upland Farm, Mayland. His eldest son William was, by then, 14 years old and all his six children from an early age had been brought up to help with the farm work.

Furniture, when removed, has a propensity for arriving late at its new home. On their removal day the Scotts rose early, loaded the last things onto a farm wagon (the normal method of removal among the farming community) and sent it on its way, with every hope that it would arrive at Bovill's well before dark. The horses pulled the wagon up the steep gradient of Maldon Hill — they had made good time — but in Latchingdon Street the inevitable delay occurred when the wagon shed a wheel, and the contingent at Bovill's waited!

Soon Harry began looking for ways to supplement his income and, as they grew older, to provide employment for his two sons Bill and Ted. At this time few seedsmen owned or rented sufficient land for the multiplication of more than 50 per cent of their requirements. Furthermore, they were not wishing to take on more full-time staff and so were on the lookout for reliable part-time agents in the good seed-growing areas. The Scotts, who were proven growers, reliable, honest and with a knowledge of fields and farmers who would be 'right' for the job, were eminently suitable.

71. A farm wagon from Halstead in Essex, 1932.

So it was that Harry Scott took on this job and began travelling around in his tub cart to place root, brassica and some flower seed contracts for such firms as Wheeler's, Hurst's, Johnson's, Taber's, Nutting's and E. W. King. Chiefly, the contracts were with farmers in the Dengie and Rochford Hundreds — maybe coriander, tares or Essex Broad Red clover for Leslie Attenborough of Landwick, Dengie, or the Squier's of Doggett's, Rochford, and to the marsh and other farms of both Hundreds, kale, radish, mustard, cress, mangel and parsnip. Or he might visit the Burroughs family at Snoreham Hall, Latchingdon, some of whom later moved to Foulness Island where they farm and grow seeds to this day. Several of these vegetable crops would have been cut with a sail reaper. During the Second World War I saw one of the last of these machines in use, at East Ware, Dengie: it was a purposeful, knowing-what-it-wanted-to-do sort of tool, which clattered its way across the field like an irritable pterodactyl occasionally choking on an extra tough seed stem.

In 1941 Harry Scott died, leaving Bill and Ted to continue the business. In 1948 Ted decided to emigrate and to grow seeds in Canada. He is still there but has not found it feasible to establish himself in the seed trade of that country.

Bill remembers that during the Second World War there was a fortune to be made from canary seed (*Phalaris canariensis*) the growing of which was strictly limited. Nevertheless, many an odd acre was secreted in the middle of a barley crop, or on an out of the way, off-hand farm. In the Dengie Hundred too, there was a little knot of Provence lucerne seed-growers. At least it had been Provence when the seed had been purchased many years previously and by 1945 it had become, by natural selection, particularly well-adapted to local conditions of heavy clay and drought. It could not be sold officially as it was difficult to get through the Germination Regulations because of its propensity to 'hard' seeds. Nevertheless, given a winter in the district's stiff clay germination seldom failed, and the seed was favoured by those farmers lucky enough to obtain a supply from Partridge Brothers of Gate and Grange Farms, Steeple, Watson McKellar of Court Farm, Dengie, or one of the other three or four growers. In the *Essex National Farmer's Union Journal* of March 1927 (p.56) is a letter to the Editor which says that on some trial plots of Provence and English lucerne the English was slower to establish itself but, once established, came earlier in the season by some 14 days.

For some years before his death, in 1980, Bill Scott was a very sick man and the farming of Bovill Upland fell on the shoulders of his son Roger. Since the Second World War fewer and fewer seeds have been grown in this country and so today Roger Scott neither places contracts nor grows any seeds.

THE SWEET PEA IN ESSEX

The first sweet peas to come to this country probably arrived in 1699 when Francis Cupani, a Sicilian priest, sent seeds to Dr. Robert Uvedale of Enfield. (Dr. Uvedale (1642-1722) became master of Enfield Grammar School and, not altogether with his employers' approval, devoted much time to his garden. He probably had the greatest collection of exotics in England and although his garden is said not to have pleased the eye it was admitted that he had an 'extraordinary art in managing his plants'.) Although sent from Sicily, these sweet pea seeds are believed to have come from plants which originally came from Malta where the flower grows wild, which it has not been recorded as doing in Sicily.[14] Plants which bore masses of sweetly and heavily scented blooms were produced but the development of the sweet pea, either as a garden subject or for cut flowers, did not reach the stage described as a 'triumphal progress' until the last quarter of the 19th century.

Originally the flowers were small, probably little larger than those of the culinary pea, with only two, or at the most three, of them being carried on a short stem. There is no certainty as to their colour but Charles W. J. Unwin writes:

> I surmise, the colour was nearer a purple-maroon, possibly a sort of bi-colour, with maroon-purple wings, for this is a 'throw-back' that one often used to meet in the old days and one which still crops up occasionally in crosses.

Any developments which took place during the century after its introduction appear to have been unrecorded. Nevertheless, something did happen, for by 1800 there were five different colours — the original purple, a white, a black (probably dark maroon), a red, and a pink and white bi-colour. These later varieties may have been imports from elsewhere or, improbably, the result of natural cross-fertilisation or, considering the behaviour of the plant in later years, the variations may well have arisen quite naturally, as 'sports' from the original purple-maroon.[15]

Towards the end of the 19th century, when several firms and breeders were taking a serious interest in hybridisation, well-known names such as Laxton, Burpee and Eckford began to be associated with this flower. In fact there was a growing interest in the sweet pea both here and in the United States of America.

By cross-fertilisation and painstakingly careful selection Henry Eckford, first and in a comparatively short period, transformed the little-known sweet pea into an annual deemed worthy of a place in every flower garden. With the consequently growing public demand every flower seed producer and merchant jumped on to the bandwagon. New varieties, or 'novelties' as they are termed in horticultural circles, proliferated. In Essex, J. K. King and Company were soon making their selections. E. W. King and Thomas Cullen and Sons first selected and then employed specialists to breed their own varieties and Robert Bolton came down to Essex from Lancashire and established his name amongst the most successful and reputable breeders and exhibitors in the country. At shows this flower, which had hitherto appeared only among collections of annuals, was then afforded special classes and the day of the sweet pea as a cut flower began. However, it was well behind the gladiolus which was already in our florists' shops by 1861.

In 1900, the National Sweet Pea Society was founded and together with its affiliated

72. 'No flower has so rapidly advanced in public favour as the Sweet Pea.' Sweet peas, 1899.

societies has played a major part in the promotion of this flower by means of exhibitions, conferences, trials for new varieties and by its publications.

The horticultural writer, Walter P. Wright, has written that 'the value of a species lies more in its capacity for producing varietal forms than in its intrinsic beauty however great that may be'. Although sweeping, this statement is particularly true in the commercial seed world and so, in 1900, when the sweet pea appeared to be marking time at what then seemed to be the height of its development (and so to be due for a gradual decline) no one was prepared for the sudden dramatic change which occurred in its form or the long-lasting popularity which has ensued.

To appreciate what happened it must be understood that the sweet pea flower has three differently-shaped petals: the large one at the back known as the standard and, spread out just below this, two side petals known as wings between which are two joined petals known as the keel. This latter envelopes and protects the fertilising mechanism of the flower and undeveloped seed-pod. It also almost invariably ensures that the flower is self-pollinated. Climatic conditions, such as a very hot summer, will sometimes result in the style emerging from the keel above its anthers and so exposing itself to cross-pollination.

It was in the standard petal that the change was most obvious. Until it happened, this petal was either hooded or shell-shaped with a slight inward curl on each side, or open and flat, as in culinary peas, with a notch at the centre top or, less frequently, at each side towards the base.

Then in 1901, for a reason not yet explained, the Eckford variety 'Prima Donna', a fairly large, pink and popular sweet pea with a slightly hooded standard which had remained true to its original colour and type for at least eight years, suddenly mutated. The standard petal of these 'sports' was larger than anything hitherto seen in sweet peas and it was not hooded but distinctly frilly. Probably this waved mutation occurred in a great many gardens growing 'Prima Donna' seed that year but only three people are recorded as having noticed it or as having bothered to save its seed. They were Mr. Eckford, at Wem, W. J. Unwin

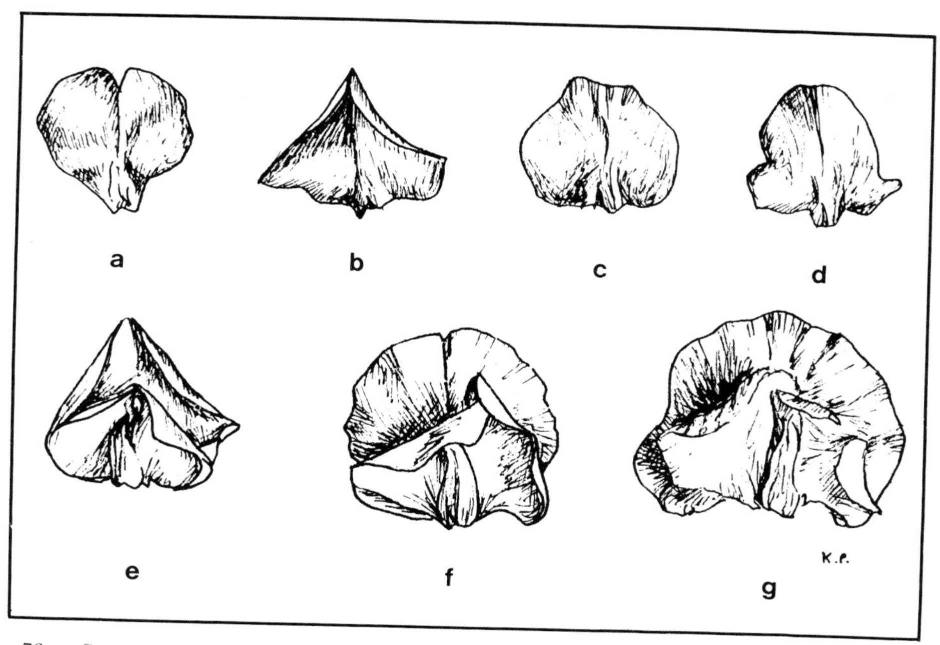

73. Sweet pea petals: (a) open form, central notch; (b) hooded, shell-shaped form; (c) open form; (d) slightly hooded notched sides; (e) true grandiflora (hooded) or shell-shaped; (f) semi-grandiflora 'rogue'; (g) true early Spencer type.

(senior) at Histon, and Silas Cole, gardener at Althorpe Park. (This was the home of Lady Diana Spencer and when she married the Prince of Wales these sweet peas were used in the decorations and particularly in The Mall.) The Wem sport does not appear to have been developed but, from his, W. J. Unwin produced and introduced 'Gladys Unwin' and other related varieties. These earned the distinguishing prefix of Unwin types and had the advantage of breeding true to both colour and type. They were also a little more robust and free-flowering than the seedling saved by Silas Cole. To begin with there was a fierce rivalry between these two breeders. However, Silas Cole's was undoubtedly the larger and the more frilled bloom and in 1908 it caused a great sensation when shown at the National Sweet Pea Society's first exhibition. It was named 'Countess Spencer' and its successors are known as Spencer types. As C. H. Curtis, Honorary Secretary of the N.S.P.S. has written in his book, *Sweet Peas and their Cultivation*,

> The sweet pea experts unhesitatingly granted the newcomer a First Class Certificate, and the visitors, charmed by Mr. Silas Cole's table decoration of this new variety, eagerly desired to know from whom it could be obtained. Secured by Mr. R. Sydenham, of Birmingham, the stock was sent chiefly to California for cultivation for seed, but alas, when it was distributed the Countess Spencer, beautiful in any form, presented almost as many variations as she had admirers. The variety was not fixed, and consequently during the next year or two everyone who grew it was able to select a dozen or so varieties from the row.

From then on private and merchant breeders searched for a large and frilled 'Spencer' which would always breed true to type. Some simply continued to select from the original Spencer stock, others tried to introduce the 'fixed' gene by crossing with the Unwin types and at last Robert Bolton, after years of tireless and meticulous trial and error, found an even bigger and better version of the 'Countess Spencer'. This he brought out in 1945 under the name of 'Mrs. R. Bolton'.

Robert Bolton and Son, Sweet Pea Specialists, Birdbrook, near Halstead

So that those not in the trade may understand something of the work entailed in growing sweet peas for seed, some notes are given below, which were made during a visit to Mr. R. B. Bolton (grandson of the founder of the firm) in May 1980. Each grower's method of cultivation will vary according to his land, labour force, training and inclination but these will serve as an example of the tremendous amount of work involved in just growing these seeds for our gardens.

The Bolton way

A light land field, where there is plenty of sun and some drying winds at harvest, is ideal except when the crop is to be sown directly into open ground in the autumn. For this latter purpose a field containing rather 'stronger' soil, which is less liable to capping, is to be preferred. In either case the field must first be suitably cultivated and fertiliser mixed into the soil before the sweet peas are put in the ground. Mr. Bolton applies two ounces a yard run of a mixture containing: 7% N; 20% P_2O_5; and 20% K_2O, or, if the ground is low in nitrogen, this constituent is raised to 20%.

For a crop started in a greenhouse

Sequence of Work

October Sow 6 seeds in 3 in. pots and leave them in a cool greenhouse until after Christmas.

After Christmas Once the worst weather is judged to be over, remove the pots of small plants to a cold frame. The frames will need to be covered if there is any danger of frost and should be opened up to harden off the plants when the weather is mild. Before planting out, apply and work fertiliser into the ground.

Mid-April Plant each pot load in clumps at 15 in. intervals in the row. Allow 7 ft. between rows for tractor hoeing and an adequate circulation of air.

Larch posts and 4 in. mesh wire sheep netting Formerly brushwood faggots were used to support the plants but these are now seldom obtainable. This support may be erected either before or after the plants are put in, but must be there within 3 weeks of planting out. Once the fence is put up growth starts because of the protection that it gives against wind. (In 1980, the cost of these posts and netting was £35 for a run of 30 metres. If taken down each year, rolled up and put under cover for the winter, this fence may be expected to last for 15 to 20 years with just the renewal of a few posts each season.) It is then necessary to loop string along the plants'

Troubles which may occur

Look out for *mice*. A few traps are a good insurance.

Slugs and snails. Control with bait made from crushed Meta-fuel tablets, mixed with bran. Apply this in good time, soon after sowing.

Greenfly — the worst enemy! This pest is often unsuspected especially in the early stages of growth. Take the precaution of spraying with a good brand of systemic spray, once or twice during October, November and March. N.B. Always use a diluted spray and never apply when there is frost about. Continue to guard against slugs, snails and greenfly throughout the growing period.

High winds. 'If there is one thing that a sweet pea will not tolerate it is wind!' For this reason netting rather than canes, is used for support, unless growing for exhibition.

Late spring frosts. These may cause 'blindness' of the terminal shoot.

Greenfly. Although still a hazard, they are less trouble at this stage because neighbouring farmers have now adopted the practice of spraying more of their crops against this pest.

side of the netting, at about 2 ft. from the ground. This keeps the plants against the netting and encourages them to climb rather than trail along the ground. Another loop of string will be required in June at a higher level.

Roguing starts in earnest once the flowers begin to appear but before this happens it is possible, between some varieties, to detect differences in leaf. Mr. Bolton 'goes through' his crops personally three times during the season: at first flower; a fortnight later and when in full flower 'just to make sure and of course we are always looking . . . you nearly always find two rogues together, it seems they must have a friend'.
Hand-picking ripe pods into half-gallon tins Ideally this should start by 25 July. If there is a June 'flower drop' it will be delayed until the second crop develops. If this fails the plants will be too exhausted to try again and the crop is a failure.
After picking the pods are put into sacks and hung up in a greenhouse where they will be shaken twice daily to assist drying.
Once dry they are put through Mr. Bolton's special thrasher and then cleaned in a Boby Dresser. The seeds must be stored in a cool, dry rat-and mouse-proof place until packaged and sold.

Flower drop. Sweet peas must have hot sunny weather in June. Cold rains cause the flowers to fall off. The same can happen to the next crop produced in July. An emergency casual labour force is a necessity to cope with bad weather and variations in the size of the crop. Delayed harvests not only disorganise the labour programme but often run into bad weather.

Hardening of the seed. In very hot weather it will be necessary to shade the glasshouse in which the seeds are put to dry. This helps to prevent hardening of the skin and later difficulties with germination.

For an autumn sown field crop

Sequence of work
It is not usual to risk more than 3-4 acres for outdoor sowing. A fresh field does not have to be found each year as each row is moved back and forth, a distance of 3 ft. 6in. to occupy the middle of the space between the rows of the previous year.
October. Having cultivated and applied fertiliser, sow in rows 7 ft. apart as for a crop sown under glass. 8-10 seeds are sown in clumps at a space of 15 in. Often this crop does not survive the winter. If it survives the worst of the weather, put the fence up quickly and proceed as for a crop started under glass. You may be lucky and harvest a heavy and early crop of seed.

Troubles which may occur
Wind damage
This will be more serious on land liable to 'cap'. The wind then twizzles the little plants' stems round and round in the tight layer at soil level. This results in bruising and laceration.
Mice, slugs, snails and greenfly must all be guarded against.

Snow — a complete covering is usually alright but if the plants poke through the snow *skylarks* are liable to graze them off. If the grazing is not too severe the crop may survive but growth will be delayed.

Charles W. J. Unwin and the episode of mice

In his book on sweet peas Mr. Unwin tells an amusing story:

> Many years ago, before the California growers perfected their methods of cleaning and grading the seeds, samples sometimes arrived which were dull and dusty in appearance and in one season, when we had to rely largely on Californian seed through a bad harvest here, my father hit on the ingenious notion of brightening the samples by working the seeds about in large sacks which had their inner surfaces slightly coated with lard. The very thin film of lard certainly brightened them, and greatly improved the look of the sample, but later on, reports from customers of mice taking the seeds

immediately they were sown reached such large and serious proportions, that he never used the lard treatment again.

Today, a look at Bolton's current sweet pea list or a walk around their garden centre provides ample evidence that this family continues to uphold the high standards of its ancestors. Most of their trade in sweet pea seeds is postal to customers who come back every year. Pictorial packets have never been used for their own seeds for, as the saying goes, 'Good seeds will sell themselves'. This has proved true, for Grandfather Bolton's seedling, the almost almond pink 'Mrs. R. Bolton', described by him as 'incapable of capricious behaviour', has remained so to this day and still sells in bulk both at home and abroad.

The genus Lathyrus, to which the sweet pea belongs, offers some interesting plant-breeding possibilities for the future.

In 1937 D. F. Archer[16] divided this genus into two sub-genera, namely *Orobus* (embracing six types) and *Lathyrus* (embracing 11 types) which, he pointed out, may again be subdivided into some three hundred species, many of which, either pure or crossed, offer great possibilities. For instance, a real blue and a yellow (as distinct from a cream) have not yet emerged among cultivated varieties and yet there are several of both colours within this genus. It also contains many wild species of a different form from the sweet pea and just waiting to be introduced as charming and interesting plants for our borders and rockeries. Yet, up to now the sweet pea has remained a pure breed developed only from the species *L. odoratus*.

There are several reasons for this but one difficulty, which by 1937 seemed on the way to being overcome, is the difference in size of the reproductive organs between one species and another. For instance, *L. odoratus* has a very long style, too long for the pollen grain tube of *L. hirsutus* to reach and fertilise seeds in the *odoratus* ovary.

One method of shortening the style is by stylar amputation and this, provided that the species are compatible, does increase the chance of success. However, to quote David Archer:

> As yet the best technique to use in the 'amputation' is not apparent; consider two methods: by cutting the style off at the base in a transverse or slightly diagonal cut, and applying pollen to the cut surface, the whole apparatus is left exposed to the air. To avoid possible contamination and drying out of the surface some sort of protection has to be devised. For this plastic capsules, or pure, sterile vaseline has been used. The alternative method is to cut the style longitudinally, down the middle and to place the pollen at the base of the cleft so formed; the next stage is to select a hollow straw of the right 'bore' and slide a centimetre section over the style. This holds the pollen in place, prevents drying out, and reduces the risk of contamination. It probably goes without saying that for this sort of job a very clean, very sharp blade is required — preferably a scalpel.

By 1975 there were plans for a display of *Lathyrus* species at the Sweet Pea Society's National Show but sadly, this most interesting work came to an abrupt end when David Archer fell to his death on a plant-hunting expedition in the mountains.

No-one knows just how much of this seed is distributed for sale each year. In his book on *Sweet Peas*, (1914), Horace W. Wright made the following estimate which was still being referred to in the N.S.P.S. Annual of 1976:

> Probably in excess of 40 tons of sweet pea seed is distributed in this country which, taking an average figure of 5,000 seeds to the pound, represents a distribution of at least 448 million seeds to British growers every year.

Sometimes the owner of a firm also functions as its specialist breeder and sometimes an experienced man is hired for the work. Hugh Dickson was Cullen's first breeder and his brilliantly scarlet and sun-proof 'Air Warden' sweet pea is still popular, and has been used in trials as a comparison for brightness of colour.

74. N.S.P.S.'s outing to Brighton.

75. Mr. G. H. Burt at sweet pea trials at E. W. King's. 'He devoted his life to this flower.'

Mr. G. H. Burt evidently devoted his life to this flower and rose to be President of the N.S.P.S. He came to E. W. King's in 1912, after several years with Unwin's of Histon, and a period in the United States. Ernest King was himself something of an authority on this flower and did much towards promoting its popularity. From 1916 to 1919 he was President of the N.S.P.S.; he twice agreed to have its trials on his ground and in 1928 was awarded the Eckford Memorial Medal in recognition of his services to the Society.

Early in its history the N.S.P.S. trials had been conducted in a somewhat amateurish manner and by 1925 many members had become anxious that the trials might fall into disrepute. So the suggestion was made that they should become the responsibility of five or six reliable seed firms, each one to undertake the task for no more than two successive years. At this point E. W. King offered to put his grounds at their disposal together with the services of Mr. Burt. The next year, under G. H. Burt's tireless and experienced direction, these trials more than fulfilled their object. As just one example of care needed in trial work, a dark seeded variety was always planted next to a light one so that if, at picking, a pod escaped from the container of one variety to the next, it was easily spotted after thrashing and could be cleaned out.

The winning of show awards is not just a matter of growing perfect blooms, vegetables or seeds. Their arrangement and presentation has often tipped the balance between one excellent collection and another. Sometimes the breeder is also expert at presentation and even of flower arrangement. However, more often than not, it is the long suffering wives and daughters who are pressed into this service and who, by way of some compensation, sometimes have a variety named after them!

Mr. J. O. Tandy followed Mr. Burt as flower seed manager for E. W. King and Company and it is he who, after many years of trial and error, at last succeeded in producing several colours of an entirely new type of sweet pea. It is unique in having no tendrils, these having been replaced by leaves and, no longer being a climber, little or no support is required. This sweet pea, which Mr. Tandy introduced and in 1982 put on the market, has been multiplied up by Denholm Seeds, Lompoc, California, and marketed initially by Thompson and Morgan under the name 'Snoopea'. It has already received at least 14 awards as well as achieving the much coveted designation of Fleuroselect Novelty for 1980.

Although now somewhat rare, there is to be found in Essex a wild, everlasting sweet pea, *Lathyrus tuberosus* — known as the 'Fyfield Pea'. It is the only species in the genus, other than the annual sweet pea, to have much scent and thus is the only everlasting (perennial) sweet pea. A cultivated hybrid, which is a cross between *L. rotundifolius* and *L. tuberosus*, has been produced.[17]

Perhaps someone will one day finish, or at least add to, the work on this flower which David Archer began so well. It is also to be hoped that some enthusiast will explore the possibilities of other species in this genus.

Chapter Eight

Tiptree and Mersea Island

Tiptree

A parish of many smallholdings and once a gay patchwork of flower seed crops.

It was in the 1840s that conditions of near famine last occurred in England and in the 1870s work on the land was scarce and wages a mere pittance. If they could, families often emigrated to Australia or Canada. Others walked to the Shires to become coal miners or mill hands, so that between 1871 and 1891 it is said that the agricultural population of Tiptree had fallen by over a hundred. Nevertheless, it was more fortunate than some villages at that time for among its inhabitants there were people[1] with sufficient drive and social conscience to do something about both the unemployment and the economic conditions of the labourers and their families. In doing so they also gave impetus to seed and strawberry growing, which industries, for many years, became such an integral part of the economy of this area.

John Mechi, a successful cutler of Leadenhall Street, London, also became a well-known agricultural innnovator. In 1841 he bought the notoriously poor farm known as Sadler's or Bigmore's on Tiptree Heath, which, having built a new house, he renamed Tiptree Hall. He was a supporter of the National Agricultural Labourers' Union and declared that, although higher wages might force farmers to replace men with machines, he believed that mechanisation would ultimately benefit the type of farm worker that would be required in the future.

On the subject of the wasteland of Tiptree Heath, he wrote:

> I shall exert all my energies to get the copy-holders to enclose and cultivate it, if I can, believing it to be a public benefit; and as an example, I shall devote a portion of my own land, in allotments of forty poles that their leisure summer evenings may be innocently and profitably occupied.

Nearby, Mr. Rand of Messing Park, in company with many another landowner at this time, was unable either to let his farms or to afford to farm the land himself in such a way as to maintain the existing labour force. So, rather than stand his men off, he split up a field into one or two acre plots. These were let to the men at a rent which they could afford and thus more smallholdings came into being in this district.

In 1864, Arthur Charles Wilkin started to grow fruit. This enterprise had been suggested by his former foreman, John Parrish, by then a seed grower whose son William is said to have planted the first two acres of strawberries at Trewlands Farm. Thus was started an enterprise which provided employment in the village and by 1885 developed into the Tiptree jam industry which maintains its fame and Royal Warrant to this day. In 1891, 400 casual workers were needed at picking time when they could earn from 2s. 6d. to 7s. 6d. a day. The factory hand took home between 15s. and 20s. a week. Those employees with smallholdings supplied themselves with vegetables and might make £10 or so a year from the sale of seeds and/or fruit and vegetables.

Imports of cheap American wheat, and from 1873 several disastrous corn harvests, added to the hardships of agricultural workers and those in ancillary trades. In Tiptree, there was great unrest which fermented until finally a strong demand was made to the employers

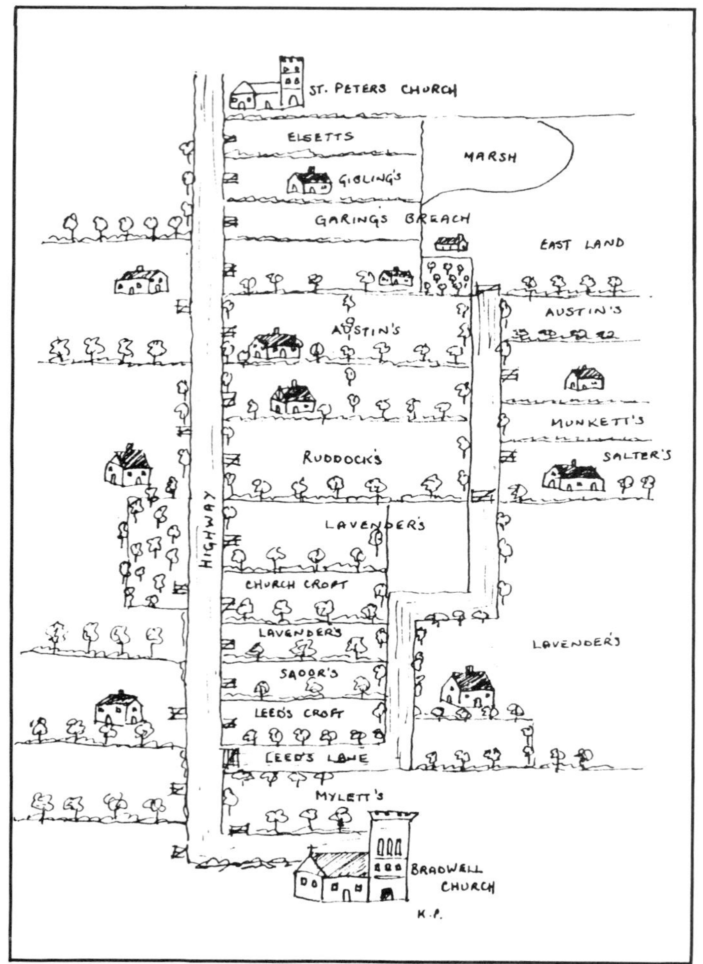

76. Elizabethan crofts at Bradwell-on-Sea, Essex, from a contemporary survey.

from the Agricultural Labourers' Union, asking them to make available to each of their employees a small piece of land which the employees might cultivate for their own use.

It is said that:

> To this demand some of the employers cheerfully agreed, and that the concession had such a good effect in satisfying the men that the majority of them settled down quietly to their old work with a new interest in life. Continuing their usual employment and living upon their wages, year by year they accumulated capital from the proceeds of the new land. The crops were good, the expenses small and the men worked with newborn vigour, early and late — often during part of their mealtimes — and occasionally getting a day off by the goodness of their employers. In three or four years a few saved as much as £100 each, and some more than that, and were so inspired with confidence in their new venture that they relinquished their work for wages and hired ten or twenty acres of land, one or two of them went so far as to hire a little farm.

One of the employers who cheerfully agreed was Charles John Wilkin. He not only lent or hired his plough and man to help people with their land but also started the Tiptree Credit Bank and the Wilkin Provident Trust. This latter provided a pension for all his employees over 65 and for their widows. It was funded by a half-share of the profits of the fruit enterprise.

It was probably in the 1900s that the third Lord Rayleigh visited Mr. Wilkin's jam factory and there is a story that when he was shown the cherries being pipped he remarked that charcoal produced from these seeds had, when heated, peculiar properties of its own with regard to the absorption of gases. The story continues that during the First World War, cherry-stone charcoal was supplied to the Ministry of Munitions for use in gas masks.

Strawberries and Green peas

Although soft fruit and green peas are by no stretch of imagination seed growing, in Tiptree and the surrounding parishes the three crops were so complimentary (the fruit and green peas providing a 'break' crop and also cash when there were no seeds ready for sale) and as seed was required to produce the green peas, it seems appropriate and gives a more complete picture of the times to diverge and say a little about these two crops.

The only strawberries available to Henry VIII were the little wild ones (*Fragaria vesca*). His accounts contain payment for a collection of these roots for the Royal garden. These same small berries were still much prized during the reign of Elizabeth I as shown by Thomas Tusser who wrote:

> Wife into the garden, and set me a plot,
> Of strawberry roots, of the best to be got:
> Such growing abroad, among thorns, in the wood,
> Well chosen and picked, prove excellent good.

In 1642, Jean Robin, gardener to the French Royal family, recorded a not much larger but better-flavoured variety, which had arrived from eastern North America (*F. virginiana*). Its offspring were to be known as 'scarlets', and Messrs. Wilkin and Sons still produce pots of delicious 'Little Scarlet' strawberry jam. But for our first modern strawberry we had to wait until 1826 when Michael Keens, a nurseryman from Isleworth, developed from his large red-berried 'Imperial' seedling (which had little flavour) an even bigger berry with good flavour, namely 'Keens' Seedling'. This caused a sensation at the Royal Horticultural Show, for it was the first modern strawberry — with fine-coloured red fruit, nearly two inches in diameter, held well above the ground and with flavour. Mr. Fred Martin believes that Thomas Partridge Brett, of Villa Farm, was the first person to grow these strawberries in Tiptree and that the plants came from Keens' Nursery at Isleworth where T. P. Brett's nephew was an apprentice.

Most of the strawberries required for the Tiptree jam factory were produced on Mr. Wilkin's farms. It was only when this fruit was in short supply and prices rose sufficiently that the smallholders sold their crop for jam-making. Before the railway came to Tiptree in 1904, produce from smallholders was sold almost entirely in Colchester, Chelmsford, Witham or other nearby towns. Some was transported by horse-carrier or a privately-owned horse and cart, and a good deal of produce was pushed into town by its owner on a hand-cart. Some sent their produce to London, first by horse carrier and later to Stratford Market by train from Kelvedon station. (As Stratford Market was (except on Monday mornings), a 'closed market' owned by the Great Eastern Railway, only produce transported by this railway could be sold in its market. Outside the market gates, in the Burford Road, there were some half-dozen buyers to whom produce was sometimes sold. This has led to confusion as to whether this market was 'closed' or 'open'.) In order to get this produce to market in time for the buyers, the pickers had to be on the job by at least 5 a.m. for it to be loaded on to the train at Kelvedon at 8 a.m. In those early days, children were allowed six weeks' holiday from school during the pea and strawberry picking season. Each day of the 'holiday' they would go with their mothers and younger brothers and sisters, including toddlers and babes in prams, to the field to be picked that day. Their aim was to earn sufficient money to clothe themselves during the coming year. When the educationists stopped this practice many families were in dire straits for new clothes.

Once the railway was extended to Tiptree, it not only carried jam from the factory but also took aboard fresh strawberry and pea crops from growers large and small. Then it was a common sight to see a half-mile queue at the station waiting to load their produce on to the trucks. Consignments of strawberries varied from two to 100 peck baskets; the smaller quantities were often brought to the station on homemade hand-carts, in a wheelbarrow or an old pram. Naturally, the station staff tended to deal with the larger loads first which caused a good deal of ill-feeling. As many as 20 truck loads often left Tiptree at one time. Individual packs might weigh anything from 12 down to four pounds and the size gradually got smaller over the years as two pound and smaller chip baskets came in.

A peck was a squat wicker basket with no handles, strengthened by a round or so of heavy duty cane two-thirds of the way up its side. The top was finished as a rim which protruded on the outside and this both made handling easier and provided a means for fastening on the paper covers with string or a withy. On this cover was the grower's code number. Names were not used, because the buyers were anxious not to disclose, to each other, from whom they were obtaining produce. In due course the empty pecks were threaded in eights on to a string and returned to the grower. As many a picker has said, 'those baskets seemed to get bigger and bigger as the day wore on. We used to put our knees into the bottom to push it up so they did not hold so much. They also made good stools to have your lunch on' — it is no wonder the sides needed strengthening.

After about 1922 there were a few local motor vehicles travelling up to Covent Garden or Spitalfields ('open markets') and quite soon the London salesmen were sending their own lorries to fetch the crops. On their way to and from Spitalfields market by lorry, the Birkins remember that they passed many carts laden with lettuce, carrots, onions and other greengrocery. These were drawn by horses and had come from market gardens down Dagenham way. They could be seen on any weekday morning, anywhere along the route, their drivers fast asleep. But the horses knew what to do and unerringly negotiated the traffic and drew in to whichever 'pull-up' was favoured by their driver who, awakened by the stopping of the cart, slid from the driving seat and stumbled inside for a cup of tea. It is to be hoped that the horses were also rewarded.

In 1914, from every village, hamlet and town, our fit young men 'joined the colours' and went singing to the war in France. Few came back and of those who did none was ever quite the same in body or mind. Once again those at home did what they could. Mr. Wilkin transferred 15 acres of his land to his returning employees as part payment of bonuses which had been allotted to them in their absence. Also, both he and a Mr. Arnold offered plots for sale to other soldiers who had returned to the village. Some of this land was known as 'Blighty Lane' and it is now Anchor Road. Captain Eaton, of Messing Park also provided land which became known as 'Warrior's Rest'. It is now part of the Anchor Press site. The patchwork quilt of little fields was thus enlarged still further.

But the hey-day of seed growing had passed and after 1918 the history of the Essex smallholders, whose living depended largely on seed and market garden crops, is a tale of hard work, ingenuity and great faith. Only those with the courage to carry on when 'any sensible member of society' would have given up, survived in this occupation for more than two generations.

When in 1939 war struck again and regulations came into force which cut the acreage of flower seeds that were allowed to be grown on agricultural land by 99 per cent, it was to these cultivators of small patches of ground and to allotment holders and owners of large private gardens that the flower seedsmen's representatives entrusted the maintenance of their precious seed stocks.

Strangely, in times of disaster, there is always an upsurge in the demand for flowers and consequently, flower seeds. Successive governments have come to recognise this need and so have tended to turn a blind eye when a small piece of land, previously classified as an agricultural holding, reverts to a garden. Anyway, that is what happened in Tiptree and because much of this soil grows flower seeds far better than cabbages and potatoes, it is possible that these acres did as much to cheer and feed the nation's soul as the vegetables did for its stomach.

There is a story which has persisted from 'Hitler's War' which I believe, but have been unable to confirm:

> In the first year of the war someone had a large piece of ground which had been sown with nasturtium seed. When it came into bloom — a glorious carpet of reds, orange and yellow — the Air Ministry

> became much alarmed, for the field shone like a beacon from the air.

It had to be ploughed under.

Birkin, Chappell, Cottee, Harrington, Hull, Josselyn, Martin, Newman and Wilks are all names which recur in the village. All these families owned small parcels of land on which they grew seeds and market garden crops but, by 1980, it was quite difficult to find any of them growing even a row or two of flower seeds. There follows the memories of some of them.

77. Great-grandfather Henry Birkin (b.1840).

Fred Birkin, Manor Lodge, Tiptree

Mr. Birkin's ancestors were Huguenot refugees who came to Coggeshall. At first they were lace makers in that village and later some of the family went to Nottingham and they are said to have started lace-making there. One of them was knighted. The Tiptree seed-growing branch of the family began either with William Birkin, who was born in Coggeshall in 1791 or, more probably, with his son Henry, born in 1840, when he rented and moved into Brook Hall, Tolleshunt Knights. Henry was a tall distinguished-looking gentleman with the family's aquiline nose. He retired twice. The first time was when he stopped farming Brook Hall and there still exists Messrs. Surridge and Son's priced catalogue for the sale of live and dead stock on the farm on Tuesday 4 October 1904.

Some of the items provide an interesting price comparison with today. We find the auctioneer obtaining:

Six mahogany chairs	£1	1s.	6d.
An iron bedstead		1s.	0d.
Pembroke table		13s.	0d.
Three two-bushel skeps		5s.	0d.
One four and one one-bushel skep		6s.	0d.
Three seed sieves		4s.	0d.
Clover seed drill		2s.	6d.

Wagon tarpaulin		16s.	0d.
Stack cloth	£1	1s.	0d.
Gentry blower	£1	7s.	0d.
Gentry dressing machine	£1	10s.	0d.
Set of Maldon Iron Works duckfoot harrows	£3	5s.	0d.
Smythe corn drill	£10	0s.	0d.
Double shaft road wagon	£4	0s.	0d.
Platform seed cart	£1	10s.	0d.
Set of plated harness	£1	1s.	0d.

It was Henry Birkin who built Birkin House, Tiptree, and lived there after his first retirement. At that time he hired Peakes Farm, Tiptree from the Du Cane family, had another farm at Cressing and was farming 'little fields all over the place besides'.

In 1920 he retired again and died about four years later at the age of 84, leaving five sons, four of whom were seed-growers. His second son, Alfred, was the grandfather of the present Fred Birkin who during the Second World War helped by serving on the County Horticultural Advisory Committee. He was a man who could be relied upon to put both sides of a question fairly and to give judgment based on sound evidence or reasoning.

Seed growing booms occurred after both world wars. That, Mr. Birkin affirms,

> encouraged over-production which hastened, if it did not entirely cause, the slumps which followed. Quite quickly after the First World War mangel seed failed to get a satisfactory price. After the Second World War it was onion seed, but after that war prices kept up for several years and were mainly brought down by foreign imports being allowed into this country, so that onion seed which had been grown in the expectation of a return of 23s. a pound plummetted to 8s a pound and no longer paid for the growing.

In his turn Fred Birkin has now retired leaving his son David to carry on growing strawberries and other crops, not one of which is now for seed. He is also very proud of the fact that David's wife has brought Tambour lace-making back into his family. When pillow lace was made, the small round seeds of the weed 'cleavers', while still green, were pushed on to the tops of the brass pins to form a protective head.

Bill Chappell, Pinecroft, Tiptree

Bill Chappell is an horticultural committee man and possibly now grows the greatest variety of flower seeds in Tiptree: forget-me-nots, pansies, aquilegia, lupins, many colours of delphinium and no doubt a few more.

Amos Cottee, Lyndene, Grove Road, Tiptree

Mr. Cottee is a jolly 86 years young! His father and his grandfather were also seed growers and they grew mangel, turnip, parsnip and swede seed for Cullen's and Cooper Taber. Later on they grew seeds for Hurst's: wallflower, parsnip, parsley and cornflower which is described as 'very slippery'. Grandfather Cottee first worked for Mr. Wilkin and then got some land at Bull Corner where he built himself a house. House names in Tiptree often indicate the achievement of a lifetime, so saved earnings from small plots of strawberries and flower seeds often resulted in nameplates such as 'Welldon', 'It's Mine' and 'Overtyme'.

After the First World War Sharpe's representative came into the district and one year the Cottees contracted to grow some runner bean seed for them. It was a dry year and green beans were making a good price so father sold a few — and then some more — so that when Sharpe's representative, a Mr. Anderson, always elegantly attired in bow tie, spats and gloves, came to look at the crop and asked how it was doing, there were very few beans left on the bines. 'The crop is very bad', said father Cottee, 'I fear you won't get your seed back'.

To which Anderson, who was no fool, retorted, 'Green beans have been a good price this year. You'll have to pay for the seed', and it all ended with a good laugh.

Mrs. Amos Cottee's mother could sort four bushels of runner bean seeds in a day, 'odd times', between doing her housework and seeing to the children and her husband's meals.

Nasturtiums were also grown for seed. 'You pick up the bines and shake them, and then sweep and pick up the seeds by hand. In Holland where they have flat fields', said Amos Cottee thoughtfully, 'you can leave the crop until the bines are sere and the seed has dropped off and then on their soil they sweep up easily. They've got the trade now.'

Bertie Harrington, Wits End, 48 Maldon Road, Tiptree

Grandfather William Harrington and his three brothers grew seeds at Tiptree, Inworth, Layer Marney and Layer-de-la-Haye, in the latter half of the 19th century. They grew for Cullen's of Witham — probably root seeds, which they took down to the warehouse by horse and cart and it is said that 'No-one ever knew when they were a-comin' back because they went into the pub to celebrate afterwards!' As flower seeds, and particularly sweet peas, became more popular they were one of the family's specialities. They usually had an acre of many varieties on contract with Carter's, who always sent their own men down to rogue the crop.

In 1979, Bertie Harrington grew an antirrhinum named 'Lipstick' for Sutton's Seeds. It proved a very shy seeder in this country and is now to be tried in Sutton's trial grounds in India, in the hope that it will do better in that climate.

Mr. Harrington also remembers that although, during the depression, some men left Tiptree for factories and mines in the Midlands and North, sometime around 1910 the reverse happened and coalmen from Durham came to Tiptree where they nearly all grew seeds for Carter's. Here again the same tale is told that after the last war the seed trade became centred on Holland where labour was cheaper and where, during and after the war, their government assisted the trade.

C. Josselyn, Oakleigh, Maldon Road, Tiptree

Mr. Josselyn remembers having grown savoy, cucumber, marrow and cress. The cress seed was grown for 6d. a pound. Once he grew a ton of savoy seed from three acres. This seed made £70 a ton in 1938 and went up to £90 in 1939. It was all hand-work from the sowing of the seed in April to the setting out of the plants in late July to August. The following year, during the first few days in August, the crop should be cut, tied into sheaves and laid across the rows to dry. Each row, because the crop had previously been earthed-up, was slightly raised above ground level. In this way not only was air able to circulate all round the sheaf, but it was prevented from blowing about in the wind by being impaled upon stem stumps still in the ground.

Once dry, some seed cases such as savoy, cabbage and kale open up and shed their seeds very readily, so it was generally considered best to thrash these out in the field because every movement meant a loss of seed. This loss was greater when the crop was dry and so it was, if possible, done when the dew was on it or after a shower of rain. First straw would be brought to a convenient place in the field, perhaps in the shade of a tree. This would be laid out to form a circular 'mattress', the rim higher than the middle (so that the seed would fall inwards). Enough straw was used for there to be three to four inches of cushioning even after it had been well trodden down. A 10-yard stack cloth was pegged out over the straw and then some sheaves, with their bands cut, were arranged on the 'mattress' with their heads to the middle. Then came a man with one or a pair of horses who, leading one and riding the other, would walk the horses round and round on top pressing out the seed.

78. Treading out cabbage seed at Rivenhall, *c.*1965. Alfred Bonner is on the left.

79. The Bonners flailing.

Two other men were needed to stand at the edge of the canvas to fork the seed stems to the middle and catch any horse dung, in a bucket, as it fell.

The thrashing of small quantities could be done with one steady old horse, who had been trained to walk round and round on its own. Mr. Josselyn recalls one such which, the day after thrashing had finished, was found still walking round and round on the thrashing place. When rubber-tyred tractors came in, these, driven to and fro across the seed, replaced the horse.

Other crops were carted to the barn or stacked to await thrashing during the winter. This thrashing might also be done by a horse walking over a heap of the crop on the barn floor, by men with flails, by putting through a simple thrashing device, or by a larger contractor's machine, which, belching smoke and smelling of heat and oil, would chug its way with defiant majesty to farm stackyards throughout the district, and today we have the combine harvester which cuts and thrashes in one operation.

George Wilks, Barbrook Lane, Tiptree

Whether or not great-grandfather Wilks grew seeds is not remembered. His son, Joseph Nathaniel Wilks (1857-1940) lived at Hill Farm, Inworth, and most probably grew root seeds as well as cereals. In the next generation the boys were of an age to go to the war. Jack, the younger son, was taken because he had no family to support and Harry stayed at home keeping Jack's land going and working for Mr. Wilkin, until he had saved enough money to buy and rent sufficient land to support his family by growing seeds — mainly vegetables, strawberries and green peas. When Jack came home from the war he settled back on to his land and in time saved enough to purchase New Park Farm, Tiptree. This small farm, when added to his other fields, enabled him to support his wife and himself by growing seed and market garden crops.

Both Jack and Harry had a field in Barbrook Lane and after Harry's son George was demobbed from the R.A.F., his father gave him his Barbrook Lane land upon which he built a bungalow and grew flower seeds and strawberries.

80. George H. Wilks dressing lobelia seed. He made this ingenious dresser in 1947.

Later, when his uncle Jack's land came onto the market, George Wilks bought the field in Barbrook Lane. In 1980, his barn was neat and tidy with his father's sieves of many sizes still hanging on the wall. In the corner stood one of the Gentry dressers which were made in Little Totham, at least a hundred years old and cleanly and carefully stored. Next to it was a Hunt's (of Earls Colne) seed thrashing machine. The gem of the collection, however, was a home-made dressing machine of 1947 vintage with which, when I called, George was efficiently cleaning up a sample of lobelia seed. It was 'kiltered up' from a wooden tea chest, an orange box, the castor off a chair and the handle from a rubber stamp — a truly ingenious and functional item of equipment. George has now retired and sadly there is no-one in this family to carry on.

Fred Martin, Grange Farm, Tiptree

About 1932, Chivers of Histon, Cambridge, came into the Tiptree area in search of land upon which strawberries might be grown for their jam and canning factory. Mr. Martin became their area agent. As well as several other members of his family, he grew seeds as is shown by a record of his farming enterprise for 1936 when on his 120 acres he produced:

	price per ton
5 acres of cabbage seed for Cullen of Witham	£56
4 acres of wallflower seed	£96
6 acres of runner beans	£50
6 acres of broad beans	£45
7 acres of mangel seed	£35
2 acres of sweet peas for seed	£90
3 acres of rhubarb for 2½d. a pound	—
25 acres of barley	£35
20 acres of wheat	£45
35 acres of soft fruit	
7 acres of grass	

The livestock consisted of six horses, 120 pigs and three cows. The labour employed was 22 men at 35s. for a 52-hour week.

Arthur Scott, Grouts Farm, Tolleshunt D'Arcy

Although not actually in the parish of Tiptree, the Arthur Scotts of Tolleshunt D'Arcy and Tollesbury were considerable flower and vegetable seed growers and so may be included in this area. When he married, Arthur took over Grout's Farm and remained there farming and seed-growing until he died in 1950. His sons, Ralph and Robert, were first in partnership with him and then, when Ralph wanted to get married, he began to branch out on his own by taking on little pieces of land and finally Carringtons Farm, Tollesbury.

Bob remembered that in the early days they grew cabbage seed for both Cranmer's and Deal's of Kelvedon, Cheltenham red beet for Carter's, and had contracts for parsnip, runner beans and radish as well as many kinds of flowers. In fact, in the early 1900s, so many seeds were being grown on their 70 acres that nine cart horses and three ploughmen were required to do the work.

The Scotts are a close-knit family, always willing 'to help one another out' and when one realises that in the two parishes they grew plots of flowers including sweet william, godetia, wallflower, cherianthus, nasturtium, antirrhinum, night-scented stock, aster, calendula, sweet pea, clarkia, and candytuft as well as corn, onion seed, round and prickly spinach and peas, there must have been several crises necessitating an extra hand during the season.

When they grew runner beans for Cooper Taber, it is remembered that the seed was never delivered before the end of April as this firm did not like it to be sown too early and their growers also had strict instructions not to flail it out until the following March. This crop, which is sown in May, is seldom ready to harvest until the end of September. You judge when it is ready by the appearance of a few brown pods, and roots which will pull out of the ground without much effort. As the bines were pulled they were tied in bundles and stood up in the field for some two to three weeks. Once the leaves and stems were dry, the bundles were put on to tripods in the stack yard or a corner of the field. Each tripod was carefully thatched against the weather and the whole left to mature until the following spring. Finally, on a bright and drying day in March, a thrashing floor would be prepared between the barn's large doors, on to which the tripods would be tipped as required by those wielding the flails.

Radish is another seed which, although now combined, really needs to mature in the stack over winter. It has a dense seedcase which takes a long time to dry out sufficiently to release its seed with any readiness and much of the unripe seed will 'make' to a good sample if left unthrashed until the following year.

Ralph Scott died from a fall from the back of a trailer in 1964. His son, Douglas, still grows a few seeds such as broad beans, rye grass and sometimes parsley for Charles Sharpe but there are now no flower seeds. At Grout's in 1982, there were no seed crops at all, but Bob said, 'if the trade looks up, we shall be at it again'.

MERSEA ISLAND

From early in the days of seed-growing certain farms on this island have grown crops of vegetables, cereal and other farm seeds. In the main it was left to the smallholders to take up the contracts that were offered by Sutton's, Nutting's and Carter's, for flower and garden seeds; and they grew these colourful crops in every nook and cranny that could be found.

As far as equipment is concerned such growers seldom yield to the high-pressure salesman. In the dark evenings they may look at what the advertisements have to offer and, when there is an opportunity — if it is not too far away — they may find time to go and see in use whatever it is that has attracted them. Then, as often as not, they go home again with no intention of placing an order but to think out how the idea may be adapted for their use, and be made from what is 'about the place' or can be obtained second-hand, in reasonably good condition, and much more cheaply.

This country is on the fringe of the flower seed-growing climate and, except for a few such as salvias which to do well in this country need to be grown at home, most contracts are now placed abroad. When I visited the island in 1982 it was thought that there were but four growers and by 1986 they have dwindled still more. There follows what three of them told me.

Edgar Heard, 18 Victory Road, West Mersea

Both as regards himself and his equipment Mr. Heard is certainly a person who can adapt. Originally a fisherman he gradually eased out of this in favour of growing cut flowers which seemed more profitable at the time. Unfortunately, with the rise in transport, packing and heating costs this scheme had to be given up in favour of flower seed growing.

Realising that irrigation would be a great advantage he gathered together from somewhere a portable irrigation system. This was powered by a three horse-power petrol engine, which he linked to the water supply from an existing well in his field. His long greenhouse was adapted to dry and condition the seeds as well as to produce plants. In it was a centre bench on which stood a home-made propagator and some seed-cleaning devices. Along part of the walls were bays for seed drying which were fitted with shelves made from two-inch by half-inch battens and over these were placed woven plastic onion nets or an old fishing net (whichever would prevent the seed pods from falling through). Each bay was enclosed by walls made either from discarded sheets, or from nets, according to the dehiscent capabilities of the seed to be dried. For instance, when pansy capsules burst, the seeds are shot several feet in every direction and so sheets are used.

The various trials and tribulations, so typical of any smallholder, are graphically put in a letter from Mr. Heard in the early 1980s:

> Tried growing cut flowers in back garden. Began by digging a well 22 ft. deep to provide supply of good water. Started in 1966 with one glasshouse 40 ft. by 18 ft. and grew sweet peas outside.

A year later put up another heated glasshouse 30 ft. by 12 ft. for trial crops such as chrysanthemums, daffodils, tulips and iris. Decided carnations would be the best crop for heated houses and bought a 50 ft. by 20 ft. mobile house for sweet peas and chrysanthemums.

This was reasonably profitable as a part-time job for a year or two but it soon became clear that to make a full-time living it would need to be done on a much larger scale.

With no capital and the ever-increasing cost of heating, transport and packing material I decided to give it up and try something else that would make use of the glasshouses. Having some of the character similar to that of a lemming, I made up my mind to try seed-growing using the two smaller glasshouses for plant raising, and the large one for drying the seed.

I then traced the owner of a 3½ acre field that had not been used for some time, rented it from him, wrote to Sutton's, got some contracts and was on my way.

To sum up, the small seed grower of the '80s needs to be a mechanic capable of keeping an obsolete clapped-out rotovator going for just one more year, a carpenter, an electrician, a biologist and an optimist supreme.

Must be prepared to work 10 hours a day, seven days a week, through spring, summer and autumn, bent double most of the time, either hoeing or picking seed, for an hourly rate that would make the most moderate trade union man scream in anguish, take the difficult in his stride and achieve the impossible at least once a week.

Cope with everything nature can throw at him and manage till the end of the year, when he will be paid, if he gets a crop, and if the crop passes the germination test. A wife who will grab a hoe or picking bucket whenever necessary and help get the job done when you just can't make it alone is absolutely priceless. In fact he needs to be a genius, but if he was, he would certainly have more sense than to try to earn a living growing seeds.

To have a better understanding of what Mr. Heard has written it is necessary to realise how much purely routine work is entailed before one can hope to make a modest living from growing flower seeds. Mr. Heard's usual contracts were for varieties of antirrhinum, lobelia, polyanthus and pansy. This necessitated attending to the needs of some 25,000 plants each year. Each type, and even each variety, of seed needs to be handled differently and one must try to choose so that their peak work requirements follow, rather than coincide with, one another. Mr. Heard became a noted grower of pansies and, barring any emergencies, work on this crop occurs during the season as follows.

It was stressed that it is very necessary first to arrange a contract with a reliable seed firm. Having done that, the seed may be sown in trays from December to the end of January. If not sown before February the plants are less hardy and setting out will have to be delayed. This job will then run into the time when all available labour is needed for setting-out lobelia and dahlias.

The seed trays are kept in the propagator until the first real leaf appears. They are started off at a temperature of 50 degrees which is lowered gradually so that at first leaf it is down to 40 degrees (about three to four weeks).

The plants are then pricked out into more boxes and put on to the floor of the greenhouse to harden off. By early March it should be warm enough to stand them outside for further hardening until the ground becomes fit for planting, hopefully by the end of March or the beginning of April.

Plants are then set out in rows three feet apart (so that the rotovator can get between to clean the crop) and 12 inches between plants in the row.

Hand hoe to clean between the plants. The crop must be gone through by hand as well as rotovated three or four times to keep down the weeds. Spraying for mildew, botrytis, red spider and aphids with Dicron-Benlate and liquid copper is routine every two weeks if time and weeds allow. If the weeds are getting the better of the crop it is thought better to hoe than to spray.

One hopes to start picking by late July. This must all be done by hand as pansy seeds do not all ripen at the same time and unlike many others will not ripen after they have been picked. There are two to three days, according to the dryness of the weather in which to pick the capsules from the time that the seed inside has turned brown (it is not ripe while still white) until the capsule bursts and flings its seed far and wide. Mr. Heard suggested that a good average yield might be 21 kilos of seed from 4,500 plants. It is not always achieved for, in 1980, he and his wife finished hoeing the pansies one evening and they 'looked a picture'. The next two days it rained and blew from the north-east and the whole crop disappeared under a soggy grey mass of botrytis-ridden flowers.

Once the seeds are picked they are trayed, put into a sheeted bay of the greenhouse and left to dry. The seed then bursts on to the sheets and falls to the floor. When as much seed as possible has been ejected (and the last one or two seeds will always be retained in the folds at the bottom of the seedcase) the pods are removed from the trays and Mr. Heard puts them through a rubber wringer to get out the trapped seeds. All is then sieved, the rubbish blown off with an adapted electric fan heater and then bagged up and labelled for the merchant.

Some points mentioned by Mr. Heard about his other crops, illustrate the management problems still further.

Lobelia seed cases if dried too rapidly become like chamois leather and do not release their seeds. Therefore cut this crop after the worst of the hot weather is over — this seed will still be being shaken out in December from a crop cut in mid-September. Although not the smallest seed, there are some 750,000 lobelia seeds in one ounce which, because they run through most mesh like water, must be put into sacks of very closely woven material. When it comes to sieving, Mr. Heard uses this fact to advantage and removes a great deal of rubbish from his sample by allowing it to run through the mesh of a fine nylon stocking. Even so, from seven kilos of seed (the produce of 1,700 plants) his merchant extracted a further two kilos of extraneous matter.

Dahlia is another seed that is picked by hand. Late spring frosts present a problem and blackfly can be a serious pest. This crop has to be sprayed as for pansies, an average yield being 30 kilos from 3,000 plants, but in 1980 Mr. Heard got 70 kilos.

Polyanthus crops spread over three years. The sequence of work is, in the first year, to sow the seed in May-June and plant out in the autumn in rows three feet apart with 18 inches between the plants. During the second year the crop must be sprayed and kept clean. In the third year continue to spray and keep clean until harvested in the third or fourth week of July.

As it is a very erratic germinator, which likes cool and moist conditions, the boxes of sown seeds should be placed in a shaded frame or glasshouse. Germination is seldom more than 50 per cent and therefore one should double the seed rate. Two grammes of seed will contain some 2,000 seeds so this amount will produce about 1,000 plants. Mr. Heard's best yield from 2,000 plants has been 12½ kilos and his worst 1½lbs. — the difference between early and late flowering. Early flowers seldom produce seed.

Antirrhinum seed is sown in a greenhouse in February at a seed rate appropriate to the variety.

In mid-March it must be pricked out and hardened off so as to be ready for planting out into the field from mid-April to early May. The rows should be 36 inches apart but the distance between the plants will vary, according to the variety being grown, from 18 to 20 inches. It will be necessary to spray at least four times against rust disease.

This is another seed which does not ripen after it is cut. However, the pod, being upright, does not readily lose its seeds and so, barring a very high wind, it is reasonably safe to leave the pods to ripen for a few more days after the first four or five are fully ripe. Some growers choose to take off the spikes as they ripen. This necessitates going through the crop two or three times from mid-August and into September. The central spike first, followed by the bulk of the crop and perhaps a few late-ripening spikes at the end. Other growers take off the whole crop as soon as four or five pods are fully ripe. Dwarf varieties like 'Coral' or 'Lipstick' are liable to be shy seeders and you may harvest only one kilo of seed from five rows of 130 plants. With most other varieties one kilo of seed may be expected from each row of 130 plants.

At one time Mr. Heard was able to employ two extra hands each season. Then, as wages rose to above the returns for his product, he had to face the work single-handed. This, for a time, he did but by 1984 there were so few contracts to be had that, at the end of the 1985 season, he packed up seed-growing and took to jobbing gardening and any other available work. This, he cheerfully assures me, provides a reasonable income with far less worry and toil.

V. T. Sams, 13a Kingsland Road, West Mersea

The late Mr. Sams is reputed to have been the largest flower seed grower on the island. He grew almost exclusively for Sutton's of Reading and was obviously one of their trusted growers for, on one occasion, they sent up 'a whole lorry load of old cabbage stubs'. These were all that had been saved of a special stock and the firm felt that if anyone could induce this unpromising material to yield a little seed, that man was Vic Sams.

He started work as a gardener and after 1939 struck out on his own as a seed-grower on Mersea Island. Here he managed to get two seed crops in one season from nemesia by cutting first when some seeds were ripe and the plants about four inches high.

This grower was convinced that it was much better to plough and hand-hoe the land than to use a rotovator, and he held to this conviction despite having had as many as 30,000 plants to set out and keep clear of weeds in a season.

J. L. Jowers, Thistle Cottage, Bower Hall Lane, West Mersea

Mr. Jowers is an ex-schoolmaster who has taken to growing seeds for the more exotic plant trade. Here are Japanese lilies of both *Speciosum* and *Auratum* types, alpines, and a cloud of *Cyclamen neapolitanum* growing comfortably under the trees in his D'Arcy Spice apple orchard. He believes that this represents the only commercial source of this cyclamen seed in this country. Otherwise it is obtained from Germany or from Oregon, U.S.A.

This crop is hand-picked and the distinctive thing about cyclamen seed is that it must remain on the parent plant for almost a year before it is ripe enough to gather. It is also an awkwardly-shaped seed which prefers to germinate in October in half shade.

As at Tiptree, something was needed on Mersea Island to provide cash at times when there were no seeds to sell, and so 26 seed growers in this area grew tomatoes and formed themselves into the Colchester Tomatoes Distribution Association which supplied markets in Leeds, Birmingham, Manchester and Liverpool from about 1960 to 1975.

Chapter Nine

The Development of Corn Exchanges

Originally corn exchanges were primarily centres where cereals were bought and sold for use by other trades. It seems that it was not until some time around 1850 that it became necessary for these establishments to provide accommodation for trading in farm and garden seeds.

Yet, from very early days it was known to be beneficial to exchange one's home-grown seed for that grown in another district and that there was a choice of variety is shown by the following chronological table. This has been compiled from the records of plant and seed remains found in the soil levels of archaeological digs and, although it does not claim to be complete, it does provide something useful from which those interested in crop history may make a reasonably accurate start.

Crop	Species	NEOLITHIC · BRONZE AGE · IRON AGE · ROMAN · DARK AGES · MEDIEVAL
Einkorn wheat	*Triticum monococcum*	- ? - - - ? -
Emmer wheat	*T. dicoccum*	═══════ = = - - - - - - - .
Spelt wheat	*T. spelta*	- = ═══════ = - - . .
Bread wheat	*T. aestivum (inc. 'T. compactum')*	- ? - - - = = = = = = = ═══════
Rye	*Secale cereale*	- ? - = = = ═══════
6-rowed, hulled barley (mostly lax-eared, ie. '4-rowed')	*Hordeum sativum var. polystichum*	= = = ═══════════════
6-rowed, naked barley	*H. sativum var. polystichum-nudum*	= ═══════ = = = = = = = - - - - . .
Cultivated oats	*Avena sativa + A. strigosa (inc. A. brevis, etc.)*	? - - = = ═══════
Horse ('Celtic') bean	*Vicia faba agg.*	. - ? = = = = = ═══════
Field pea	*Pisum sativum*	. . - ? = = = = = = = ═══════

81. Crude summary of temporal changes in cultivation of some of Britain's major field crops.

Given these facts, one might expect an earlier organised seed trade but perhaps, before the demand for a large volume of seeds arose for both home use and export, this was unnecessary.

By 1970, many corn exchanges had fallen into disuse and had been closed and, of those still left, most if not all seem doomed to become an anachronism. Nevertheless, no history of the corn and seed trade can be complete without some mention of a few of them and particularly of this country's most famous centre, which for many generations has been known throughout the world as Mark Lane.

Mark Lane Corn Exchange

In October 1972 a banquet was held to commemorate the centenary of the incorporation of the Corn Exchange Company by Act of Parliament in the reign of Queen Victoria. It is from the fascinating booklet produced as a souvenir for this occasion that much of the following history of this great corn and seed market has been abstracted.

The small section of the City of London that lies to the east of Mark Lane and Bishopsgate is the most historically interesting if for no other reason than that, at the time of the Great Fire, it was saved from destruction by an easterly wind. It is here that the London Corn Exchange, known as Mark Lane, was built in 1749, in a market area of great interest and antiquity. We know it is an old market place because it is recorded[2] that in the 13th year of the reign of Edward I (1285) 'a lane behind Blanch Appleton was granted to be enclosed' and that this land was then known as Mart Lane, from some discontinued market held nearby.

Blanch Appleton is also mentioned as a district in which, by an Act passed in 1464, foreigners were allowed to carry on the trades of basket-making and of wire-drawing, which they were not allowed to do in any other part of the City. This name later became corrupted to Chepelton, just as Mart was to become Mark. In the Mart Lane and Crutched Friars districts the foreigners were chiefly of Teutonic origin from the near European states, all then referred to as Dutchmen. In contrast, Mincing Lane was the place to find Italians and merchants from the Levant. Mincing has no connection with butchery: it is a corruption of Minchin, an order of nuns who once lived there.

From its earliest days this market had been in the busiest part of the City. It is close to the Tower of London which, for some centuries, was not only the Sovereign's palace but the main fortress of the city, wherein was the Ordnance (War department), a state prison, the Royal Mint and the seat of Government. Trinity House and the Customs House were not far away, and the Navy Office (Admiralty), before being moved to Seething Lane, had actually occupied a space in Mark Lane.

Throughout the Middle Ages London's corn was supplied from Kent and Essex. Later, as it became necessary, the supply was augmented from Norfolk, Suffolk and Sussex. For many years Essex farmers and dealers met at Aldgate and those from other places at Bear Quay in Thames Street.

Until, however, some millers expanded their business to include seed corn, imported fertilisers and oil-cakes, and other allied commodities together with the services that became associated with them, it is probable that farmers usually saved seed corn from their home-grown stocks. Or sometimes they may have exchanged their seed for that of a neighbour or even have bought some from a particularly successful crop that they had seen. Whatever happened, it appears to be the case that until well into the 18th century the main grain trade was simply to provide flour for bread and food for essential livestock (e.g. crushed oats for horses).

There is an Act of Parliament passed in 1551-2[3] which makes a direct reference to the buying of corn for seed. However, it appears to be more concerned that this might not be a means by which a supply could be purchased to sell again, rather than a recognisable trade in seed corn. It states that persons engrossing corn were subject to heavy penalties, and on a third offence to the pillory, forfeiture of goods, and imprisonment. Persons were, however, permitted to engross corn provided that they did not forestall it or regrate (hold it for a rise), when the price of corn did not exceed 6s. 8d. a quarter. Farmers buying corn for seed were compelled to sell an equivalent amount or forfeit double what they had bought.

In the 15th century corn came in to Queenhithe and Billingsgate quays, at which point it was weighed before being carried, by pack-horse, to the London Corn markets at Cornhill and Cheapside.

By the beginning of the 18th century the metropolitan corn market was held at Bear Quay, in Thames Street, and during the same period the corn trade began to use the services of factors. This arose from the practice of a number of Essex farmers who, instead of spending time attending the corn market, left their samples with the landlord of an inn at Whitechapel, on the understanding that he would sell it for them and for his trouble take an agreed commission. Very soon the profession of factor or farmer's agent became established and as their number increased they set up their stands on almost every unoccupied space in the vicinity of the Bear Quay market. In time this caused a nuisance and the necessity to gather them together, on one site, became a matter of urgency. A suitable place was found in Mark Lane and by 1749 the first London corn exchange (then called the Corn Factors' Exchange) was built around an open quadrangle.

It was perhaps because this was not always the warmest place in which to work that the factors became regular customers of Jack's Coffee House. This was near to Bear Quay and they evidently decided that it was a more comfortable and pleasant place in which to hold their meetings, for there exist Minute Books[4] for a period around 1759, which record that their meetings were held at 'The Corn Exchange Coffee House'.

By 1827, the Factors' Exchange had become too small for their needs and, in an attempt to improve matters, additional accommodation was added. Clearly this addition was not considered adequate for, 'there was such agitation and complaint by a section of the members' that in 1828 they broke away, formed the Corn Exchange Company and built a new corn exchange to adjoin the original factors' offices. These two exchanges were both under charter and remained as separate entities for just over a hundred years. It became necessary for dealers, merchants and bankers to become members of both exchanges until after their amalgamation in 1929 and for this special parliamentary powers were needed to give effect to the merger.

The importation of foreign corn, particularly after the repeal of the Corn Laws in 1846, caused an increase in this trade. By 1850 the Factors' or 'Old' Exchange was again enlarged, and at this stage the quadrangle was given a roof. Once again the enlargement was insufficient and this time they decided to knock down and rebuild on the same site. So in 1880 there was opened 'a handsome and commodious Exchange' and it was this building which was destroyed by enemy action in 1941. Copies of a quite splendid picture of its interior, entitled 'The New Corn Exchange and Seed Market 1897' are still to be found in the offices of at least two of today's seedsmen (R. H. M. Hasler, Dunmow, Essex and Messrs. Van Lessen, Richardson & Company, Headland House, Solebay Street, London E.14). It was published by Barclay Brothers of 47 Old Bread Street, London E.C. and, since from front to back of the picture the seedsmen's faces do not diminish in size, they must have been from separate photographs superimposed upon a line drawing of the building. Unfortunately no record of their names has been found. Nevertheless, the picture provides clear evidence of the formality of dress then demanded for those engaged in this profession, and which persisted with only minor changes of fashion until after the Second World War. In fact, many of the older members of the profession were still wearing their top hats until well into the 1930s, though amongst the black and grey 'toppers' and the bowler hats in the picture is one daring young blade in a straw boater! Maybe he was the relative or friend of a seedsman, for visitors, provided that they were accompanied by a

82. The New Corn Exchange and Seed Market, 1897.

83. A *Punch* caricature of the Corn Exchange, reproduced on a Christmas card.

member, were allowed into the Exchange. Membership was dependent upon the formal recommendation of a member and of its approval by the majority of the Board. Any non-member found to be trading 'on the floor' was first warned off by the beadle and, at a second offence, received a solicitor's letter.

As the internal combustion engine gradually ousted horse transport this, in its turn, had an effect upon the volume of trade conducted on the Exchange. The hitherto extensive oat, straw and fodder market was completely upset, and it was this which was very largely responsible for the decision to amalgamate the two Exchanges in 1929, for the accommodation was then, for the first time, too large for their needs.

When the Corn Sales Act, 1921, came into operation on 1 January 1923, it no doubt caused a great upsurge in the sales and servicing of weighing machines. Beautifully made wooden measures for a bushel down to a pint, were now discarded and often left to rot, until they became the cherished 'collector's piece' of more recent times. Except in quantities less than one hundredweight, it was now illegal to sell all corn and some seeds by measure, all had to be sold 'by weight' (avoirdupois). Ryegrass, clovers, vetches, swede, turnip, rape, sainfoin, lupins, linseed, buckwheat, wheat, barley, oats, rye, maize, cress, mustard, peas and beans, all had to be sold by weight. Of course, the indefatigable J. K. King was already warning his customers that this was about to take place in his catalogue of 1921.

Mark Lane corn and seed market began by being held on Mondays, Wednesdays and Fridays, the Monday market being the main one for business. Then, when Saturday work became unpopular, the Friday market was moved to Thursdays so that the ensuing paperwork could be completed before the weekend. Lieutenant Colonel C. A. Brooks (Brooks of Mistley, Essex) says that the market for seeds, other than cereals and pulses, had begun to develop in the last half of the 19th century.

Other memories of Mark Lane have come from Mr. H. C. Russell of Van Lessen, Richardson & Company who, in April 1982, and at the age of 96 years, was still to be found at his office desk for a few hours each day. (This is one of the half-dozen or so large seed importers in this country. The firm specialises in seeds for pet birds, pigeon fanciers and zoos. One of their largest lines is peas from New Zealand. In 1948 they were the sole importers of the produce of the New Zealand Pea Growers' Association. They both buy from and sell to the Martins of Earls Colne.) During the Blitz, when the offices of this firm were on the opposite side of the road to the Corn Exchange, Mr. Russell vividly remembered his experiences as a Fire Warden on the roof, with bombs falling all around. Of Mark Lane he also recollected that,

> A bell was rung by a beadle at noon and after this, trading might officially begin and smoking was disallowed. Samples were then examined and any seed taken from the packet or sack had to be discarded — it was thrown onto the floor.
>
> Essex merchants were met at Liverpool Street station by a porter sent from the market, who would carry their bags to Mark Lane and bring them back to the station at the end of the day. They were NEVER to be seen carrying their own bags!

The late Mr. Harold S. Wyncoll, of E. Marriage and Sons Ltd., Colchester, when speaking about Mark Lane, laid great emphasis upon the fact that at this market,

> No lies were told. Verbal agreements WERE honoured and on the rare occasions that anyone did misbehave, he was very soon eliminated.

One such is remembered to have been fined £7,000 as well as to have been banished from the Exchange for three years. For some years, until and including 1939, on the last day of trading before the Christmas holiday on the provincial Corn Exchanges, business ended with a traditional relaxation of formality. In fact, it was prudent not to wear one's best pin-stripes on that day for a flour fight was very liable to break out. Although rather frowned upon by some of the older and more staid members 'on the floor', Christmas trading at Mark Lane often ended in a good-humoured free-for-all when old samples were cleared from desk drawers to be used as 'snowballs'. The daily papers and *Beerbohm's List*[5] reported with such phrases as, 'Towards the close samples were exchanged very freely'! On more than one occasion, and no doubt attracted by the noise, young bloods from the vegetable and flower seed market in the north wing invaded the floor and a football match developed. Goals were scored when a bag of seed hit the face of the clock. Tony Cullen remembers, more than once, having to contribute to the repair of this imposing timepiece, which was mounted high on legs and plinth at one end of the central aisle.

Mark Lane, after the bombing

During the night of 10/11 May 1941, tense fire watchers on the tops of London's buildings hunched their shoulders and hoped that nothing would fall too near to them — the air raid alert had already sounded — the Luftwaffe was on its way. This time, the eastern corner of the City was not to be saved by a wind from the east, for minutes later, among a hail of bombs, one watcher remembers noticing that 'something rather large had hit the Corn Exchange'. This bomb had gone right through the glass roof, between the imposing line of pillars and into the centre aisle. The pillars and the side aisles were left more or less intact. Mr. Dennis Bonner (then working for Richardson and Preece of Witham) remembers that on the following Monday, 'everybody was in a huddle together behind the pillars, which they had draped with tarpaulins to protect themselves and their merchandise from the weather — people just found a space for their desks wherever they could'. Soon it became apparent that this inconvenience was to be added to for 'bombing pigeons, obviously delighted by the new arrangements whereby they had access to every opened sack, were a constant source of irritation'.

So it was that this market carried on its business until re-building was once more set in hand. This time the design was to be on modern lines 'worthy of the City of London's post-war reconstruction programme'. Meantime a few immediately necessary repairs were done to the L-shaped part of the building which had suffered less damage and into which, as their business had increased, the vegetable, flower and grass seedsmen had been moved since the latter part of the 19th century. By 1954 the first stage of the Exchange planned after 1941 was opened. It now occupied two-thirds of the space of the former two markets and an eight-storey office block had been built on the remainder of the site. During 1973 further major reconstruction was completed: there was now a first storey, and the corn merchants were moved from 'the floor' to a new suite of offices upstairs. The business of the vegetable, flower and herbage seed traders, having by now completely changed in character, was no longer in need of an Exchange as such at Mark Lane. Nevertheless, on most Mondays, these gentlemen may still be found 'attending' the Seething Lane Restaurant bar where you may meet them if you care to patronise this restaurant for a meal.

Mark Lane has been described as being, 'The main trading centre for all agricultural products . . . One of the most essential markets of Great Britain . . . For many years . . . the most important cereal market in the world', and we leave it in the knowledge that it is still where it started. Today, because they were also bombed out, the traders in Commodities have joined the Corn Trade in a building known as The Combined Commodity Trading Centre at Mark Lane. This modern building is owned by The Corn Exchange Company Ltd. which is a wholly-owned subsidiary of The British Land Company plc.

Provincial Corn Exchanges

Although there are earlier examples, it was mainly in the latter half of the 19th century that the tall, glass-roofed buildings called corn exchanges became a feature of many of our market towns. They had to be tall and glass-roofed because it was necessary to admit as much daylight as possible if the quality of malting barley and any defects in a sample of seed were to be correctly assessed before a price was offered.

The social and educational benefits which accrued from the necessity to attend the market and Corn Exchange are difficult to appreciate in today's age of advertising literature, the telephone, two-car families, radio, television and the computer. For the restricted narrowness of life experienced by a great many country dwellers was then such that their only chance to escape the daily routine of work and to hear something of the outside world was this visit to the nearest market town. Exchanges, as well as being the place to take your samples of corn, also provided an opportunity to meet the hay and straw buyers, representatives of the various seed firms, maltsters, seed potato merchants and the sellers of rope, sacks, oil and even insurance — and we think today that supermarkets are a modern idea! Here, a jostling throng 'edged and elbowed their way to and fro', in an attempt to find and to catch the eye of whichever merchant, firm's representative or farmer with whom they wished to do business. Once a potential buyer was engaged in conversation, the correct moment to produce the sample had to be judged, and was then withdrawn from one or other of a coat's capacious pockets. The sample was contained in either a stiff brown paper bag, a small linen sack or a canvas bag, whichever was most suitable for the type of seed. Then came an anxious moment, for the difference between a malting sample of barley, or a bread sample of wheat, and one which was only fit for livestock feed, might easily determine whether bills, often of long standing, could be paid or not.

At times the exchange became so crowded that the beadle was called upon to mount the rostrum, ring the bell, and announce that Mr. — would be grateful if Mr. — would meet him under the clock, or indicate where he was to be found. Geoffrey Browning Smith (E. Marriage and Sons, Colchester), when still a small boy in the 1930s, had attended the Exchange with his father. He remembers one terrifying occasion when he lost hold of his father's coat tails, was drawn away into the throng, and spent a very long time in finding him again.

Many merchants hired stands, which were part of the 'furniture' of the exchange. Others simply occupied a space on the floor, sometimes with their goods spread around them. (This latter practice was not allowed at Braintree.) Gradually these buildings became out-dated for the following reasons: the advent of the telephone allowed orders to be placed and enquiries made, without the necessity of attending the Exchange; the use of the combine harvester resulted in the thrashing operation being crowded into a mere four to six weeks, rather than being spread conveniently over much of the year; also the adoption of laboratory testing removed the mystique of biting through a kernel of barley or wheat to enable inspection of the cut surface for any 'steeliness' or lack of whiteness, in order to determine its suitability for malt or for bread. Today, a great many provincial corn exchanges have ceased to exist. They were closed with sad little ceremonies such as that which took place at Colchester in 1967 and of which the *Essex County Standard* reported on 2 June that the Colchester Corn Exchange, which had been opened in 1884, had been 'closed ceremoniously with a champagne party the previous Saturday, but the general mood was one of nostalgic sadness'.

Mr. Joe Percival, a farmer from Wakes Colne, vividly remembered that when he first attended this exchange in 1901, it was common for about a thousand people to be thronging this building. Then, as a final piece of nostalgia, the heavy brass bell, which had always been rung to open and close the exchange, was given to Mr. Harry Gray, the secretary of the Smallholders' Association, who for many years had performed this duty.

Building started on the Chelmsford Exchange in Tindal Square in 1856 and eventually, in 1969, it was pulled down to become part of a shopping precinct.

Of Braintree Corn Exchange, in 1964, Mr. Douglas Church is reported as saying,

> If I got here at 2.05 p.m. 20 years ago, I was late. Now, if I get here at 3.05 p.m. I am early. Trade is dead now in the exchange but it would be a calamity if the place were closed down. The farmer does not know how much of the truth he is being told when dealing with a representative outside.

This exchange was discontinued in about 1966.

RISKS TO THE SEED FROM BIRTH TO RE-BIRTH

The hazards that a seed may experience, even before it is gathered, sown, and germinates again to become a plant, are many and varied. The remarkable thing is that any, not to mention the required statutory percentage, arrive in seed sacks and packets in a satisfactory condition.

Each seed, down to the smallest fern spore, carries within it a fragile embryo living plant, just waiting for the opportunity to continue its life cycle. Seed storage is designed to hold this urge in abeyance, but at the same time to maintain a satisfactory standard of germination, until it is expected that the seed will be sown. Today, despite the research and technological literature which has been building up on the subject since about 1832, all the results are by no means understood or the questions answered. This is one of the many examples of a practical man doing the job who has by trial, error and instinct found the answer to a problem long before it has been scientifically proved. To appreciate this we have only to ponder the success of an Iron Age farmer's clay-pit grain store or the almost fail-safe method of cutting, drying and stacking seed under a well-thatched roof, thus preventing much pre-storage mechanical damage as well as giving unripe seeds a chance to mature within the protection of their hulls, chaff or glumes.

Nevertheless, 10 factors at least have been scientifically proven to have an influence on the storage potential of a seed.[5] These are its genetic make-up; the pre-harvest conditions that it has experienced; its composition and structure; whether or not it is a hard seed; its stage of maturity when harvested; and its size, dormancy, moisture content, vigour and any mechanical damage that it may have suffered.

Genetic make-up

Even within a closely-bred stock the genetic make-up of individual seeds may be as variable as children in a human family. For instance, some will age and be likely to die more quickly than others. Such seeds, if present as a large percentage of the bulk, will reduce the time that the consignment should be stored before being sown. This ageing process can vary from still being viable after 500 years to less than a year (especially under poor storage conditions). Harrington[6] quotes four kinds of seed that are known to have survived for a century and over: albizia, 147 years; cassia, 158 years; goodia, 105 years; and trifolium, 100 years. All are members of the *Leguminosea* family, noted for its ability to produce hard seeds, On the other hand peanuts, which are of the same ilk, are relatively short-lived. It is the Indian lotus (*Nelumbo nucifera*)[7] which holds the records for viable longevity. Estimates vary from 50,000 to 120 years. The likely period seems to be well over 500 years.

Egyptian tomb wheat — the Kelvedon Report (1981)

It is quite extraordinary how seed from Egyptian tombs continues to be reported viable after storage for over 2,000 years. At regular intervals this myth crops up somewhere in the world. Each time the 'fact' is headline news and is believed by many. Now, in Kelvedon, I find someone who knew someone who actually had some of this wheat — and it grew! The story, as told by Frank Siggers of Leapingwells Farms, is that it came from Carter's Seeds establishment, having been brought back from Egypt by the last James Carter, who was an archaeologist. Apparently, a son of one of Carter's representatives worked for Hurst's of Witham. This young man had some of this 'mummy' or 'tomb' wheat in a bottle. It was duly sown and grew, but is reported as having been 'no good for our climate and only yielded seven pounds'. Since all wheat so far found in tombs has been found to be completely carbonised it seems likely that, for a long time, the Egyptians have recognised a market for otherwise unsaleable varieties of their native wheat, such as *Triticum turgidum*, which together with their 'mummy pea' have been sold to gullible tourists as 'miracle seed from the tombs of the Pharaohs'. There are illustrations in a European herbal of 1590 which show a fasciated form of pea, similar to the 'mummy pea' now being sold. Perhaps they were on to a good thing even at that early date! We can let the matter rest with a statement from J. H. Turner of Kew Gardens:[8]

> It is popularly asserted that 'miracle wheat' and 'mummy peas' originated in Egyptian tombs and that such seeds germinate when sown, but in every instance the statements prove to be without foundation.

Pre-harvest considerations

Those wishing to store seeds have to take into account the experiences that the seed has undergone even before it was harvested. Rainfall, temperature (especially extremes), photoperiod, soil moisture and mineral nutrition all need to be considered. Seeds store best when they are mature, of normal size and weight, and are relatively free from mechanical injuries and adverse storage micro-organisms. Where a seed is produced (provenance) may also have some effect and, as all farmers and seedsmen know, the kind of weather just before and during harvest can make all the difference between profit and loss.

Composition

One example is that there may be difficulties connected with rancidity when a seed contains oil.

Structure

Hulls, chaff and glumes all help to protect seeds both by cushioning against mechanical damage and because of their inhibitory effect on mould growth. Today, the combine harvester removes these protective coverings at the time the crop is cut. Beans, which have large cotyledons, are structurally very vulnerable to mechanical damage especially when dry. Not only is the embryo liable to be jolted off the cotyledons, but this seed, like the onion, has a very poorly protected seed root. Therefore whether and how a seed is thrashed before storage, if its essential structures are well or badly protected, its size, shape and biochemistry will all have their effect.

Hard seeds

There is little information on the storage capacity of hard as against normal seeds. Nevertheless, many crop species can develop hard impermeable seed coats if produced or stored under certain environmental conditions. This leads to problems, particularly with the current requirement of 'once over germination', which demands that all seeds germinate at approximately the same time. In most cases it is also more than a nuisance if seeds, because of delayed germination, continue to come up in future years.

Maturity

Having reached its maximum dry weight a seed is generally considered to be mature. However, as many crop species flower, produce and mature their seeds over a period of days or even weeks, it is necessary to know how immature the particular seed can be before it is unable to ripen after it has been cut. Some seeds, such as wild oats, will ripen from a very immature stage, but pansies must be watched very carefully if they are not be picked too soon. To make matters worse there are differences even within a species and, with crops like carrot, parsnip and antirrhinum, the flower heads occur and produce seed on at least three different dates. When labour was relatively cheap and even today with antirrhinum, such crops were gone over two or three times — the first seed heads being kept separate either to be sold as quality seed or to be mixed with some of the later cuts to produce an acceptable sample. In this connection an Essex seedsman earned the nickname of 'Three-in-one, m'boys', because this was the order he always gave when he had some inferior seed of which to dispose. One hopes that he meant three parts of good seed and not the other way round!. Even so, we should not totally condemn this practice for it often meant that it enabled him to buy slightly less reliable seed from some smallholder, so saving him from financial ruin when the crop, upon which he was entirely dependent, had suffered damage.

Seed size
Little work has been done on seed size relative to storage but there are indications that, to some extent, small seeds are at a disadvantage.

Dormancy
Some or all seeds of many species are dormant at harvest. This causes problems for those who test seeds for germination. The cause may be due to any one, or a combination of factors. For instance, there may be a germination inhibitor or some other block present. Again, the physiology of the embryo or the structure of the seed can be the limiting factor. In this last case the seed coat, bracts, glumes, pericarp or membranes are all capable of limiting the exchange of water and gases necessary for germination.

Moisture content
Storage conditions, particularly those of temperature and moisture, can also maintain or break seed dormancy. Whether dormancy either lengthens or reduces a seed's life span there is, as yet, very little evidence. Probably life span is most influenced by moisture content. Certainly, mature and relatively dry seeds will remain in better condition, and will be less liable to mechanical damage or attack by moulds and other pests.

Vigour and viability
It often proves difficult to separate vigour and viability in storage experiments. Their decline is sometimes shown as a sigmoid curve which, provided that the seeds are dry and being stored under favourable conditions, may be divided into three sections. The first, the period of maximum seed vigour, ends when germination has fallen to between 90 and 75 per cent. This is followed by a rapid deterioration to a survival level of between 25 and 10 per cent after which the pace slows down until all the seeds are dead.

Mechanical damage
Whoever it was who first said of potatoes 'they are very easily damaged and should be handled as if they were eggs', might well have been advising upon the handling of seeds. Just dropping a sackful from a height onto a hard floor may sever the connection of the embryo from its food supply and cause cracks and bruises through which moulds and fungi can gain easy access, or the primary roots or shoots may be damaged, resulting in crippled seedlings. Today, the many mechanical devices through which a seed has to pass all take their toll as each one, large, small, ripe and unripe, hurtles its way through combine harvester, dresser, grader and elevator, suffering impaction at every drop and bend or being

cracked or squashed by a wrongly set drum. Sometimes, to assist germination, seeds are scarified or rubbed down: their storage life is thereby shortened.

In-store considerations

Once grown, cut, thrashed, dried and cleaned, seeds may be held in a number of ways until required for sowing or manufacture. It all depends upon the purpose for which they are to be used; where they are going; the hazards likely to be encountered on the way and the length of time before they are expected to be used.

Apart from attending to such mundane matters as seeing that no water is entering the store, that before use all bins, sacks and bags are clean and fumigated, that electric points are spark proof and wiring is not being chewed by rats or mice, a constant watch must be maintained for infestations of insects, fungi, birds, rodents and the tell-tale smell of heating in bin, bag or sack. Sometimes, even when seeds have apparently been dried sufficiently, after a few weeks in store they will begin to heat because they had dried too rapidly, and although their outside coats were dry enough, there was still too much moisture within.

Where a farm has good storage facilities, seed will probably be purchased during the winter and stored for sowing the following spring. This usually provides a useful discount on the buying price, as well as having the seed ready to hand when conditions for drilling are right. This practice not only provides a merchant with ready cash at a time of year when he is likely to be in need but it also relieves congestion in his store and delivery problems in the spring.

Again, both farmer and merchant may hold seed in store for more than one season. A good harvest often produces a glut and a consequent fall in price. It may pay to keep the seed in the hope that in the next season there will not be so much on offer. This is one of the many gambles which the seedsman is forced to take and it often happens that there are one or two good seasons in a row. In this case he will have incurred the cost of storage and still only be able to sell his goods on the relatively cheap manufacturing market for oil, bird seed, or food for livestock.

Because warehouse space fills up rapidly after harvest, particularly if the season has been wet, merchants will usually offer an increase on purchase price to growers who will dry, clean (at least partially), and store their crop until a later date.

To be able to satisfy his customers' requirements a seed merchant is wise to hold over a supply of those seeds which will remain viable for longer than one year. Otherwise he will find himself short of supply and he will have to buy in at an enhanced price if a bad harvest has resulted in his contracts with growers not having been fulfilled.

Environmental conditions which can have a marked effect upon a seed's life span include temperature, both above and below freezing; seed moisture content; the relative humidity of the atmosphere; and the inter-relationship of temperature, seed moisture content and storage life. There are also the possibilities of vacuum and gas storage, the effect of light and the speed or slowness of the seed's respiration. Furthermore these conditions may be altered by an inter-relationship with such factors as bio-chemical changes which occur as a seed deteriorates. This varies with the type of seed. Again, the seed may have been dressed with an insecticide or fungicide, perhaps both, which are having an effect.

Transport, even when still within Great Britain, can cause problems. Container lorries or rail trucks may not be waterproof, or may be left too long in the hot sun causing their contents to overheat. When travelling by ship or plane, to or from countries abroad, the problems are further increased. Even when the consignment arrives at the dock a seed merchant worth his salt will have his man there to see that his lot is not mistaken for a manufacturing one and is being sucked through conveyors at too high a speed, which would bruise the seed and so endanger germination.

84. 'A seed merchant worth his salt will have a man at the dock to see that his consignment is carefully handled.'

Retail storage is seldom ideal, although new types of seed packets have now greatly improved shelf life. If they are to be kept in a hot and humid climate, seeds must first be dried to between five and eight per cent moisture and then enclosed in packages with a moisture barrier.

With the increasing refinements of plant breeding there is a necessity for the storage of small quantities of various cultivars. Seed Banks already exist in various parts of the world, and are established in this country at such centres as Wellesbourne Vegetable Research Station, The National Institute of Agricultural Botany, and The Bush E. Pedigree Sugar Beet Breeding Station at Woodham Walter, Essex.

Packaging

Packaging methods and the kind of containers used also have their effect upon the life of the seeds. Packaging methods vary from the use of a spoon, seed scoop, or 'thimble', to a manually controlled gravity flow from bin to container, through to high-speed, automatically-controlled fillers of small packets. Packages may be of burlap, cotton, paper or film plastic and there are foil bags, metal or fibreboard cans and drums, glass jars or fibreboard boxes, and containers made from various combinations of these materials.

During the mid-1920s equipment was developed for placing seeds within a roll of tape ('seed-tapes'). The idea did not become popular at the time and a revival of interest in 1979 has suffered a similar fate.

To meet the requirements of precision drills, seeds are sometimes enclosed in a coat of inert material to bring them all to a prescribed size. Sometimes the opportunity is taken to incorporate some fertiliser and/or a seed dressing into this coating and this under adverse conditions may impair germination. It should be borne in mind that seeds so coated are likely to be more successful in the hands of the professional rather than the amateur grower.

Chapter Ten

The Effect of Location

After Great Britain's population rose to the extent that it could no longer be adequately fed from the produce of its farms, increasing quantities of grain, both cheap and free of import duty, was brought into this country. Concurrently, for a while, our home-grown acreage of corn considerably decreased. Therefore, those millers and maltsters whose premises were situated inland, or were inconveniently placed for, or far from, a well-metalled road, railway or port, then had difficulty in obtaining supplies of grain with which to carry on their businesses. Some met this situation by diversifying their trade and, to a greater or lesser degree, have become agricultural merchants supplying a range of goods, including farm seeds.

Both these trades have always taken a lively interest in finding out which varieties of cereal seeds are most suitable for their purpose, for there are sharp distinctions between those wheats that are sought for bread-making and those which are best for biscuits. Again, very different malts may be obtained from different varieties of barley and even from two samples of the same variety grown under different conditions. Consequently, these trades have always had close connections with both seed merchants and growers.

Three millers and one maltster have been chosen as examples of the way in which, especially because of differences in location, their businesses have responded to, or have been limited by, the changes in water, rail and road transport and particularly for the movement of grain for sowing, malt, grist or flour. (The histories of these firms have in one form or another appeared in print: the most recent a book by Mr. Norman Pertwee, entitled *Not Roses All the Way*. E. Marriage and Son Ltd. brought out *The Annals of One Hundred Years of Flour Milling — 1840 to 1940*, Hasler, of Dunmow, their centenary publication entitled *A Hundred Years of Agricultural Trading*, and an account of the seed trade carried on by Brooks of Mistley has appeared in the magazine of the Country Gentleman's Association for August 1958. All are interesting and informative documents.)

Until the railways came there was no real rival to water for the transport of such goods, since to send them by road over long distances was formerly both slow and expensive. For several centuries ships with evocative names such as barque, brigantine, sloop, cutter, hoy, coaster, barge and square-rigger have sailed up and down the Rivers Stour, Colne, Blackwater, Crouch and Thames. These rivers and some smaller inlets were once navigable for far greater distances than today. All have a wide and long tidal estuary, are unbridged for several miles inland and have along their banks a heterogeneous collection of small ports, inlets, jetties, wharves, quays and hards at all of which goods were once picked up and delivered. Not all deliveries were within the law. Up these creeks, on a moonless night, many a cask of brandy or bale of silk has been 'slipped in'. In such places as Tollesbury, Tolleshunt D'Arcy and Goldhanger there are still tales of one-time underground passages from cellars to the water.

With some overlapping, and changes due to the development of the boats built in each period, this shipping may be divided into three categories: transport up-river, above tidal water and including canals; transport down-river, in tidal water to the sea; and sea-going transport, coastal, cross-Channel and ocean-going. The upstream traffic was used, more or less exclusively, for work above the highest port on the river's tidal water. The boats were small sailing craft able to pass under bridges or barges and lighters towed by a horse on a tow-path either singly or in gangs of two. These barges were built smaller than the Thames barges, perhaps 47 feet long with a 10 ft. 9 in. beam, to carry 25 tons and to draw 2 ft. 9 in. of water. Up-stream cargoes included agricultural seeds; coal for a gasworks or a foundry, for domestic use or to stoke the engine of the thrashing tackle, or clover huller when it came to a farm to 'do some stacks'; loads of chalk; chemical and organic fertilisers; pig-iron; oil cake for cattle; tallow for candles; and ragstone to mend the roads. These were all taken up rivers and canals to fulfil orders from customers with access to their banks. On the return journey, these boats carried all kinds of agricultural produce, machinery, castings, leather, chalk, bricks, wool, velvet and other cloths. Once delivered to points downstream, these goods were either distributed overland, used for manufacture at the point of delivery or trans-shipped from the tidal port to points along the coast, across the Channel or even across the oceans of the world.

On the tidal reaches, a variety of craft are still in use. Some are for hire from the ship owners, others are the property of individual companies. Generally speaking, they are all relatively small boats of shallow draft which ply up and down the estuaries. A few creep round the coast to London but seldom go to the open sea, although they are not afraid to do so when called upon for a little job such as the evacuation of Dunkirk. These boats once served every little hard and jetty and glided in and out of small inlets to tiny quays, which were once the lifelines of coastal farms, villages and hamlets. 'Nearly 100 places in East Essex had quays during the Elizabethan period and in 1630 it was stated that the majority of the Dengie farmers sent their corn to London by sea rather than to the country markets'.[1]

As late as the 1920s, three small barges were built especially for this work on the rivers Orwell and Stour. They were the *Muriel*, the *Alice* and the *Cygnet*, of 23, 22 and 16 tons respectively. All three were able to 'get to any farm where it was wet' and some said that 'the *Cygnet* could go anywhere after a heavy dew'.[2] (Lieutenant Colonel C. A. Brooks believed that the *Cygnet* was built earlier and was trading before 1914.)

These river craft are also in use for the partial or complete unloading of ships carrying heavy cargoes such as grain and seed and which have too great a draft to sail up-river to the port. For instance, a square-rigger, carrying loose barley, would sometimes anchor in the tideway at a sheltered spot a little up-river, to be bagged and off-loaded there, although most of the barley was brought round from the London docks by smaller ships and barges.

Sea-going transport

For a county with so many miles of coastline, it is remarkable that, in Essex, Harwich is the only sea port of any size. Nevertheless, barges and small ships once traded in considerable numbers all along its coast which is both protected and made hazardous by long lines of parallel sandbanks interspersed with navigation channels which are often narrow, and may dry out at low water.

On the Essex coast the Thames barges of this era were swim-headed, square-sterned, generally cutter-rigged and with lee boards. They were 50 to 60 feet long, 16 to 18 feet wide and carried 40 to 50 tons. The addition of spritsails was only just coming into use and the route to London was via Havengore creek to a channel through the Maplin Sands which led to the Thames estuary. These barges were therefore able to reach London without having to leave the coast for the open sea. This channel no longer exists.

Barge racing came about through a naturally competitive spirit among the skippers which was fanned by a very real need to augment the extremely low wages of those days. Races for and with cargoes took place between rival barges from Essex and Kent. Between 1801 and 1908 Thames barge matches became a regularly organised event and more than anything else may be said to have led to improvements in design and handling capabilities of these most functional, beautiful and dignified trading ships.

The ratio of a barge's length to beam began to be increased early in the 19th century and finally it reached a near ideal ratio (for trading) of 82 to 84 feet by 18 to 20 feet. Above this, although possibly better for racing, it was not so suitable for carrying goods. During the 1880s-90s, some barges were built entirely of iron or with iron beams and carlings. It was an attempt to give added strength but was not a success.

Because of seasonal differences in harvesting between such places as Australia, the Argentine, Iraq, Morocco, the United States of America and Canada, there was a continual movement of imported grains throughout the year, but the movement of home-grown grains tended to slacken off after early summer. It was then that the barges had time to pick up the produce of the coastal and marshland farms; they called at little jetties, hards, quays and even picked up directly over the sea wall. For the return journey the boats filled up with coal, stable manure, starfish or sprats for manure, Kentish ragstone to mend walls, and a year's supply of essential groceries such as sugar, salt, currants, raisins and possibly some flour. Where it was an economic proposition there would be a jetty but, more often, there was a hard to which barges drew up and waited until the tide had receded sufficiently for them to settle on the bottom when, most conveniently, their deck was at much the same height as a farm wagon. Associated with the hard there is often an especially constructed hatch in the sea wall from which stout, horizontally-slotted boards can be removed to allow a passage at low tide. Otherwise, it was a matter of taking the goods straight over the wall. I am indebted to Mr. Douglas Joslin, one time farm bailiff of Sandbeach, Dengie, for a description of how this was managed in a part of the Dengie peninsula where the coast is protected by saltings which extend for some half a mile out to sea, and the only approach for a barge is up a land-drainage outfall. The barge was turned by hand at the seaward edge of the saltings so that its stern faced the sea wall end of the outfall. It was then winched up stern first to as near to the wall as it was possible. A long, stout board was then placed across the gap from the top of the wall to the deck of the barge. Carts, tumbrils or wagons, whichever was most convenient, were then brought to the wall to load or unload. If they were full of trussed hay, men at the wall would carry two half-hundredweight trusses at a time up the wall and across the plank to the deck to be stowed in the hold or elsewhere. (A one-inch leather strap with a 'ringel' at one end was used to hold the trusses together. The method was to put one truss on top of the other, pass the strap round both and through the 'ringel', make it fast and then use what remained of the strap to make a sort of attache-case handle. The men worked in pairs. The one who had just unloaded gave the second man a lift of the trusses onto his shoulder and then prepared his own load ready for the return of his partner.)

Walking the plank was an art, for its 'whip', if wrongly judged, could easily catapult transporter and goods into the water or thick ooze below. It is said that many an old score was wiped off by someone jumping on the plank when the loader was half way across! Mr. Herbert Yeldham, farm bailiff at Holiwell Farm, Burnham-on-Crouch, can remember that there was once a hatch in the sea wall at Holiwell Point through which corn, hay, straw and sugar beet were despatched. Also, that at Coney Hall sugar beet was carted in skeps, over the wall and via a plank to a barge which had come up alongside (no doubt destined for the Cantley factory in Norfolk).

At ports such as Mistley and Maldon planks were often used because they needed far less adjustment as the boats rose or fell on the tide. The 'lumpers' as the men were called took the sacks on their backs from the wagon, trotted up the plank in time with the 'whip' and then either slid the sack down a chute into the hold to be stowed, or if the shipment was in bulk, released the tie at the neck of the sack allowing the grain to pour down from shoulder height.

Cargoes of beans, wheat, maize and barley, in that descending order, were the most economical freights. Malt and oats, because they are more bulky, fill up the barge before its dead-weight capacity has been reached and therefore the charges per quarter or ton were higher.

The men were paid 1s. 6d. a ton for loading over the sea wall. Where access to the barge was direct from a quay (as at Bradwell-on-Sea and Holiwell) the payment was reduced to 1s. 3d. a ton. It is claimed that the height of the Thames barge trade was reached in 1898, and that by 1930 the numbers of working barges had fallen to approximately 1,100, which by 1939 had dwindled to 600 and that these had virtually ceased to work by 1950.

True or false?

There is a story which crops up so frequently along the Essex Blackwater that one feels that it must have some firm foundation. With minor variations it asserts that because the barge skippers from Maldon, Tollesbury, Brightlingsea, Bradwell-on-Sea and Burnham-on-Crouch carried wheat to London at a time when the plague was rampant they were rewarded by a remission of port dues on grain for evermore.

Despite research in various quarters I have been unable to obtain any verification of the facts but it is perhaps significant that no-one, not even the Customs and Excise Authorities at Maldon or London, has said that it was untrue. Former skippers from Mistley tell much the same tale, but add that not many people know about it. It would be nice to know if anyone ever finds out the truth.

Brooks of Mistley

The almost racial division between Suffolk and Essex occurs between the north and south banks of the river Stour. In the early 18th century the opening up of this river for at least as far inland as Sudbury (and it may once have been navigable to the village of Clare or even beyond) gave access to a considerable inland trade between points upstream as well as downstream to and from the tidal port of Mistley. This two-way trade around the coast and into other rivers was of great interest to Edward and Francis Norman who, by the end of the 18th century, were the owners of a fleet of sizeable ships including the brigantine *Iris* of 92 tons, the *Lark*, a cutter of 83 tons, a schooner of 85 tons, the *Good Intent*, and the sloop *Traveller*, all of which were in use to transport goods for their thriving business as maltsters and grain merchants at Mistley. It was with this firm that William Brooks, the son of a local farmer, took employment in 1799 and from it developed the family firm which, from 1862 for over a century, was known as Brooks (Mistley) and which earned the respect and trust of farmers and seed growers in the Tendring Hundred of Essex, over the river on the sands of Suffolk, and beyond.

This firm was early to specialise in seed corn and it was brought to them by both land and water. By horse-drawn wagon barley sent from Suffolk could take two days to arrive by road. In times when a farm labourer seldom left his own village this was looked upon as a perilous journey, and Mr. C. N. Brooks (b. 1856) told his son that as the drivers of carts and wagons crossed the centre of Cattawade Bridge — and so left Suffolk for Essex — they would turn round in their seats to look back, wave their whips and shout 'Goodbye old England — I'm goin' foreign — I may never see you n'more'! (This story is corroborated quite independently in the letters of the artist, John Constable.) Memories passed down in local families claim that in the early 19th century a queue of wagons and carts, some

85. Mistley Quay, showing Brooks's mills after 1929.

quarter of a mile in length, was on occasion to be seen waiting to discharge its grain at the quayside maltings and granaries, for use or to await despatch by sea to London.

Along the half-mile quay, sometimes there was hardly a berth to be had and the congestion was such that barges had to lie two and three abreast. Even as late as the 1930s, Frank Ainger, the mill foreman at Brooks', remembers that over 100 barge freights came to their quay in a 12-month period and that on one occasion nine barges came up on one tide.

In the early 1800s Mistley was undoubtedly a busy little port. By 1817 there were 36 barges working up and down to Sudbury. It was a trip of 26 miles and took a day and a half (depending on the state of wind and tide at Brantham) to negotiate the 15 locks and to ferry the horse, standing on a platform in the bows of the leading barge, across the river every time the tow-path changed from one bank to the other. This happened 33 times on this stretch. The day's work had not then finished, of course, until the horse had been groomed, fed, watered and bedded down for the night. Downstream, where the tow-path finished at Brantham, the 'gangs' had to complete their journey to Mistley by other means. Given a favourable wind (not a usual occurrence), skipper and mate would rig up some sort of sail, light their pipes and complete the journey at ease but more often it was a case of 'poking' the boats or barges, by means of long poles, the one and a half miles to Mistley, which under unfavourable conditions of wind and tide, especially on the upstream journey, could require the efforts of five able-bodied men. Even on arrival at Mistley quay, the unfortunate mate-cum-horseman had to tramp the two and a half miles by road back to Brantham to see to his horses and to be back at Mistley quay in time to start work the following day. When it is realised that the volume of trade between Mistley and Sudbury amounted to between 60,000 and 70,000 tons annually before 1848, it can be appreciated that these men worked hard and for many hours each day.

From 1840 the railway began to extend from London into Essex, after which date both main and branch lines of the various companies sprouted out in all directions. In Essex the rail goods traffic was very largely confined to the movement of agricultural goods and so when one line reached Sudbury in 1854 and another passed Brooks' maltings, granaries and coal yard on its way to Harwich, the up-river transport was doomed to decline. This decline was serious by 1900; in 1916, the last trading barge is said to have negotiated the whole stretch and, after 1930, none passed through Dedham Lock. After this time, therefore, no more seed-corn or other goods from Brooks travelled by water to their customers on the upstream reaches of the river Stour. A similar story may be repeated for the upstream goods transport on most rivers during this period.

William Brooks's son, another William, followed his father into the Norman's firm and became its manager. Then, when the last Mr. Norman died in 1862, he left the goodwill of the business to William Brooks (b. 1813). The remarkable collection of grain and seed samples which has been built up by this firm dates from that time. Among many more it contains the first sample of Chevallier barley that was handled by this firm. It was from the 1830 crop and, for malting purposes, proved to be a great advance on any other barley then known.

At the Great Exhibition held in Hyde Park in 1851, Brooks exhibited a sample of barley from a crop grown by Robert Mason of Brightlingsea Hall. It had a bushel weight of 53¾ pounds and had been purchased for 29s. a quarter (72s. 5d. a hundredweight). During the Festival of Britain in 1951 this same sample was exhibited at the Victoria and Albert Museum and it was the only item of its type to have been exhibited 100 years earlier.

As the 19th century progressed, Brooks' interest in grain for seed increased and one crop of Hallett's Pedigree barley, grown in 1873, was exported to India for seed purposes. They also produced one of the first commercial crops of Plumage Archer barley, a variety introduced in 1905, which later became very popular. This crop, grown on their own farms, yielded 12¾ sacks an acre, and was exported to Chile for seed. An outstanding crop of white clover seed grown in 1911 made the then large sum of £5 a bushel. This firm also branched out to sell animal feeding stuffs such as the well-remembered Brooks' cow cubes, as well as other agricultural requirements.

Between 1888 and 1925 a number of family deaths gave rise to the formation of a private limited company in 1927. At this same time the amount of land farmed, some 1,000 acres, was reduced and the capital so released was used to finance an extensive development of the firm's seed-cleaning plants. It was fortunate that at the outbreak of the Second World War a new seed granary had just been completed. Even during the war it is evident that Brooks' kept up the standard of seeds that were sold for, in 1944, a sample from a crop of barley grown from their seed won the championship in the Red Cross National Exhibition against barleys from all over the country. Many successes have also been achieved with samples entered at the Royal Winter Fair at Toronto, Canada. These include, for rye: a World Championship, a Reserve World Championship and two other awards; for peas: a Reserve Championship and a Second Prize; for barley, rape and red clover seed: four prizes; for wheat: a winter wheat Championship, three winter wheat Reserve Championships and, in 1957, the most resounding triumph of all, the Supreme Championship of the World, with a sample of the variety 'Capelle Desprez'. During the 29 years of this international competition this trophy had never before left Canada.

For family reasons, the equity of this business was sold in 1962 to Ranks Ltd., the large flour millers. Almost at once, Ranks merged with Hovis McDougall to form, with Hasler's of Dunmow and several similar businesses from all over Britain, the organisation known as Rank Hovis McDougall Ltd. (R.H.M.). It was announced in August 1983 that agreement in principle had been reached for the sale by R.H.M. of all the companies owned by R.H.M. (Agriculture) Ltd. to Dalgety Ltd.

Recent improvements have helped the port of Mistley to remain viable. A few years ago, Brooks' sold their maltings, mill and quay (by then too shallow for modern shipping) and new warehouses have been built on this site. Another part of the quay has been deepened and trade figures for the port over the last quarter century show a healthy expansion. It follows that the firm of Brooks, now under the Dalgety Ltd. umbrella, is particularly well-placed for moving goods by water, rail and, as nearby improvements continue, by road.

E. Marriage and Son Ltd., East Mill, Colchester

Apart from difficulties that arose from changes in transportation, once engine-driven rollers had been invented and installed, either to supplement or replace water or wind-powered stones for the milling of grain to flour, this process and that of the baking of bread gradually concentrated itself amongst fewer and fewer individuals. (In England, the first completely automatic roller mill was installed by Messrs. McDougall of Manchester in 1879. By 1878 two sets of roller mills and a centrifugal dressing machine had already been added to the equipment at East Mill, Colchester — presumably they were not fully automated.) For instance, the late Harold S. Wyncoll of E. Marriage and Son Ltd. told me that in the late 1920s his work, on every Tuesday, was to visit 27 bakers in Colchester. He sold them flour and, for their van-horses, oats, hay and sometimes straw. On his return to the firm's office, if he had not done business with at least 22 of the 27, he recalled, with a chuckle, that 'there was a raspberry from the Guv'nor!' and that 'by 1979 not more than four of these bakers were in existence'.

On the whole, it was the small mills with insufficient capital and little or no opportunity to branch out into lines other than flour who were forced out of business. This shortage of capital was seldom due to any fault of their own. In times of depression such as followed the wars against Napoleon, the Boers, and in 1914, Germany, corn merchants often found it necessary to supply their farming customers with such essential items as seed corn and animal feeds, with no hope of payment until the crop or the animals had been sold at, it was hoped, a realistic profit. It was a vicious circle, in which farmer and corn merchant sank or swam together, their capital reserves dwindling with each successive year of depression. In fact, during the 10 years before 1890, 'some 3,000 small mills throughout the country had . . . been closed and all but one of the ten or twelve windmills that formerly existed in Colchester had disappeared'.[3]

Other millers, more favourably placed, managed to continue in business by making use of every opportunity, however small, to expand and modernise and/or to develop along new channels such as the provision of coal, balanced rations for livestock, fertilisers, sprays and dusts to combat pests, products for health food stores and to a greater or lesser degree becoming suppliers of seeds of cereals, pulses, grasses and clovers. In so doing these millers, in their new role as agricultural merchants, became an arm of the seed trade.

The Marriage family came to Essex as French Huguenot refugees and when, in 1647, the religious denomination then known as Quakers came into being, Francis Marriage, a farmer in Stebbing, became the first of the name to be known as a Friend. It was his great-great-grandson, Edward Marriage who, in 1840, bought East Mill, Colchester.

A mill is first recorded on the site which is reputed to be that of East Mill, in *Little Domesday Book*, which covers Essex, Suffolk and Norfolk. At that time it belonged to Leflet

86. Edward Marriage, the founder.

87. East Mill, 1840, a timber-framed brick building with weather-boarding to the eaves.

or Leofleda, apparently a Saxon lady of some financial substance. Situated upstream of the bridge which carries East Road over the river and out of Colchester, East Mill is some one and a half miles above the Hythe Quay, both of which facts were to have a considerable effect upon its future.

Before adequate road-drainage and surfacing became commonplace, Essex, with its large areas of sticky clay soil, presented all travellers, and particularly those moving heavy goods, with roads which became a morass in wet weather and deep, hard-baked ruts and a cloud of dust when they were dry.

These were some of the problems faced by the horse-drawn traffic which brought corn and other supplies to East Mill. Loads of up to 10 quarters of wheat can be drawn by two

88. Horse-drawn road wagons taking wheat to Marriage's mill.

cart-horses and, unless it was a small consignment, the sacks of corn were usually sent from the farms in one or more low, stoutly built, four-wheeled wagons, with a piece of sailcloth tucked in somewhere to cover the load if it rained. On arrival the sacks were hoisted up to the corn-floor of the mill. Between 1846 and 1866, a branch line was extended from Colchester North railway station to follow the bank of the river Colne, to a station at the Hythe and on to another in the St Botolph's district of the town, as well as from the Hythe to Wivenhoe and Brightlingsea. Unfortunately, this railway was not built close enough to East Mill to allow a convenient siding for the mill's use and so any goods sent by rail had to be fetched or taken by horse and cart to the station or transferred to or from a lighter at the Hythe. Therefore, although the River Colne was once navigable to well upstream of East Mill, during the whole of its occupation by the Marriage family transport has become increasingly difficult.

When Edward Marriage purchased his mill in 1840, the channel between the mill and the harbour was in such a deplorable state that only very small boats and lighters were able to come up even as far as East Road bridge. However, as the result of considerable efforts by Edward Marriage and the co-operation of a few other interested parties with establishments on this reach of the river, permission was obtained for the river bed to be improved from the Hythe Quay to East Mill and in 1865 the barge *William and Mary* was able to come up and under the bridge to the mill. On arrival the barge crew had to bag up and weigh the loose grain in the hold before it was hoisted into the mill by chain and winch. This method was improved upon by the turn of the century with the installation of a mechanical bucket elevator, and again in 1927 by a pneumatic grain discharger. Storage was also increased to keep pace with greater output from the mill.

The River Colne Improvement Scheme, which in 1882 straightened and widened the passage from Hythe Quay to East Mill, further improved the facilities by affording a free passage for the bigger sea-going barges, a large number of which were then coming to East Mill.

One might have thought that this mill's transport difficulties had then been solved. However, already by 1897, steam propulsion had been introduced and was replacing sail. To meet this change, in 1905 the Marriages acquired a property at Felixstowe Docks, where they built one of the best equipped mills for its capacity in the country.

By 1908, mechanical road transport began to replace the score or more of fine draught horses at East Mill. As more and more goods began to come in by road, those mills which had been built to serve a local need found themselves having to expand to cover a much wider area and, in many cases such as at East Mill, the extensions which were needed had to be sited where there was room, rather than in the most convenient place. Again, not only did road and rail transport replace barges, but barges became obsolete as they were replaced by motor-propelled craft which, as these grew larger, were unable to come far up-river. East Mill, in company with many others at this time, then found itself with buildings for the reception and despatch of goods which were back to front!

In 1913 and 1914 this firm had the M.V.s *The Miller* and *Flacon* built for their use. These were replaced in 1932 and 1934 by even better M.V.s — another *The Miller* and *Golden Grain*. There also exists a photograph of a beautiful sailing boat. It was taken on 1 January 1949; the boat was built for the company by the exceptional firm of Messrs. Cann of Harwich and is appropriately named 'Leofleda'.

Mr. Wyncoll told me that the transport cost of freight by water from Mersea to Colchester was, in 1908, 6d. a quarter for a load of 300 quarters (i.e. 504 pounds at 2s. 3d. or 11p for each ton).

Throughout their years at East Mill the Marriages met the challenge of difficult times by expanding their capacity for milling and storage; by taking advantage of educational foreign travel, the introduction of well-chosen modern machinery and equipment, and the setting-up of a fine laboratory and experimental baking department. There has been some diversification such as the provision of balanced rations for every kind of livestock from a pack of foxhounds to a goldfish, but essentially they have remained millers whose bread and biscuit flours are well-liked by their customers.

Nevertheless, in 1970, transport difficulties caused by the irremediable restraints of the location of this mill finally resulted in the sale of this property for conversion to an hotel. East Mill's milling business was then transferred to the Felixstowe Dock mill, which was enlarged to enable full use to be made of its excellent road and port facilities.

Frank Pertwee and Sons Ltd., Harbour House, Hythe Quay, Colchester
After the massacre on the eve of the feast of St Bartholomew in 1572, the Huguenot family

89. East Mills, 1890.

90. East Mills, 1940, after the installation of a provender mill.

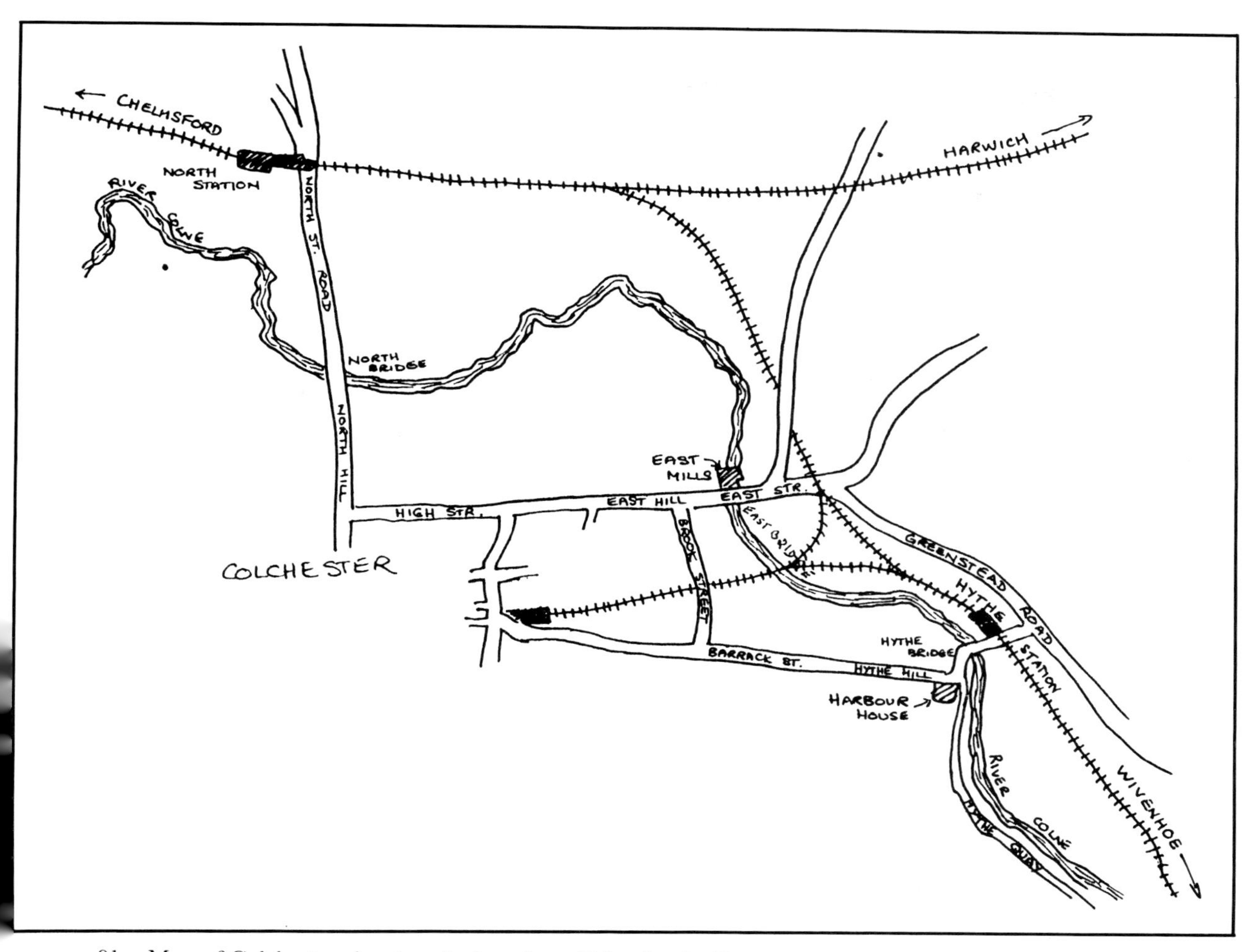

91. Map of Colchester showing the location of Marriage's (East Mills) and Pertwee's (Harbour House) establishments.

of Pertwee somehow escaped to England and for many generations they farmed in the Colchester area. Towards the end of the 19th century Frank Pertwee, in company with many others whose livelihood depended on the sale of corn, was looking for other ways to make an income. At the same time, there was a growing tendency for mills to concentrate at ports through which consignments of foreign grains were coming into this country.

A mill came up for sale at Hythe Quay, Colchester; Frank Pertwee saw the opportunity that this offered, bought the property and in 1899 started to trade in corn. So began the family's many-faceted business which includes a well-known agricultural seeds division known as 'Perseed'.

Even well downstream in the River Colne silting and bridges have continuously caused problems to shipping. Despite this, from quite early times a varied export and import trade has been maintained at Colchester hythe.[4] It is believed that the Saxon haven was lower down the river, at what should be called Old Hythe but which has been corrupted to Old Heath. The creek which served this haven was still recognisable as late as the 17th century but, by 1276, the present harbour was referred to, in Court Rolls, as the New Hythe (A.S. *Hetha*).

Attempts to improve the channel continued throughout the 18th and 19th centuries. During the 19th century various engineering schemes were put forward for the improvement of both channel and port. Of these the most daring was that of 1842. It proposed that the river should be straightened and deepened right up to the main railway station, that a dock of 11 acres be constructed to accommodate 100 vessels at the Hythe, from which a canal should be cut through to a lock at Wivenhoe. As is so often the case with far-sighted long-term projects, the schemes were not received with any great enthusiasm. The harbour commissioners were much more concerned with keeping down harbour dues than spending large sums on long-term improvements.

However, during the 19th century, previous Acts of Parliament relating to the port of Colchester were repealed and replaced by a new Act. This provided for both the upkeep of the river and for the roads that lead to it, which were to be paved and lit. Then, when the owner of East Mill, Mr. Wilson Marriage, pointed out to the Town Council that from 1865 to 1879 the harbour dues had fallen from £1,068 to £514; and that vessels with a draft of only eight to nine feet sometimes took up to seven days to sail between Wivenhoe and Hythe Quay; that the *Pilot*, from Hull, was stranded midway between Wivenhoe and New Quay on Christmas Day 1879, until 30 December, and the *Jane* from Grangemouth in 1880, although it arrived at Wivenhoe on 3 January, and despite transferring some freight to a lighter, was forced to delay there until 11 January before there was enough water to take her up. The complaint had an effect and on 13 July 1890, the first meeting of the Town Council's Harbour Committee took place under the chairmanship of the Port Reeve, Mr. Wilson Marriage.

Therefore when Frank Pertwee started his business, the transport position was that both road and rail were seriously competing with the port but, with the Town Council now taking a direct interest in its economy, there was hope for improvement in water transport.

As the century advanced other industries began to gather in the vicinity. Both World Wars increased coastal traffic and, although the Hythe was twice bombed in 1940 and seriously flooded in 1953, the Council's, by then, firmly-established policy was to keep the harbour in good working order and also to improve the port. Today, dredging during the summer removes mud deposits so as to allow a vessel drawing 11 feet of water to come up at high water during spring tides. The port is also provided with a radio system and, during peak periods of night tides, the river is lighted from Wivenhoe to the Hythe. The result is that over the last 20 years its trade has doubled, the link with the main rail line continues from Hythe station, access roads to the port are gradually being improved, and after a modest start and some setbacks the Pertwees' business has continued to expand.

A glance through their records reveals that, since Frank's son, Norman, entered the firm in 1924, various other members and relations of the family have followed suit and in 1956, when Frank's grandson, Christopher, joined the staff, there were three generations of the family working for their firm at the same time. Motor transport began with the purchase of a lorry in 1923, to be followed by eight-ton and then ten-ton lorries as the barge fleets were superceded by modern road and river transport. The one-hundredweight sack was introduced by this firm in 1944 and by 1953 their fleet of lorries had been fitted with hydraulic loaders. Bulk handling began with the purchase of a grain tanker in 1956 and, to provide greater port facilities and merchandise for this transport, from 1935 onwards there has been a steady acquisition of nearby premises for storage, seed cleaning, testing, drying and when, in 1949, Harbour House was purchased for conversion to office accommodation, it may be said that their large expansion programme had begun.

It is not generally appreciated that today this country is in a position both to export home-grown grain and to import grain from other countries. Norman Pertwee says that in 1971, when he was President of the National Association of Corn and Agricultural Merchants, Great Britain's grain harvest reached a record of 15 million tons, and that only 12 years later, when his son Christopher held this position, the record had risen to almost 22 million tons. What other industry can match this for increased productivity? Furthermore, it is claimed that because of the county's sunny climate, Essex produces seed wheat so full of starch, and therefore able to be a good mother, that germination can be about a week earlier and harvest some seven to 10 days earlier than crops grown from seed produced in counties further north. It has to be admitted, however, that the best wheats for gluten content generally come from Lincolnshire.

This firm found it necessary to appoint an export manager in 1946 and by 1954 was able to load its first seed directly into ships from its premised on Hythe Quay. These freights were being sent to Ireland, France, Belgium, Germany, Denmark and Finland. 1955 shows their first dollar sales to America and Canada and, during 1961/2, 20 shiploads of seed corn were despatched to France and Germany and in the 1980s the firm makes use of small merchant ships of 300 to 1,000 tons now plying between Colchester and ports in Germany, Belgium and Holland.

The Pertwees do not breed or select varieties of corn but have proved themselves very successful promoters of new and promising varieties. The growing crops are all inspected by their trained representatives and then sold to the wholesale trade. It was from their seed that R. & W. Proctor, of St Lawrence Hall in St Lawrence, won a First Prize and Reserve World Championship at the Toronto Fair of 1963. The firm has also pioneered such innovations as 'Operation Airdrill', in the terribly wet season of 1960-61; the 'Mini-Bulk' (one ton) fertiliser bags, and a spreading service for customers for which they made a machine — the Landforce Spreader — which won an award at the Royal Show of 1978. They have diversified and when Norman Pertwee retired from chairmanship of the company in 1977, there were some 10 sides to this family firm and still the position is by no means static.

The *Essex Farmer's Journal* of July 1982 provides some information on Colchester's port and the Pertwee's latest project:

> The opening of a new £¼ million transit warehouse complex at Hythe Quay in the Port of Colchester marks the completion of the first stage in the redevelopment of five acres of dockside land by the Pertwee group.
>
> One of the largest privately-owned agricultural merchanting organisations in the country, the group has its headquarters alongside the docks through which more than 250,000 tonnes of grain were exported last year, putting Colchester into third place in the 'league table' of grain-exporting ports.
>
> 'Our group accounted for a significant proportion of this tonnage', said Chief Executive Christopher Pertwee. 'With our new deep-water silos at Haven Quay we intend to increase our exports in the future.'
>
> 'Imports through Colchester are also increasing. We are sitting on five acres of land ideally suited to play a major role in the handling of materials coming into the port in addition to the grain we already handle. We have, therefore, decided to carry out a phased development of the site. These new warehouses are the first stage. Demand for transit storage facilities is keen and our new units are being kept busy.'

In 1986 this firm's bright blue lorries are to be seen everywhere — and it is still under the energetic direction of members of the original family. For some years their advertisements and publications were enlivened by an amusing 'sprite' who surely must have done something awful as he has been banished. Perhaps he can be reinstated?

Hasler's of Dunmow

On the seed side of its business, Hasler's progressed further than most country merchants in the actual production and development of reliable farm seeds. They are also an example of an inland milling business which, with direct access to the railway and good road connections, was not dependent upon inland water transport. It began when Robert Hasler, of Throws Farm, Great Dunmow, put up a windmill with which to grind food for his livestock. He soon found himself 'obliging' near neighbours and then, when those further afield started to ask if he would mill their feed grain, he decided to open a milling business. This was in 1863 and it was the first of the many businesses which were later to become a part of the well-known firm of Hasler's of Dunmow. By chance, at about the same time, he supplied a bunch of pigs to the head of a large London grain firm. The pigs must have done well for, through that transaction, he gained an introduction to Mark Lane Corn Exchange and here he was able to obtain imported maize and other products for inclusion in his animal rations.

With the lifting of all import duty on cheap foreign corn, Robert Hasler reasoned that the fall in arable acres was likely to result in more grassland and livestock. He then made plans to increase his firm's milling capacity, as well as to explore the possibilities of obtaining and multiplying for sale better quality grass seeds than were currently available. By the turn of the century an amalgamation had been arranged with G. F. Clapham, the owner of a windmill, stabling and stores in Great Dunmow. Very soon the firm's office was moved to Dunmow and, long before the Post Office telephones reached this town, Messrs. Hasler and Clapham installed their own private line to connect the office at Dunmow with Throws Mill and another store in Felsted. As now more buildings were required, such as additional grain stores and cottages, a brickworks was purchased. Also, as farmers began to need large quantities of steam coal for their ploughing and thrashing machines, there was an amalgamation of businesses with Walford the coal merchant in Braintree.

When Robert's son William joined the firm, it became Robert Hasler and Son. As competitors in trade their combined talents were formidable. As employers they built up a staff which became more like a family and, very early on, Robert instituted an employees' profit-sharing scheme within the company and several staff houses were built. In fact it may truly be said that the influence of these two men, and indeed of several subsequent directors of this and other leading agricultural merchants, was not only within their firm but extended throughout the agricultural life of their county and sometimes also of the nation.

During the First World War, William was already highly enough thought of to be called upon to be a member of the county's War Agricultural Committee and afterwards, throughout the depression of the 1930s he,

> never ceased to campaign for government measures to improve the plight of the average farmer and it was from his ideas and at his incentive that, at last, a few years before the Second World War, a measure was introduced to help the wheat grower.[5]

Amongst many other activities he helped to form the National Association of Corn and Agricultural Merchants. He took a lively interest in the N.I.A.B., was associated with the setting up of the Dunmow Bacon Factory and at one time he farmed over 2,000 acres in Essex.

The agricultural and national benefits of growing our own sugar had really come to be appreciated during the early 1920s. In 1925 the Government gave assistance, in the form of a subsidy, on home-grown sugar and William Hasler not only promoted the growing of the crop on his own farm but actively persuaded farmers that this crop was a good one for Essex. There are three essentials for a beet-sugar factory site: a plentiful supply of fresh water and easy access by road and by rail. Two of William Hasler's fields at Felsted fulfilled these requirements and he sold them to enable a factory to be built. It opened for the production of sugar in 1925 and continued to function until 1970.

Both father and son held the conviction that the primary aim of an agricultural merchant should be to buy and sell from farmers, to give them good service coupled with reliable advice, and to be at least one jump ahead of their needs. This they most firmly believed could best be done by working from small local branch offices rather than from one large, and almost inevitably impersonal, central establishment. To this end the firm opened local branches at strategic points and all, although under the general supervision of the Dunmow office, were equipped to work on their own and, as well as providing everyday local needs, each had its own specific purpose.

Ingatestone, their first and largest branch, opened in 1921 and it was developed as the Company's main compounding and cubing plant. Here John G. and his son John E. (Jack) Roper (no known relative of mine) 'reigned' to the extent that once, when David Hasler, the chairman of the Company, was in London, and offered a sample of 'Essex Pearl' wheat to Mr. Drakeford, of Spiller's, he was told politely but firmly that Spiller's only did business with Hasler's through Jack Roper! Mr. Drakeford did, in fact, subsequently buy the wheat from Jack Roper and in due course sent him a seven-pound bag of the flour for his wife to try for making pastry. Maldon branch added an up-to-date mill, port facilities for barges of up to 350 tons, and a nearby branch railway connecting with the main London to Harwich line at Witham. Over in Suffolk, the Cockfield and Cavendish branches worked together to mill trefoil seed, to clean grass seeds and to dry and store both grass seeds and grain. For some time there had been a firm's representative travelling the Saffron Walden area and Hertfordshire border and in due course two more branches were opened, one in Saffron Walden and the other at Braughing, Hertfordshire. When it became necessary, and in company with all the main branches, these two were adapted to handle grain in bulk from the ever-increasing number of combine harvesters.

William Hasler was much concerned with the variable quality of the seeds that were then being offered for sale and, long before there were any national schemes for field approval, his firm was contracting to grow its own stocks of cereal seeds and carrying out field inspections during the growing season. When, in 1933, Essex decided to form a seed-growers' association, he helped to set it up, and gave support by allowing trial plots of grasses and clovers on the firm's trial ground. This was at Throws Farm and had been laid out and supervised by Robert Fry, and a Miss Smith, who did the laboratory tests. It was in Robert Fry's time that Hasler's bred the wheat variety first known as 'Hasler's 37' (because that was the year that it became a commercial proposition) but which was later renamed 'Essex Pearl'. The variety had a comparatively short life and was always more popular in the Midlands and north of England than in the eastern counties. The Seed Growers' Association developed into The Essex Herbage Seed Association, and it is believed that this was the first such body to cause the Government to be aware of the need for and to start certification schemes for herbage seeds in this country.

William had four sons and he had expected that the two elder ones would come into the business. In fact, both were undergoing preliminary training on the continent when the war broke out in 1914. They immediately volunteered for active service and both won the Military Cross. Leonard was killed on the Western Front and when the war ended the twice severely-wounded David, minus one foot, returned home to enter the newly-formed limited company as a director. When Robert, his grandfather, died in the early 1920s David bought Throws Farm and became Hasler and Company's landlord, but for some time it was not thought that his health would stand the strain of business. That he intended to be an active member of the firm became apparent when, on William's death in 1935, he became a Managing Director and in 1941 took over the chairmanship of the company from Francis

J. Nicholls. Although not a farmer, David fitted well into the agricultural world. It was he who encouraged the search for a variety of sugar beet to suit our conditions, and when Sir George Stapleton bred the 'S' strain of grass seeds at the Welsh Plant Breeding Station he encouraged the growing for these for pasture and seed.

During the Second World War there was a search for tough fibres to make such items as fire hoses and parachute ropes. (I have been told that the toughest fibre was found in the inner layers of the nettle stem and not, as one might expect, in the coarse outer stem fibres from which a kind of linen can be woven.) David Hasler became one of the directors of English Flax Ltd. and Hasler's became chiefly concerned with their factory at Glemsford, in Suffolk. Many a fire hose that was used during the London blitz was made from fibre produced at this factory but the enterprise was hampered by the wild oat. This weed not only clogged up the flax-pulling machinery, it was also difficult to remove after the crop had been pulled.

David Hasler was made Chairman of the N.I.A.B. in 1942 and after suffering two coronary attacks he died in 1946 whilst on a fishing holiday in Argyllshire. Of him it has been said that his value to the company was incalculable.[6] Certainly it was during his regime that this company took the then unusual, if not unique step of employing a Cambridge post-graduate to look after its 400 acres of farmland and to build up a research unit and enlarge the trial ground. Even he can hardly have foreseen how successful this unit was to become. All through the summer months parties of farmers, agricultural representatives and advisers came to Throws, at first probably just to see what sort of a job the young man from college was making of practical farming. Then they became interested in what Philip Hayward was trying to do for them until, finally, the visit became at least an annual event which on no account must be missed. Throws was a place where trials and experiments were taking place which were of a practical nature relevant to the district. There was also a licensed seed testing laboratory equipped to carry out tests on seeds, soils and feeding stuffs.

A smooth running system of speedy collection and delivery of goods is essential to an agricultural merchant. For many years one of Mr. F. T. W. Baldry's responsibilities within this firm was the organisation of transport by road, rail and water. First there was a team of horses to be maintained in good health, their feet trimmed and well-shod and their harness, carts and vans to be kept clean and in good repair. Then came the somewhat temperamental Foden Steam Wagons, the problems of which included a tendency to break down and so block the traffic when in the road tunnel under the River Thames at Blackwall; and the first of a fleet of petrol-driven lorries, vans and cars — there were 80 of these by 1963 — and all were maintained in the company's own workshops.

Alan Hasler, William's youngest son, joined the company in 1929 after a period of Army service in India and he became its chairman after Jack Roper retired in 1954. He was a man with vision and during a period of much change at the formation of the Common Market, and Great Britain's subsequent entry, his work as a council member of the N.I.A.B. and as a member or chairman of many of its associated committees has been described as outstanding. He retired from the company in 1967 and died in 1980.

At about the time of their centenary in 1963, Hasler's Board of Directors came to the conclusion that, as far as the future of the firm was concerned, they had two alternatives. They could either sell and become part of a larger company or raise more capital and remain independent. Increased capital would be required as only one-third of the company's shares were held by the shareholders, the remaining two-thirds being held by the Hasler family trust, and there were no Haslers likely to follow Alan to keep this money in the firm.

The decision was made to sell to what was then Joseph Rank Ltd. This became a consortium of businesses which, around this time, absorbed some eighty smaller companies,

Hasler's of Dunmow and Brooks' of Mistley being two of them which in 1967 with C. W. Byford of Suffolk became Brooks Hasler (R.H.M.). In 1969 Philip Hayward was appointed as a director of R.H.M. Ltd.'s Activities Section; he became reponsible for this company's marketing and development programme throughout the United Kingdom, and Throws became its national research and development centre. On 1 May 1983, Philip Hayward retired from R.H.M. (Agriculture) but not as a governor of the N.S.D.O.; a member of the United Kingdom Seeds Executive; a council member of the R.A.S.E. and chairman of the N.I.A.B. In December 1983 he had by no means stopped working.

The story of Hasler's cannot be finished without further mention of the excellent Nicholls family. Like his father, Henry F. Nicholls became this firm's chairman and managing director. He was also chosen as an adviser to the Ministry of Agriculture for cereals during the negotiations arising from Great Britain's entry into the Common Market. Henry's son, Alan Nicholls, was the third generation of this family to work for Hasler and Company Ltd., and after holding several positions of note in the Company and in B.A.S.A.M. and C.O.S.E.M.C.O. (the E.E.C. organisation for the representation of breeders and seed companies), in 1984 joined John K. King and Company Ltd., Coggeshall, in which his cousin Francis Nicholls is the managing director.

Chapter Eleven

The Sugar Beet Crop in Essex

The history of sugar production provides as good an example of political manoeuvring and vested interest as could be wished. It is an interesting story of which there follows only sufficient to provide a background to explain why sugar beet became a necessary crop for Britain and the involvement of Essex in the breeding and production of its seed.

Before the development of sugar cane plantations and later the discovery that an identical sugar could be extracted from the roots of certain plants, people living in temperate climates relied entirely on honey for the addition of extra sweetness to their food.

Tropical and sub-tropical countries had been extracting syrup from their indigenous sugar cane from very early times. The practice is mentioned in Indian literature by 500 B.C. and by A.D. 600 had spread, together with the sugar-making art, to countries round the Mediterranean Sea. In the Middle Ages, sugar cane plantations occurred in Asia Minor and a trade in sugar then started with Europe.

From the 12th century, in Great Britain, cane sugar gradually began to supplant honey. Its use may have been given impetus by homecoming Crusaders, perhaps bringing some of this new sweet substance as a present for their children or as a novelty for their wives. Although from this time, however, the flow of cane sugar into this country may be said to have reached marketable proportions,[1] for several centuries the price remained high enough to restrict its use to the richer households and for it to have remained a suitable gift to thank, please or ingratiate personages of rank and influence. No doubt this is how the saying 'given as a sweetener' has arisen.

92. Sugar loaves: these could be up to 30 inches high and weighed approximately 14lbs.

Europe's great sugar market was Venice, and the Venetians, who also transported the sugar, held a monopoly of the trade. As the centuries progressed the Venetian sugar monopoly became increasingly irksome to the rest of Europe, until in the 15th and 16th centuries the Spaniards and Portuguese decided to do something about it by developing an alternative supply from plantations of sugar cane in Madeira and the West Indies. Very soon English financiers and shippers joined in this promising enterprise. The result was that, as this country's population increased, it found itself in the fortunate position of being able to supplement its former sugar supply with that now coming from the West Indies. Moreover, we had a Navy capable of keeping the necessary sea-lanes open for its transport to this island — an advantage which we denied to Napoleon.

Other European countries were not so fortunately placed and so continued to search for an alternative, and preferably home-grown, sugar supply. In 1747 Andreas Marggraf, a

German chemist, found a way of obtaining crystals from 'fodder beet' identical to those from sugar cane. His work was not immediately recognised as the breakthrough that it was, but by 1801 sufficient interest had been aroused for a sugar beet factory to be constructed at Künern, in Silesia. Sadly, although the sugar produced was of high quality, the extraction percentage was low and the process stood no chance against powerful cane sugar interests in both the Colonies and the refineries built for cane sugar, which had been established at many of the larger European ports. However, when the British blockaded France, Napoleon speeded up continental beet sugar production to the extent that, before 1815, there were 213 small factories in France producing an annual 4,000 tons.

It was not until Britain was startled by the blockade in the First World War, that the Government saw any need for home-produced sugar. Even after the war, advances in this direction were firmly and effectively thwarted. In fact, just about all means were employed to prevent this crop from being grown here, and it was not just by interests in this country alone. Today we still hear it said that beet sugar is no good for jam making. It was a clever supporter of cane sugar who put this idea into the mind of just about every housewife in the country! Nevertheless, there were a few far-seeing souls, believers in private enterprise, who were alive to the agricultural benefits of this crop as well as having a deep conviction that the slave labour, used in the early days of cane production, was wrong. These few were prepared to do more than just march and wave banners in protest.

The 'gallant adventure of ethics and sugar'[2]

Essex Quakers have reason to be proud that in 1832 it was here, in the parish of Ulting, that the only protest of its kind in England, and most probably in the world, was made. In fact a number of young Essex members of the Society of Friends made several visits to France to learn how to set up a sugar beet factory. A company named Marriage, Read and Marriage was formed and a building put up at a cost of £2,000. Two Frenchmen 'who well understood the process'[3] were employed and the most modern, steam-heated copper pans were installed. This considerably reduced the fire risk and prevented the sugar from burning. Thirty hands were employed (men, women and children) and the pressed pulp, from which the sugar liquor had been taken, was used as cattle food.

That in two years the project failed through lack of capital in no way diminishes this splendid attempt to undermine the sale of cane sugar by replacing it with sugar from beet, grown under more humane conditions and on our own farms. Today no part of this factory remains and it is unlikely that many of the anglers on the bank of the nearby canal realise the derivation of the name Sugar Bakers Hole.

The difficulties which can arise with the introduction of a new crop are seldom appreciated except by those immediately concerned. The breeding of sugar beet was, and still is, particularly difficult and so will serve as an example of what may have to be overcome.

This is normally a biennial plant which stores a reserve food supply in its roots during the first growing season to enable it to survive the winter, and to throw up a flower and produce seed in the following year. Seed for the early attempts at growing the crop was bought from the country's various seed firms who had obtained it from continental sources. John K. King does not list this seed until 1897 in which year he offered White Red Topped at 70s. cwt and Vilmorin's Improved at 80s. cwt. Also at that year's root shows he exhibited plants of wild sea beet 'for interest'. This incredible seedsman really never missed a trick!

By 1902, J. K. King informs us that, 'Considerable interest has been manifested during the past two or three years in the question of sugar beet growing in England'. There followed a summary of the results of experiments carried out by the Earl of Denbigh (not the first he had instigated) at Home Farm, Newnham Paddox, Warwickshire in 1902.

At some time before 1914 a Government grant became available to finance a demonstration of beet cultivation for the guidance of farmers. Evidently by 1905 the Essex Education Committee, through their 'Technical Laboratories' (the precursor of the present Writtle Agricultural College), laid down experiments to find out how sugar beet, produced in Essex, would compare with that grown in other countries in Europe. The results reported in the *Essex Weekly News* were from trials at St Osyth, Great Yeldham and Stambridge Hall, near Rochford. John K. King repeated this report in his catalogue of 1907, his firm having supplied the seed, namely Improved Large Green Top, and King's New Empire. By 1908, both John K. King's catalogue and the *Essex Weekly News* claimed that 'Results show that Beets have been grown in Essex equal and in some cases better in quality than those produced in sugar-making countries'.

Although some factories had been erected, and small acreages and a few experimental plots of sugar beet had been grown before the First World War, broadly speaking it was not until after 1925 that this crop received really serious consideration in England. To begin with, it was just the strategic need for self-sufficiency in a key commodity in the event of another war that prompted Government interest. However, as the acute depression of the 1920s and 1930s wore on, it also came to be realised that the benefit of the sugar beet crop to agriculture and the farming community was of equal value. Indeed, apart from improvements to the soil (deeper ploughing and more fertilisers) and the provision of rural employment, the relatively profitable and assured sale of this crop prevented much of the light land of our eastern counties from going out of cultivation. By 1928 the last of the 18 factories in operation during the Second World War had been built, and sugar production in Great Britain had risen from 13,000 tons in 1923 to 420,000 tons in 1930.[4] Concurrently the acreage of sugar beet increased and this reduced the acreage of mangels and turnips in the farm crop rotation as well as providing tops and pulp which were able to replace mangels for livestock feeding. This, in turn, reduced the mangel seed trade. Furthermore, after 1936, the 18 factories amalgamated to become the British Sugar Corporation Ltd. which replaced the seed merchant as the only direct source of sugar beet seed for farmers. Seed then came from the breeder or the breeder's agent to the British Sugar Corporation which distributed the appropriate strains to each factory to fulfil their beet seed growing contracts. When these crops were harvested the seed was returned to source for re-testing before redistribution.

Looking back, the improvements achieved in this one crop, both during and after the Second World War, are quite remarkable. British farmers and farm workers together with the Government's War Agricultural Executive Committees and Advisory Services, backed up by teams of scientific workers and the makers of tools and machinery, succeeded in producing the whole of this nation's rationed sugar supply.[5] The general public, irritably grumbling at the smallness of their allowance, had little idea what a monumental achievement this sugar and sweets ration represented. Furthermore, for a time after the war, the necessity to restrict imports from non-sterling countries continued to encourage the growing of the crop. This cut down our cane sugar requirements and also made a saving on imported animal feeding stuffs through the by-products of leafy tops, dried pulp and molasses. For example, in 1947, the home-grown sugar would have cost $72 million bought at official Cuban prices, while the tops, dried pulp and molasses also represented a large dollar saving in imported feeding-stuffs and played an important part in the home production of meat and milk.

The first seed obtainable was imported from Europe but because, in our latitude, there were more hours of daylight than this seed was used to, some varieties bolted badly in the first year. Therefore a programme to breed more suitable types had to be put in hand by some of the continental breeders. Seed supplied by K. Buszczynski and Company, in Poland, had this trouble which they tried to put right in their own country, but came to the conclusion that the only satisfactory way was to breed the crop in Britain. This, in 1934, is where Essex came into the picture. In that year Buszczynski approached the National Farmers' Union for a site for a breeding station. As Stanley Oldfield Ratcliff, an Essex farmer, was the Union's President that year, he was in a position to help them to set up a business in Maldon which was known as British Pedigree Sugar Beet Seed Ltd., with a breeding station at Great Beeleigh Farm under the direction of Lutoslawski, a Polish breeder. He helped to solve the crisis in the supply of sugar beet which hit Britain when war broke out. In 1939 he was recalled into the Polish armed forces and was presumably killed, for he was never heard of again. After Lutoslawski's recall to Poland, J. C. Cullen, a post-graduate from Cambridge, was responsible for the breeding.

Then in 1942, under the auspices of the British Pedigree Sugar Beet Seed Company, a tall, lithe student, with a quiet manner and a quizzical, amused smile, who had recently finished his studies at Cambridge, came to Essex. Dr. Sydney Ellerton was first tolerated as a boffin, soon became an interesting boffin, and finally won not only the admiration but the genuine friendship of many of the Essex farming community. He was our local breeder of sugar beet seed whose task was at first to breed traditional multigerm varieties with a better performance. In 1944, the Hall at Woodham Mortimer, Essex, together with some adjoining land for trials, was purchased and thus began what was to become one of the most interesting places for farmers, plant breeders and agricultural advisers to visit in this country. By this time the Essex firm of Hasler and Company, of Dunmow, held shares in the British Pedigree Sugar Beet Seed Company. One director, Mr. David Hasler, was on the council of the National Institute of Agricultural Botany (N.I.A.B.) and, because he had a great appreciation of things academic, was responsible for much of the fruitful co-operation which came about between the two companies. For instance, when Dr. Ellerton required greater isolation for some of his stock seeds he was allowed to grow them at Throws Farm, Dunmow, which Hasler's farmed and where they had their trial grounds. Today, Dr. Ellerton is said to have retired but can seldom be contacted because of frequent sorties to many parts of the world, picking up and passing on knowledge which may help in the production of better varieties of this most awkward seed.

Some of the problems which arose

Sugar beet seed presents difficulties all along the line. To begin with it is not really a seed but a fruit of irregular size and shape which contains from one to four viable seeds tightly enclosed in a strong corky husk. Then, before germination can take place, the husks need to be thoroughly wet. Sacks of mangel seed, which are of the same species, used to be put into the horse pond to soak the night before sowing and gardeners often soak their beet and spinach seed today.

In a dry period germination may be tardy which will result in an uneven braird, delayed cultivations and a subsequent reduction in yield. Furthermore, when using natural seed, from one to four seedlings will result from each seed cluster. These will come up in close proximity to one another, their roots tangled together so that the removal of surplus plants, at singling, is almost impossible without damaging the single plant which is to be left to mature.

Natural seed has both male and female flowers on the same stem. This, until the discovery of varieties which are male sterile, meant that the only way to hybridise to a plan was to pick off the stamens of one of the parent varieties with a pair of tweezers!

Attempts to produce a more convenient seed

Clearly it was necessary to find a way of producing, either by mechanical means or by breeding, clusters which contained only one viable seed. Various mechanical ways of

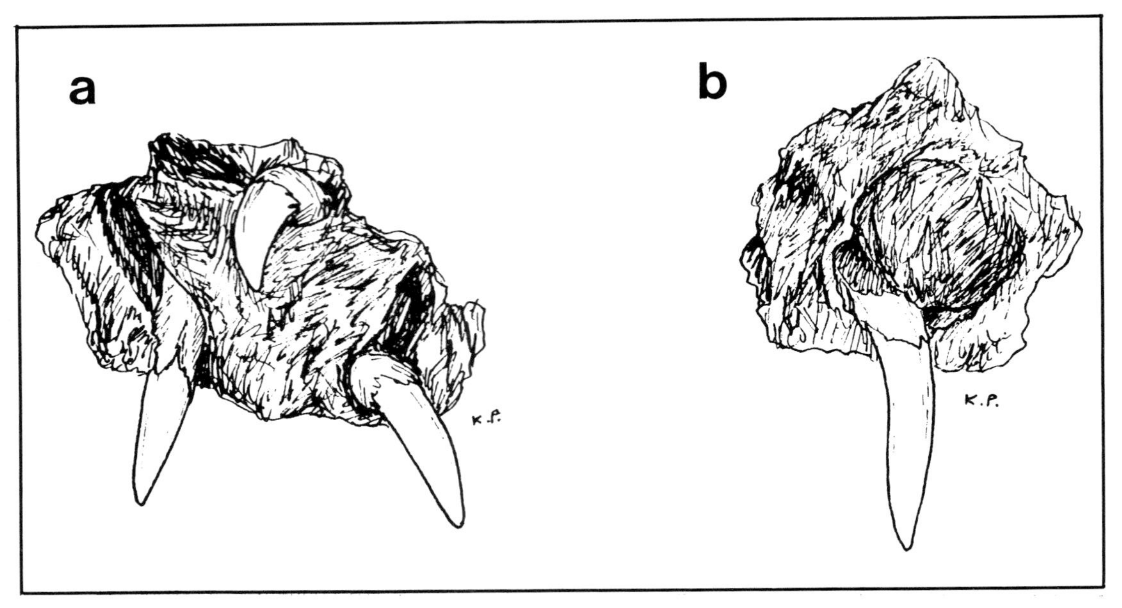

93. Sugar beet: (a) germinating multi-germ fruit; (b) germinating mono-germ fruit.

removing or diminishing the husk have been tried. These include an attempt to dissolve some of it away with sulphuric acid; trying to crack the clusters either to release the seed altogether or to produce portions of husk containing an individual seed; and by rubbing away some of the husk. None of these methods goes far enough although the last has now been further developed to a stage of satisfactory practical use. One of the reasons for failure has arisen because the clusters have no natural lines of cleavage. Therefore they neither crack nor divide readily and this, because the seed inside the cluster is extremely susceptible to damage by rough treatment, often results in poor germination. During the Second World War a milling process was tried for the removal of some of the husk. Then came *segmented seed*, produced by cutting the clusters into segments which were of various sizes. The dust, small pieces of husk, and damaged seeds were then removed and this left segments which, for the most part, contained only one seed. The wastage was considerable and only one pound of clean, graded and segmented seed was obtained from three pounds of clusters. Unfortunately field germination of this seed was also low and although the processed seed contained 50,000 seeds to the pound as compared with 20,000 from natural seed, the seed rate an acre was not able to be reduced. Again, there was some evidence that segmented seed suffered more severely than natural seed from poor seed bed conditions and unfavourable growing weather. In time a method less drastic than chopping up the clusters was tried. In this the seed was passed between a stationary rubber pad and a rapidly revolving carborundum stone. The severity of the rubbing can be varied but still, in addition to reducing the cluster size, there is a tendency to graze some of the true seeds, thus destroying their germinating potential. Seed so treated was given the name *rubbed and graded* and produced a higher proportion of single-seeded segments which were also capable of being graded for size. This was essential when using a precision drill. By this method the initial recovery of seeds is about 70 per cent by weight of the original bulk; however, this percentage is reduced much further during grading and gravity separation. Germination is almost as good as with natural seed and on the basis of seeds to a pound, three pounds of rubbed seed equals four pounds of natural seed.

Although precision drilling is possible with properly prepared unpelleted seed, the uniform roundness of seed which has been coated with some inert material to form a pellet is an advantage. Therefore the use of *pelleted seed* has now become the common practice in this country. Nevertheless, the process has produced its own difficulties such as when pellets disintegrate in the bag during handling, or when passing through the drill while being sown. Sometimes the pelleting material remains intact but fails to break down readily when in contact with the soil. This, particularly in a droughty season, leads to an impeded and uneven germination with the likelihood of chemical scorch, if a fertiliser, fungicide or herbicide has been incorporated into the pellet. Compared with rubbed seed, however, the cost of pelleted seed is high.

Today, the final preparation of sugar beet seed for market involves *gravity separation*. It is carried out after the seed has been rubbed and graded for size and shape. Such separation has made it possible to put on the market monogerm seed with over 90 per cent germination. This is a great advance on the early days of this seed for then even multigerm seed, with its possibility of two, three or more seedlings from each cluster, was accepted with a germination of no more than 60 per cent. Today, 75 to 80 per cent of all sugar beet seed sown is monogerm.

During the war, farm labour supplemented by the Women's Land Army and later also by prisoner-of-war labour struggled with the seemingly endless hand labour demanded for this crop. After the war, when most of the land girls had married or gone home and the P.O.W.s were repatriated, the shortage of labour became acute and there was a consequent rise in the agricultural wage without a corresponding rise in crop value. Clearly, for this country to continue growing sugar beet, machines to cover the labour gap had to be invented and the crop itself changed by adapting the seed to meet the situation.

A useful summary of the problems connected with the mechanisation of this crop may be found in the Ministry of Agriculture's *Bulletin*, No. 153 (1970 edition). As much of this summary may also be applied to the seed crop only brief notes will be given here.

In Essex, until approximately 1958, the seed crop was cut by hand with a sickle, and then built up on to a quadrupod to dry before being thrashed. When direct combine harvesting was attempted this was found to be impossible. Even with the help of Paraquat spray — to remove the leaves — the harvester has been described as 'having failed to do the job because its works became gummed up with white goo which issued from the pith of the undried stems'. With the advent of the Leverton pea cutter and swather, cutting on to a high stubble whilst the crop was reasonably green was tried, the cut crop had to be cut, swathed and left for 10 days or more until sufficiently dry to be picked up and thrashed in the combine harvester.

As the seed crop spreads into two years the seed used to be sown in a small plant bed in the summer. The little plants (stecklings) then had to be planted out in the field by mid-April but Essex spring weather seldom favours this operation nor, in this county, is it usually possible to achieve a good plant bed in June/July, so it is now realised that the stecklings have often to be put out in the autumn, as is usual in Lincolnshire.

When in the late 1930s it was appreciated that the yellowing of the leaves was not a normal senescence but a yield-reducing virus disease transmitted by aphids, and that over-wintering aphids were spreading infection in the steckling beds, attempts were made to grow the crop in hitherto non-sugar beet growing areas. This was not successful. By this time H. H. Hansen in Denmark, however, had found that there was no infection if the beet were sown under a covering crop of barley. Dr. Ellerton heard of this and was allowed to adopt

Hansen's methods in Essex. They were successful and are still current practice. Around 1958, two of the farmers who helped by allowing early trials of this method on their farms were Arthur Bentall, of Wakering Wick, Great Wakering, and Bill Edgar of Butler's Farm, Shopland.

It may truly be said that the sugar beet crop survived in Britain because of three simultaneous developments, namely: the advent of the precision drill; suitable herbicides; and monogerm seed. Without *all three* there would have been no dramatic reduction of labour requirement.

The unravelling of the full breeding story of this crop would require a very large book and has so far defeated those far more capable of tackling the subject than I am. It will, therefore, be dismissed with the statement that breeders continue their search for more suitable seed by employing such devices as male sterility, polyploidy, and gene manipulation. Eventually they may also be able to insert into the beet chromosomes additional genes to provide resistance to at least some major pests and diseases together with greater tolerance to herbicides. Anyone wishing to disentangle this subject further should seek access to a publication of the International Institute of Sugar Beet Research, Avenue Monoyer 47, B-1040, Brussels.

An acreage of sugar beet roots, for processing into sugar, is still grown in Essex but, when harvested, these roots now have to be taken to factories elsewhere because that built in 1925 at Felsted was closed down in 1980. Sugar beet seed still continues to be grown successfully in Essex. Nevertheless, the acreage of this seed grown for the British Sugar Beet Corporation has fallen sharply from its peak of some 1,400 acres in 1980 to a mere 300 acres in 1983. Nationally, however, the breeding programme has not slackened and such problems as eelworm control and genetic throwback to Wild Beet are currently matters of concern to breeder and Government alike.

Note. This genetic Wild Beet must not be confused with the sea beet (*Beta maritima*) which grows wild and profusely on our east coast. Cross-pollination with *B. maritima* is guarded against by care in isolation and, to some extent, by the spraying carried out by the Water Authority to help prevent weakening of the sea walls by this deep-rooted plant.

Chapter Twelve

A Miscellany of Inter-related Seed Interests

> The utilization of iron and steam can therefore be summarised as the main means by which the manufacturing industry of England was revolutionized in the 18th Century . . . Essex was at first aloof from this because smelting did not, in the nature of things, take place and the steam engine was . . . only gradually adopted. In this sense, Essex missed the primary causes of the Industrial Revolution and certainly, on the social front, the primary results; what it did not miss were the second stage consequences of iron making and long-term involvement with the continuing pattern of industrial development.
>
> John Booker, *Essex and the Industrial Revolution*[1]

The amount and type of employment that is available, during any given period, greatly influences the social history of an area. This, in turn, is governed by such factors as fashion, politics, powerful vested interests and the opening-up of new possibilities brought about by additions to our knowledge and by new inventions.

In Essex, employment of various kinds became abundant when Great Britain stopped selling its wool clip to the continent and took to weaving cloth. In fact, the ramifications of the subsidiary industries which were engendered, by both weaving and the milling trades, are sometimes surprising and both developed links with seed-growing.

Before aniline dyes came to be produced from coal-tar, dyes for cloth were obtained from many kinds of naturally occurring materials including specific parts of certain plants. Essex grew some of these plants. The main source of yellow dye was weld (*Reseda luteola*) which was needed by the fustian weavers around Saffron Walden and Haverhill. Therefore, many acres were planted to yield both saleable seed and stems, leaves and roots from all of which the dye was obtained.

Of weld, Alma Oakes quotes[2] Worlidge as having written:

> This is a rich dyer's commodity and grows also in many places in Kent, to very great advantage. It will grow on any ordinary or barren land, so that it will be dry and warm. A gallon of seed will sow [under sow] an acre of Barley or Oats, very small, and not much the first summer. [Be] Cautious in gathering it, seeds must not be over-ripe. Pulled, as they do Flax, by the roots, and bound in little handfuls, set to dry and then housed. Beat or lash out the seed, which is of good value, and dispose of the stalks and root to the dyer, which is of singular use for dyeing of bright yellow and lemon colour.

and she continues that, in 1748, a Swedish traveller, Peter Kalm, recorded[3] that *Reseda luteola*/Dyer's Weed grew everywhere outside London on the earth walls (commonly built around a holding both to define its extent and as some protection). Here it survived the drought conditions and hot sun and stood 'green and in flower more than 18 inches high', and cattle did not like to eat it. She also records that, from Gravesend, Kalm wrote,

> Dyer's Weed, which is cultivated for its yellow colour, was in several places drawn up, root and all and bound in small sheaves which were set one against another in the fields to dry with Hemp and Flax. It grew here wild in places abundantly, and in other places it was expressly planted.

Once woven, the cloth was subjected to a process known as fulling. This not only provided work for water mills but also gave rise to a trade in human urine. In Kelvedon this is said to have been collected each morning, for a few pence a gallon, and was used to soften and condition the woollen cloth!

To raise a nap on certain cloths large quantities of fullers' teazel heads were needed and the seeds were saved for re-sowing (see pp.224-7).

When weaving became mechanised and moved to the Midland woollen mills, many an Essex family was forced to look for other work. For some time it was both thought, and written, that the 19th century, as experienced in Essex, was a period of unalleviated trade depression. That this was a misconception is now clear and, as far as Colchester is concerned, was firmly dismissed by John Booker[4] in 1974 when he wrote,

> It is often thought that Colchester spent the last century in a period of depression following the collapse of the baize trade . . . The truth is that Colchester, like Lincoln and Ipswich and other towns in Eastern England, became a centre of national importance in the working of iron for agricultural purposes.

His statement is borne out by the history of the Atlas Iron Works at Earls Colne. Therefore, since it is situated in a seed-growing area and numerous pieces of equipment needed by seed-growers all over the world are made there, the story of this works will provide an example of all similar businesses which have supplied the needs of seedsmen in Essex and beyond.

Today, when it is easy to obtain the services of a mechanical engineer, for indeed there is one or more on almost every farm, it is difficult to believe that this was not always so and that Alderman Mechi of Tiptree could in 1845 have been complaining that were he to instal a steam engine he would have to go 50 miles for a repair.[5] Formerly it was the millwright with his knowledge of gearing, shafting and pulleys who, as he travelled his circuit, was sought for when anything of a mechanical nature required attention. This explains why, amongst the many ironmongers and blacksmiths who became foundry owners, millwrights also frequently occur.

As pig-iron became more plentiful many identical castings, in standard sizes, became available. (The effect of the discovery that iron ore could be smelted with coke, as distinct from charcoal, was that pig-iron became more plentiful and that large numbers of cast-iron objects could then be made from it. *Chambers Encyclopaedia* (1966), vol. 7, p.752, states that between 1700 and 1806 the annual production of pig-iron in the United Kingdom leapt from some 20,000 to 250,000 tons.) Then, instead of having to have each iron part made from wrought-iron by a blacksmith, it was possible to obtain, or to keep in stock, castings which could be fitted immediately. Later, possibly when customers began to order their machine parts direct from the maker and also because there was a growing demand for more local producers of machinery, millwrights and others learned to cast iron and to use it for a variety of purposes.

Robert Hunt, Atlas Works, Earls Colne

Robert Hunt is first heard of as a travelling millwright who it is said left Soham, in Cambridgeshire, in 1824 and came to Earls Colne where by 1823 he already held the lease of a mill. He seems to have started in quite a small way, probably first buying in his castings and perhaps also working in conjunction with a local blacksmith. At some time between 1838 (when a tithe map[6] shows no foundry on this site) and 1860, he built a foundry which was to develop into the existing Atlas Iron Works.

Robert's four sons were partners in his business but when, seemingly quite young, the two eldest died, Reuben, the next in line, came home to become the managing director, with his brother Zach as works manager.

A photograph of Reuben Hunt suggests that he was like the products that he sold: strong, reliable and built to last (in fact he died in 1927 at the age of 91). His expression is one of considerate and intelligent shrewdness with no hint of guile and one senses that this was a man who, because he expected them, always received good manners from those with whom he associated. It was Reuben who put these works on the map and, as he did so, ensured work and provided amenities of many kinds for his work-force and also the inhabitants of the village.

At first, in order to facilitate transport of heavy goods, foundries were sited beside navigable water. Later, when the railways were extended, sites were looked for adjacent to these lines. The Eastern Counties Railway had come as far as Colchester by 1843, and it reached Harwich in 1854. The Hunts had land at Aldham near to this railway, and it is said that they once hoped to build their works there. For some reason this was not allowed and it was probably after this that land in the area was rented to the Percival family who for many years have supplied Hunts with barley straw for use when packing machinery.

94. Reuben Hunt, *c.*1905.

The aim of the Atlas Iron Works, Earls Colne, England (apparently it was not considered necessary to add Essex to the address), has always been, and very refreshingly continues to be, to supply a customer with exactly what he needs. The smallest requests are listened to with attention and well-informed suggestions will be offered if it is thought that some improvements might be made.

When Reuben Hunt travelled abroad, and he first went round the world in 1887, he not only looked for new customers but also at the conditions under which his machines would be used, to what other work they might be put and, where necessary, how costs to the customer might be cut without harm to the quality of the machine. For instance, there was no need to send wooden legs, or a wooden stand, to a remote African village on the edge of a forest full of trees. On the other hand, for a customer who had no local source of timber, costs might be saved by making the packing case for the ironwork from wood suitable, and of just the right size for, say, the table of a thrashing machine. In fact, however great or limited are a customer's resources, something can be supplied or made to meet almost every contingency. Their machines can be supplied to be powered by hand, mule or one or more horses, as well as by engine.[7] Proof that the wooden parts were regarded as optional may be found in a list of 1900[8] which advertises a 'Light one Horse Spur Wheel gear "The Tasmanian"' with a note added that, 'It is easily fixed, to sleepers that can be cut from a tree in the neighbourhood being all that is required, or these can be sent with the gear if preferred'.

To give an idea of their range of machines suitable for seed growers (and this was by no means their only line which could be supplied in 1905) there were: thrashing machines, corn and seed dressing machines, rollers, general-purpose carts, horse rakes, water-carts

95. A Peg Thrashing Drum in action.

with spreaders, seed-barrow drills, one-row bush and one-row cup drills and barrows, as well as clover and trefoil drawers (presumably what would now be called a 'huller'). There were, of course, also gears of all types to operate the stationary machines such as the Peg thrashing drum. The Peg drum was superseded by the combine harvester; the last one was made by this firm in 1950 and, possibly in 1948, the last horse gear that they were to manufacture went to the Fiji Islands.

Reuben Hunt had five sons, all of whom came into the firm after having been given a sound practical and technological training both in this country and abroad. At the time of his father's death Reuben James Hunt was a director of the business. He became its chairman in 1947. Also, from 1951 to 1963 he was a director and Deputy Chairman of Ransomes, Sims and Jeffries Ltd. of Ipswich and from 1963 to 1965 was the Chairman of this firm. In 1953 he was honoured with a knighthood.

On his retirement in 1967 he was made a Life President of his company. Sir Reuben had four daughters but no son, and in 1984, before this firm became Christy Hunt (January 1985), the last one to carry the family name and to be active within the company retired. He is Mr. R. B. Hunt, a great-grandson of its founder Robert Hunt.

Tony Bonner, of Threshelford's, reports that when visiting an archaeological site in Africa (so remote that they had to leave the Land Rover and walk the last few miles) they passed two splendidly topless ladies using one of Hunt's handmills. It was mounted on tree trunks, was still in perfect working order, and is believed to have been supplied by the firm some 50 years previously.

The Percivals of Great Tey

Possibly for much longer, but certainly for five generations, Mr. Alan Dann's ancestors have farmed and worked on the land in and around the Teys.

His great-great-grandfather, Frederick Percival, was a farm labourer in this area and he had a son, also named Frederick, who was born in 1857. When this son married, he took his bride to live in one of the little knot of cottages that once adjoined Great Tey churchyard. Here their two sons, George and Alan, were born and, after Alan's birth in 1885, the family moved to Smyther's Farm. Later, when Frederick (b. 1857) was looking for a farm of his own, it was Mr. Reuben Hunt of the Atlas Works, in Earls Colne, who 'set him up' in farming by allowing the young man to buy one of his farms for, it is believed, £5 an acre. This was Windell's Farm, Great Tey, which became the family home. Perhaps included within the agreement was a purely verbal arrangement for the Percivals to supply the Atlas Works with barley straw for packing purposes; in any event, I understand that the custom holds good to this day.

Frederick's wife died in 1903, and about that time he took his two sons into partnership. At some date before 1906 Frederick was married again, this time to a widow, a Mrs. Firmin, who had one daughter, and when his son Alan married this daughter, in 1906, the young couple went to live at Trumpington's Farm, Great Tey. Thus things continued for a number of years during which Alan and his wife had two daughters, one of whom married Roderick Dann of Kelvedon, and they had a son, Alan Dann, and a daughter.

The family continued, through good times and bad, to farm their land well and to become known as reliable seed-growers, so that by 1940 George and his brother Alan were farming some 700 acres at Windell's, Smyther's, New Barn, Brook House, Marshall's, Trumpington's and Cuckoo's, all in the parish of Great Tey, and Checkley's Farm in Aldham.

Around 1950 the partners decided to sell all the land, except about 300 acres, at Windell's, Trumpington's and Cuckoo's, which land is still being farmed by Mr. Dann. In 1966 George decided to retire and his place was taken in the farming partnership by his nephew Alan Dann. When Alan Percival died in 1978, he was buried in Great Tey churchyard, not 50 feet from the house where he had been born, for by then part of the land on which his father's cottage had stood had become an extension to the burial ground.

Seeds of all kinds were, and to some extent still are, grown at Trumpington's. There were contracts to grow Hilleshog sugar beet seed for the Martins of Earls Colne, cabbage, peas, runner beans, and grass seeds (particularly S.37 Cocksfoot) and once, for Pertwee's, some poppies which yield morphine from their seed capsules and also oil from the seeds.

For some 51 years Mr. Bertie Wilby helped with the crops on this farm and, until his death in 1982, cast his experienced eye over everything that went on, giving a word of encouragement, commiserating when the weather spoilt a crop, or offering sound advice when required. As was said when we were introduced, 'Bertie is now retired but I have asked him to come up and help us for everyone knows that he is 'The Authority' on Trumpington's'. Both Bertie and his wife had worked on the farm and their fathers were there before them. It was a work-relationship seldom found today and one which was much treasured by both sides.

Mr. Wilby's remark that 'there was always a crop of mangel seed on Trumpington's until we stopped growing it in 1980' prompted the thought that these five generations had seen every change in the method of growing this country's mangel seed. There have been two main changes. To begin with the crop occupied the same acreage for two growing seasons and the amount of work entailed was prodigious; then came the change to a 'steckling bed' and this would provide sufficient plants in one growing season to plant the required acreage of seed in the next (so that 28 pounds of seed sown into a bed of one eighth to one quarter of an acre should supply enough plants for 10 acres). Furthermore, the stecklings, being sown close together, would normally protect one another from frost and so, in the first autumn, there would be no laborious pulling up and carting off the field of many tons of large roots, which would then have to be properly clamped under a seal of straw and earth or be otherwise protected in a building. Then in the following spring, instead of having to open up the clamps and cart the whole lot back to another field to be planted, the little stecklings would simply be lifted into apron-like dropping bags, ready for debbing into the seed field; by 1948, the mechanical planter had modified even this procedure, sprays replaced hand hoeing and removed the blackfly problem in the 1960s, sickles were put away in favour of the windrower and then came thrashing in the fields using a combine harvester and pick-up attachment. This cuts out building a stack and covering it with thatch and today even the steckling beds have gone. The modern method is to sow two and a half pounds of seed an acre at the same time as a crop of (usually) spring barley, but not in the same row. Then, when the barley is cut, to leave a reasonably tall stubble to protect the little mangel plants over the winter.

The interested reader may well be fascinated to read Mr. Dann's memories of the steckling bed method, outlined above, in Appendix G.

Differences in the size and shape of seeds and in the earth, chaff and trash which become mixed with a seed crop as it is harvested, make separation possible. Removal of such extraneous matter is necessary in order to improve the appearance of the sample, to remove weed seeds, small clods of earth, stone and plant material (particularly that which is still full of sap) for these will cause the seeds to heat, discolour and lose germination potential.

Since sieving, in one form or another, is usually the most practical way to do this job, it follows that every seed grower and merchant has sets of round-, square-and oblong-meshed sieves of appropriate sizes for the seeds that they handle. Small quantities are generally sieved by hand; larger parcels are passed over suitable sieves of the same or different mesh size, which may be incorporated into one or other of the many types of thrashing, cleaning or dressing machines. An Essex firm which became noted for its taut and well-made sieves was:

Isaac Brazier and Sons, the Eastern Counties and Halstead Wire Works (wholesale and retail), Head Street, Halstead.

Isaac Brazier opened his wire works and shop in 1870, at the bottom of Head Street, Halstead, in a lath and plaster house with a bow-window on the corner near the church. He had three sons named Ernest, Sidney and William, and when Ernest took over the business he employed his two younger brothers. Ernest, who was the father of the present Gerald E. Brazier is recalled by his son as,

> . . . A good old boy and he was thrilled to death when I was old enough to leave school and could help him in the shop. I wanted to be a farmer. I should have loved it. But I drifted into the family business — you know how it is.

A photograph of Ernest as a young man shows him beside his solid-tyred bicycle clad in cap, knickerbocker suit and spats, with the addition of toe clips and a large buttonhole. He was a keen cyclist, and on occasion would ride to London and back. Ernest's wife is remembered by her son as,

A happy, sweet-faced lady who lived to be one hundred years and eight months . . . she had a hard life but she was happy.

Gerald became head of this firm after his father died in 1933. It was he who moved the business to Mallow's Field, Halstead, where there was an Army hut of suitable size for a workshop. At the same time an extra hand was employed in the shape of an ex-carpenter and cabinet-maker who was 'an excellent worker named Stanley Drury' and soon learnt to fit into this business which made everything from sieves to hanging flower baskets, and was also able to instal or repair the floor of a maltings. Gerald Brazier says that, in a wet year, seed crops were often dried on a malting floor. Malting walls have to be made very thick and strong, in order to withstand the strain when the metal floor bars which pass right through them are tightened by a nut on a plate on the outside of the wall. The Braziers put in many such floors of which two were in Halstead and six on Colchester Hythe where on one occasion they repaired the middle of a floor used by Brooks of Mistley because it had burnt through with use.

The *Essex County Standard* of 26 August 1960 reports that this was 'a little factory in top gear production, doing specialised work requiring individual attention'. The report also states that the firm made the wire crowns which were used in the street decorations of London for the Coronation, but Mr. Brazier says that this is incorrect, although he did once make a wire fireman's helmet for use as the base of a wreath!

There is much more to a sieve than meets the eye. For instance, if it has not got two rims it is not a sieve but a riddle. For the seed trade, they may be made from split willow osiers — these sieves are three feet across, deeper than most, and nice and light for the removal of 'cavings'; or from perforated zinc, such as is found in the round-holed brassica sieves; or from wire, which had been laid and tightened by hand to form a mesh of relatively large size; and there are fine sieves for little seeds, made from woven metal mesh which may range from 6,400 mesh per square inch (80/linear inch) to 16 mesh per square inch (four/linear inch). Weaving wire gauze is a specialist's job and this material was obtained from factories in Edinburgh or Warrington.

96. George Wilks's set of sieves. 'Every seed grower and merchant has sets of round, square and oblong mesh sieves.'

The Braziers specialised in making every kind of square meshed sieve that is required for flower and vegetable seeds and, if you wanted something a little out of the ordinary, they would do their best to construct it for you. For instance, when Ralph Goodwin of Brick House Farm, Kelvedon became concerned about the danger of his seeds becoming contaminated through seeds which became trapped around the rim of his sieves, he asked for the rims to be packed with soft flocky string, so that no seed could creep into the crevices. For someone who needed to remove split from whole garden peas, a straight mesh of three-sixteenths by three inches was made from the relatively pliable mild steel wire. There was also an occasion when

Gerald Brazier was asked to make a sieve which would remove wild oats from barley. This was not at all an easy task but he found that a wire mesh sized six-and-a-half to a linear inch turned the oat on its side and 'just about did it'. Sadly, when Gerald retired in 1970 the business was closed down.

Some seeds do not sieve well because of their shape or if they are very light in weight. In such cases seed is 'ryed' by putting it into a sieve, the mesh of which will not let it through, and then rotating the sieve in a tilted semi-circle. In India this is performed most gracefully by sari-clad ladies, who rotate the sieve on their fingers and held high above their heads, with the trash being blown away on the breeze as it separates. Essex folk grasp the side of the sieve, and with a semi-crouched and bouncing action manage to separate the seed to one side of the sieve and the trash to the other. The trash is then either gently blown away or swept up onto a piece of stiff card with the aid of a goose feather. There is also a method which requires much skill and practice, whereby a small quantity of seed may be cleaned by placing it on a sheet of paper which is held, curved up at the edges, between the hands and expertly flipped until separation is effected.

The Fuller's Teazel, Coriander and Caraway

The fuller's teazel had almost certainly been grown in Essex since the reign of Edward III (1327-71) and possibly even earlier. Surviving accounts of the Lady of Clare,[9] Elizabeth de Burgh of Clare Castle, Suffolk, who also owned the manor of Bardfield in Essex, lists sales of surplus produce. These for the year 1336-7 include green beans, leeks, apples, pears, onions and garlic, fuller's teazels, madder and hemp. In the same year she purchased for sowing a bushel of beans, a quart of teazel seed and both sets and seeds of garlic and onion.

Because the Latin names of both have been altered several times during the last hundred or so years there is some confusion between the wild teazel, which grows on the roadsides all over Essex, and the cultivated teazel which I have never found growing wild. Fortunately, however named, they are very easy to tell apart. The wild teazel has a relatively fat and more conical seedhead than the cultivated. Also its much softer and unhooked awns sweep upwards whereas the seedhead of the cultivated teazel is slimmer and almost straight-sided, with awns that are very stiff, downward-turning, positively lethal hooks.

The current nomenclature, as given to me from the Royal Botanic Gardens at Kew, is that given in the *Excursion Flora of The British Isles*,[10] according to which the wild teazel is *Dipsacus fullonum* subsp. *sylvestris*, and the cultivated fuller's teazel is *Dipsacus fullonum* subsp. *fullonum*. These Latin names differ from those in the second edition (1962) where the fuller's teazel is given its old name *Dipsacus fullonum* subsp. *sativus*, but are the same as those in the first edition of 1957.

It might be expected that modern technology would have been able to devise an effective teazel substitute and, indeed, hooked metal material has been made.[11] However, for the highest quality pure wool trade there is nothing to beat the natural product for, when its hooks meet an obstruction, they give way and break off, whereas metal hooks hang on to the cloth, causing damage by tearing or pulling the threads.

As with other flower seeds this crop, because it requires a great deal of individual attention and hand labour, was usually grown in little patches either by a smallholder with a family to help him, or by farmers with an oddly-shaped corner of a field or a piece of otherwise waste land. Arthur Brown[12] writes that a special Essex crop was caraway, coriander and teazel sown broadcast in the same field. At Great Maplestead, a centre of its cultivation, farmers,[13] after having ploughed the land, frequently handed over the growing of the crop to trusted labourers and divided the ultimate profit with them. This arrangement ensured meticulous hoeing, timely and careful cutting and removal of coriander and caraway, as well as a careful sorting of the teazel heads. The coriander and caraway seed was sent to

London for use in medicines, condiments, distilling and brewing. The teazels were hardened in the sun, and sent to Halstead for the roughing of cloth. Returns, he says, justified the high costs. At Great Maplestead over £40 an acre might be received in three years from yields of 20 hundredweight of caraway, 15 hundredweight of coriander and over half a load of teazels. This crop also attracted enterprising small farmers, who sometimes rented a field and took the whole of the proceeds for themselves. In the Dengie Hundred such men travelled around farms, growing these crops as an introductory arable crop on land ploughed out from pasture of long standing, and here it was customary to share the profit with the landlord. Again Mr. Brown mentions that singly or in combination teazels, coriander and caraway were grown on individual farms elsewhere in Essex, for instance at Kelvedon, Bradwell-on-Sea, Inworth, Great Wigborough and Tolleshunt D'Arcy, teazels usually being omitted except near to the textile towns.

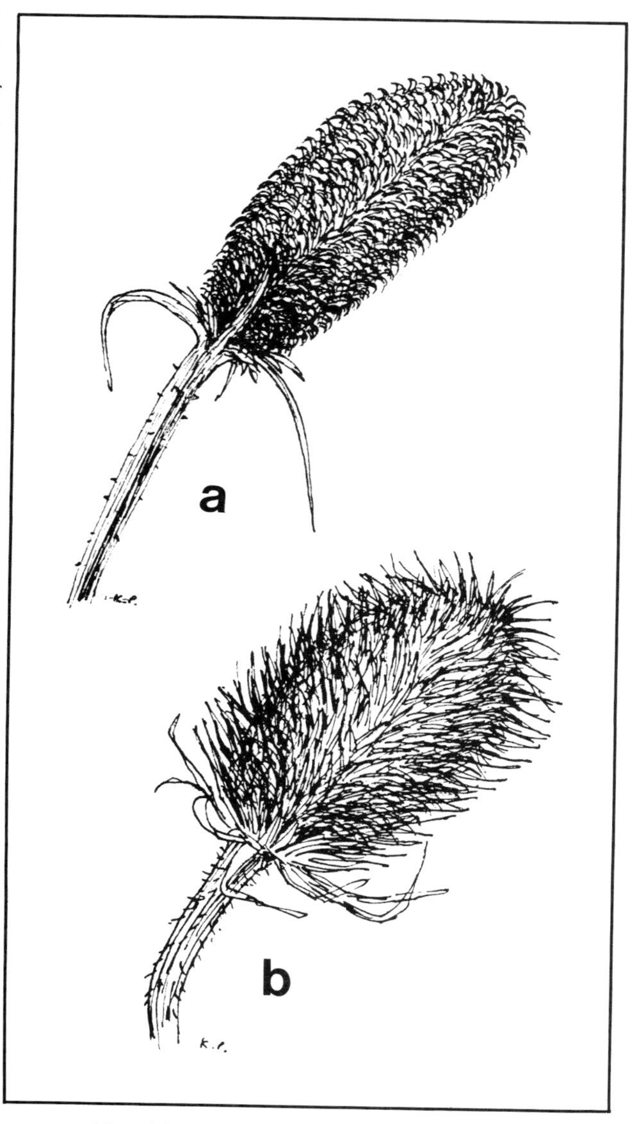

97. (a) Fuller's teazel; (b) Wild teazel.

Roughing mills and teazel stores are mentioned in records relating to Braintree and Bocking. For instance, in the 1740s one of the largest cloth firms in Bocking belonged to Joseph Savill, of Boleyn's, who in 1760 purchased a roughing mill, after which he kept a supply of teazels and roughed the cloth on his own premises. Roughing mills were being used in Essex from 1750, some 50 years before they were adopted in Yorkshire. They required less labour than was needed to raise a nap by hand and the mill consisted of revolving cylinders which were covered with teazels — the whole being powered by a horse gear.

In the 19th century landlords were very particular about the cropping of their land. They disliked any crop which drew the land (removed fertility) or was liable to leave it in a dirty state, full of weeds. The teazel crop, which remained in the field for two or even three years and also possibly in combination with caraway and coriander, was unlikely to have found favour. An agreement between Samuel Blyth of Barn Hall, Tolleshunt Knights, and Joseph

Firmin Green, of Sturgeons, Writtle, is preserved in the Essex Record Office (ERO D/D BL T1). It states that the tenant was expected,

> To pay an increased yearly rent of ten pounds an acre and in that proportion for every less quantity than an acre of the before mentioned lands which shall be sown with Flax, Hemp, Woad, Brown Mustard, Coriander, Caraway or any other pernicious or destructive seeds or roots.

In this instance teazels also would surely have rated as 'other pernicious or destructive seeds'.

Yet another mention of teazels having been grown in Essex[14] occurs in an account of a court case of the 1820s, between Edward Royce, the owner of the smock mill and *The Compasses* public house in Great Totham, and Mr. Polley the owner of the post mill which was near to *The Bull* public house in Great Totham. Polley was accused of seducing Royce's daughter and, when the case went against him, he bolted with amongst other money, '£135 owed to his mother for the sale of teazel sent by her to Yorkshire'.

Paul Lees, in his informative article on teazels,[15] brings their cultivation to the present day. In summary, when it was found that teazels could be successfully grown on soils suffering from an excess of molybdenum, this crop became a profitable alternative to grazing cattle on the 'teart' soil of south-west England. The excess molybdenum is such soils is responsible for the metabolic disorder of copper deficiency. This, if ignored, results in the animals suffering from a progressive unthriftiness. Today, it has been discovered that if copper sulphate is added to feed which is then given to cattle grazing 'teart' pastures, this disorder can be cured or materially controlled.

Fifty years ago the demand for English grown teazel heads was seemingly insatiable. Some 10 million heads were harvested each year, which is not so surprising when one considers that a 30-metre roll of densely textured cloth may wear out 3,000 heads.

Profits from the crop are still attractive but those prepared to take the trouble to grow it have steadily declined. Today, it is said, only one teazel merchant, Edmund Taylor (Teazel) Ltd. of Huddersfield, remains in business, and he is supplied by but a few growers, one of whom was, until 1984, Alfred Male of Fivehead, Taunton, Somerset, whose family have been growers of this crop for several generations. There are still four growers in Somerset, one of whom is Mr. Foote of Encie Farm, Penselwood, near Wincanton.

Teazel seed is, so to speak, a by-product from the heads, for, when these are hung upside down and dry, the seeds drop or may be gently tapped out with ease. Alfred Male always saved seed from his largest and best heads, and he reckoned to grow about 0.8 hectare each year. He sowed 3.36 kg per hectare in a seed bed in March, with a ratio of seed bed to crop of 1:20. Weed control, particularly in the early stages, is vital, for the small plants suffer badly from any competition. In early autumn he lifts the plants and shortens their roots before putting them out in the field. The rows should be 30 in. apart and the plants spaced at 24 in. intervals.

In the next year he expected a good plant to grow six feet high and carry some 25 heads of varying sizes, which will be ready for harvest in July/August. (From my own experience, I can add that, as the whole plant is armed with extremely vicious hooks, anyone working in this crop will need to wear tough and all-enveloping clothing.) The heads are ready for cutting when the hooks harden and before they lose all their greenness, and as each head is ready (the top 'King' size ones will be first) it is cut off with a small sharp knife, to leave some 23 cm. of stem attached to the head.

When gathered, the heads are tied into bunches of 50 and then fastened on to long poles each of which holds 18 bunches (900 heads). By one means or another the poles are then hung up — outside if the weather is dry, but at the least suspicion of dampness, they must be moved to an open-ended barn, for the heads will very soon go mouldy under wet or even damp conditions. When the cut heads are thoroughly dry the stems will crackle when squeezed.

Teazel is sold by the pack of 20,000 heads. Mr. Male gives an average yield of 30 packs per hectare, with a good crop perhaps yielding forty-two. Teazel crops should not follow one another on the same ground.

The merchant inspects the harvested crop before it leaves the farm to go north by road to his premises. Here it is sorted and graded a process which may result in up to a quarter having to be rejected because the heads are either misshapen or of inferior quality.

All home-grown teazels are graded into lengths ranging from small buttons of two and a half centimetres to the 10 centimetre king size. The larger heads, which are the strongest, are cut off the stem, drilled and slid onto spindles. These spindle-mounted teazels are for use on wool, cashmere and mohair. The smaller teazels are trimmed so as to retain a small stem and these are packed into heavy metal rods, 24 of which are mounted onto a drum, and this when revolved in the opposite direction to the cloth being teased produces the nap.

To this day, for the production of the finest and densest nap, there is nothing to beat an English-grown teazel. Look closely at a guardsman's uniform, and reflect that the smooth, almost waterproof, finish given to the material from which it is made has been achieved by the hooked seedheads of a plant.

An insight into one of the uses of coriander (*Coriandrum sativum* is given by J. C. Drummond[16] who writes that *The London and Country Brewer*, first published in 1738, proved so popular that several editions were brought out before 1800. In it the anonymous author stated that it was written to inform the public which had for so long,

> Suffered great Prejudices from unwholesome and unpleasant Beers and Ales, by the Badness of the Malts, underboiling of Worts, mixing injurious Ingredients and the Unskilfulness of the Brewers.

His undesirable ingredients include the seeds of *Cocculus indicus* (a poisonous drug used by Italians in medicine), which gave a bitter flavour and a 'heady' character to weak beers. The effect on the drinker was stupefying due to the presence of the poisonous compound picrotoxin. Coriander seeds, which are less harmful than *cocculus*, were also used and were relied upon to mask flavours in 'off beers' or to give flavour to one which was too 'thin'.

A. W. Squier, of Doggetts Farm, and other farmers in the Rochford district, had been growing coriander seed, which was sold for its oil, from about 1920, when in 1961 something happened to the crop, which resulted in its dying-off at the flowering stage and even the small quantity of seed that was produced was devoid of good quality oil. For the next five years much work was done on this problem by all sorts of bodies (see correspondence in possession of the Squier family), but no firm conclusions were reached. After this supplies of coriander were imported from Morocco, where the climate gave rise to seeds with a high proportion of oil and, for a time, little or none of this crop was grown in Essex. Nevertheless, distillers of gin still maintain that English-grown coriander produces the best flavour in their product and during the 1980s there has been some revival of this crop.

E. H. Ashby, Insteps Farm, Wakes Colne

'Father is at the other farm, in the barn. He's expecting you and will like to talk — you follow me'. So said David Ashby one cold, bright morning in January 1979. It was two-coat weather and we found Mr. Ashby well wrapped up and with an electric stove blowing heat at his back. There was an extra seat at the bench under the window where he was picking over a bag of runner beans. Clearly we were to talk and work, so I put my notebook and pencil to one side and settled to enjoy sorting beans and to learn many things. For about an hour Mr. Ashby reminisced, and every now and again interjected, 'You'd better leave off a minute a note that down'!

It was 60 years since this old gentleman had first trodden out seed by riding one horse and leading another, round and round on a heap of ripe and matured cabbage, turnip or swede seed.

Of beans and parsnips he recalled that in his young days they were thrashed with a flail, and that later a peg or a cylinder drum was used. These thrashing drums were made by Hunts of Earls Colne, and for beans have to have their concaves set just right or the germination of the seed is spoiled. To begin with both these crops were cut by hand, beans with a hook and parsnips with hook and hank. They were then built up into large pikes made round a fork full of straw until they measured six feet from one side to the other. With parsnip seed you had to wear your shirt and roll the sleeves down because the juice from the stems can cause nasty blisters. Once completed, the pike was thatched and left to mature and dry until it was ready, and there was time to 'knock the seed out'. This they did on a cloth in the stackyard or in the barn on the then boarded floor of the throughway between the great doors. Tripods replaced pikes in the early 1940s but, until 1946 when the Leverton Pea Cutter came on to the market and was found also to be useful for cutting runner beans, these crops continued to be cut by hand.

In those days flea beetles, known as 'Jacks', destroyed acres and acres of crops each year and the land had to be re-sown, at least once and sometimes twice. Control was attempted by tying two paraffin-soaked sacks to a hurdle and then dragging this over the beetle-ridden crop. By this means the beetles were deterred but not totally prevented from eating the leaves of the crop.

Today, one does not think of 'debs' as recent implements but in fact they were an innovation as recently as the late 1700s. Previous to their use it had been customary to sow seed broadcast (as distinct from in rows). In this case seed in a wooden or basket container, or a cunningly fashioned 'Lip' or 'Fan' of coiled or plaited hay or straw, was held by a strap fastened across the shoulders of the sower. It was after a visit to Norfolk in the late 1700s[15] that someone introduced 'debbing' into Toppesfield. At first it was ridiculed but when the 'debbed' crop outdid that which had been broadcast, the idea gained wide acceptance. Furthermore, this tool, unlike many of its successors, created rather than saved labour as is shown when, in 1800, John Saville, of Braintree, is recorded as having financed a business for the making of hemp into cloth in order to provide employment for the workless weavers, and he also created extra work by introducing 'debbing' on to his farm.[16]

By Mr. Ashby's day a set of 'debs' would have been found on almost every holding. There were three main types:

i. those for putting in seed corn, which were made in pairs, of iron, and had handles the length of a walking stick (these sometimes had a row-marker, angled from one side of the handle at a height to mark the soil as the deb was pushed into the ground.
ii. a stouter and shorter version, with a wooden handle, for beans.
iii. another, with an angled wooden handle (which had usually been made from a root in the hedgerow that the owner had marked down for the purpose because of the angle of its growth) fitted to a stout iron or steel point which was used for setting out plants. When these plants were swedes 'it was a cold old job' for the leaves of this plant hold the dew.

It was the custom around Witham to cut peas with a hook and hank. By this method a man would cut an acre a day. Around the Colnes and some parts of Tendring Hundred they used a tool known as a 'peasmake', which was considered to be more old-fashioned.

As might be expected of one who had spent all his life among seeds, Mr. Ashby could

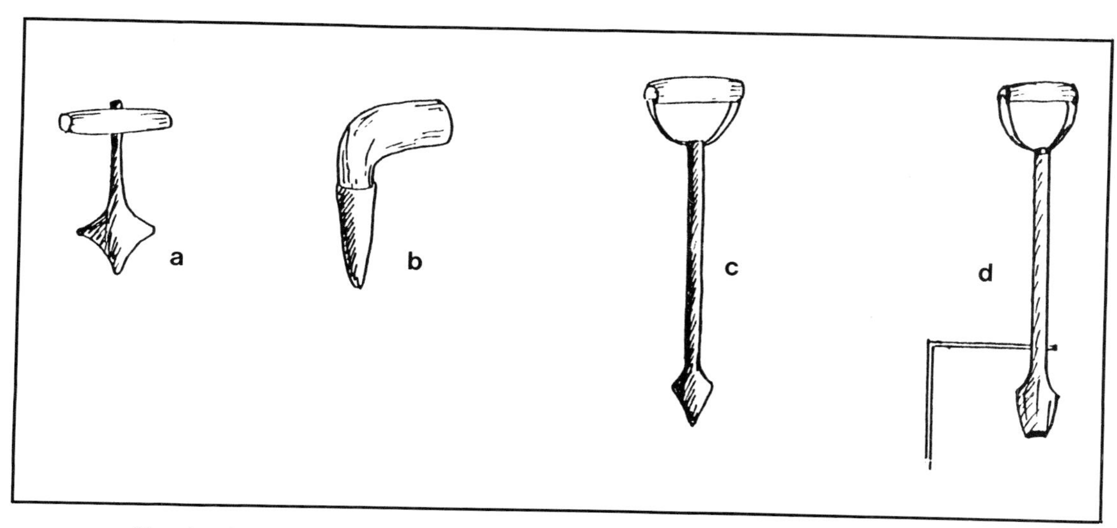

98. A selection of debs: (a) bean; (b) plant; (c) corn; (d) corn with row marker.

make a flail. Not many people are still able to fashion this ingenious and functional tool and so, despite his warning that 'you will have to have several tries before you can make one that is any good', I took down his instructions with care.

> The piece which rotates round the top of the handle is the most difficult. Make this first as two or three attempts may be necessary. Select a straight-grained and unknotted piece of ash, elm or hazel (he prefers hazel). Mark this along its length into three equal sections. Bore out the inside from each end section and leave a wall some quarter-inch thick. Cut away the central section so as to leave just a one and a quarter inch wide by a quarter inch thick connection between the two ends. Then split the ends along their length and both in the same place, so as to ensure that when they are bent over the top of the stick they will come together neatly. The two end pieces should now open up sufficiently to allow a groove to be hollowed out at about half an inch from the loop end. This groove is to take the knob at the top of the stick (handle) and the fit should be easy so as not to impede the movement of the top when in use. Next, hold the middle cut-away section of the top over a saucepan of boiling water and, as it becomes pliable, gently but firmly bend it so as to make a loop. Fit the hollowed-out end sections of the top over the knob end of the stick with their sides meeting. Then secure with a leather thong tied some half an inch from the lower end. (A small groove is often cut here to prevent the thong from slipping off.)
>
> The stick is made to fit the man and should reach from the floor to the chest of the owner.
>
> Now make the swingle. Ideally this should be of whitethorn but holly wood will serve. It must be half the length of the stick and some one and a half inches in diameter. Over the top of the swingle fix a loop made from a stout piece of harness leather. The total length of the leather will need to be about 15 inches and the width, one to one and a quarter inches. Tie the swingle to the rotating piece on the top of the stick by loosely threading a half inch thong of strong leather, or an eel skin, twice through the leather and the wooden loop. Tie securely with a reef knot.

The late Mr. E. H. Ashby was a member of the original Essex Seed Growers Association, and he later became active on the Essex Root and Vegetable Committee. His son David is currently a member of the Seed Zoning Committee. and Chairman of the Root, Vegetable and Flower Seed Committee of the Essex National Farmers' Union.

W. A. Church (Bures) Ltd., Bures, Suffolk

W. A. Church Ltd. is an Essex border firm which has already been directed by four

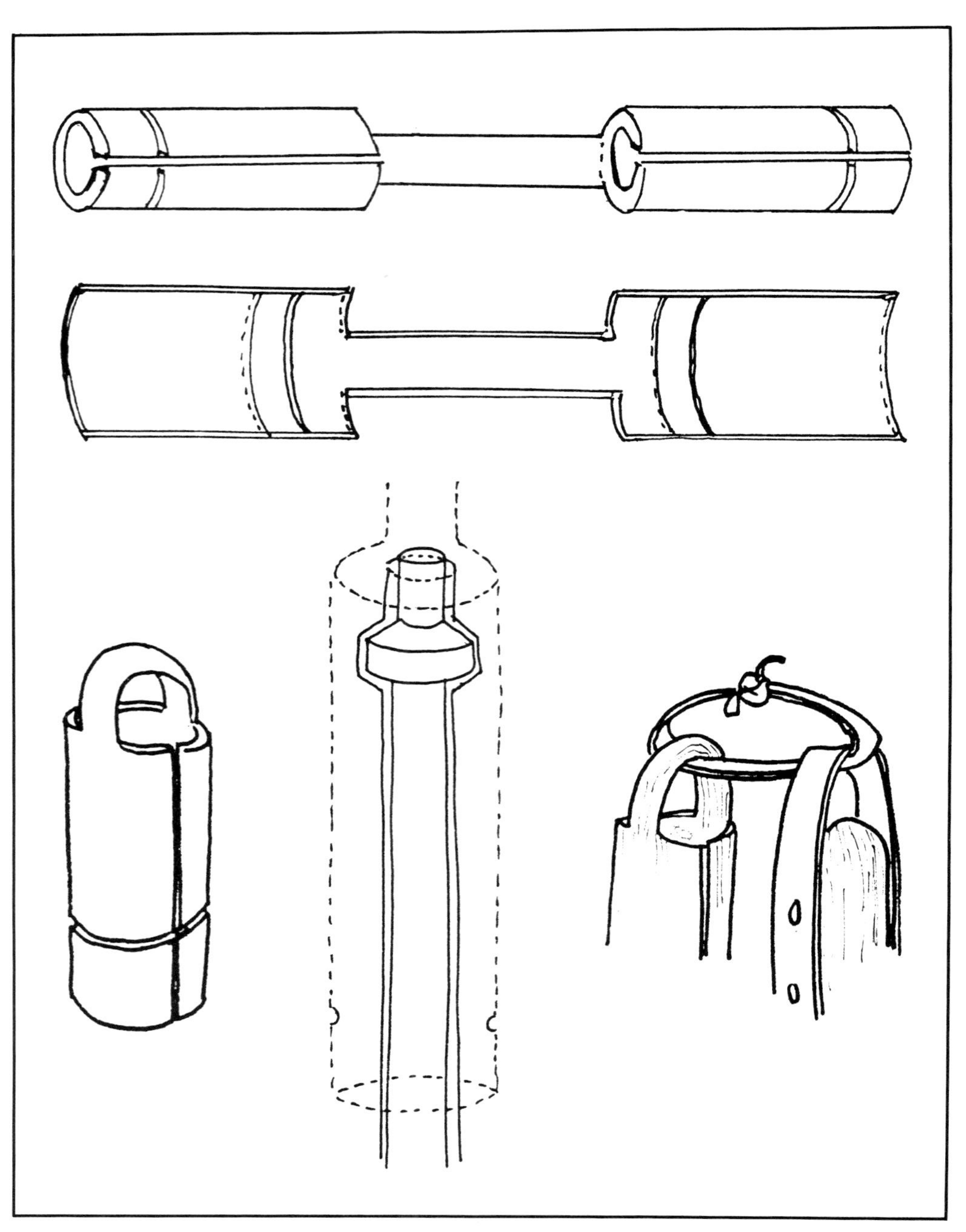

99. Parts of a flail.

generations of the founding family. Arthur Church of Hellen's Farm in Birch came from a long line of farming stock and his three sons seemed to be set to follow this tradition until, with the outbreak of the Boer War in 1899, William (b. 1879) the eldest left home and went abroad to fight with the 43rd Company of the Imperial Yeomanry.

It is never easy to settle into one's home environment after a period of unshared and traumatically different experience and, on his return, William probably reasoned that now the war had finished corn prices were likely to plummet and arable land to go back to grass. It is probable that he also needed a wider interest than that provided by the farming life of the day as well as some addition to his income. There was at this time a promising trend towards the production of more suitable varieties of reliable grass and clover seeds for pasture and, therefore, in 1902 he started his agricultural seed firm.

All went well until 1915, at which point William Church began to suffer from pernicious anaemia. As a very sick man he held on until 1919 when he died leaving a family too young to take on the responsibility of the business.

100. Willam Arthur Church who founded the firm.

101. D. W. and A. L. Church examining samples of seed in their Bures office.

The executors of William's will were his two brothers G. T. and J. G. Church and they decided to manage the seed business between them until their nephews were old enough to take over. This they did and during their time the firm continued to make steady progress until, in 1934, a private limited company was formed and control was handed back to William's sons, Leslie and Douglas Church.

A most interesting scrap book has been kept by this firm. It contains newspaper cuttings telling of the closing of some local corn exchanges; a record of yields and prices of red clover seed from 1914 to 1963 (Appendix H); accounts of awards won by growers of their seeds at the Toronto Seed Fair and itineraries of tours arranged by the Seed Trade Association (United Kingdom) in collaboration with the Federazione Internationale Sementi.

When French seedsmen are under discussion it is inevitably the establishment of Vilmorin-Andrieux which takes pride of place. If for nothing else, they are universally known, and deserve to be, for their beautifully illustrated books *Les Plantes Potageres*, *The Vegetable Garden*, and *Les Fleurs de Plein Terre*, which continue to be used for reference to this day. The remarkably good illustrations are copper engravings, set on wood. Electrotypes of these were sold and have since served to illustrate many books and catalogues throughout the world. This firm has in its library an early unpriced seed list for the year 1766.

When reading the report issued after a visit of British seedsmen to this company in 1950, one has the impression that a certain standard of charming formality was, and one hopes still is, maintained. It is also apparent that the party was impressed by what they were shown for the report contains remarks such as:

> Undoubtedly the largest seed firm in France, and must be one of the biggest in the world. Established in 1747 and their ramifications really terrific . . . have never seen so much seed cleaning machinery in one place, or so much storage accommodation. It is larger even than the premises of Messrs. Weibull in Sweden . . . 200 employers; grain and seed-cleaning machines turn out 150 tonnes a day; and the mangold seed cleaning machines turn out 70 tonnes a day . . . There was an air of distinction and dignity about this seed firm which made a most favourable impression.

Church's certainly brought back some new ideas for it was not so long after this visit that their seed cleaning machinery was brought up to date by the addition of a Craven Nickerson (Cravnic) needle pea sorter.

102. The picturesque offices of W. A. Church Ltd.

Over the years and as the demand for root and cabbage seed diminished, this business has continued to hold its own by expanding its contracts for herbage seeds and for garden peas and, when the national scheme for the inspection of herbage seeds came into being in 1956, Church's representatives were among the first to go for training.

The firm moved to its present picturesque offices in 1959, at which time also a laboratory was established of sufficient standing to qualify for an official licence for the testing of seeds. Today, if you find yourself in Bures, make time to visit these offices, for, even if you have no business to transact within, along their frontage is a beautifully carved beam, the paint of which has been restored to its original Tudor colours. The building is thought to have been the house of a weaver and it is a great credit to the Church family that they have restored what had become an almost derelict workshop, living accommodation and grain store.

Over the years this firm has developed an export and import trade through the ports of Ipswich, Felixstowe, Southampton and London. Mr. D. W. Church also remembers that,

> freight was arranged through W. Fieldgate and Son, on Hythe Quay, Colchester. The Fieldgates had established their business in 1899 and they were shipbrokers, warehousemen, stevedores and Lloyds agents. Their boat sailed twice weekly from Colchester to Holland.

By their Diamond Jubilee, in 1962, the foreword to W. A. Church's spring catalogue indicates that they were still well into the grass and clover seed trade:

> W. A. Church (Bures) Ltd., have an excellent connection in this country, also abroad, having sold over 300 tons of Red Clover and Herbage Seeds this season to America, Canada, Germany and Holland . . . In recent years the firm has been one of the pioneers of Certified Essex Red Clover and the now popular strain of Kersey White . . . A new grass cleaning and pea-picking plant has recently been installed, also several other important features to assist you.

Further details of what became known as the Eastern Region Local Clover Varieties are given in Appendix I. Many seedsmen and growers became involved with these crops. Mr. H. C. Percival of Lane Farm, Wakes Colne, is remembered by W. A. Church as having grown the basic seed of Kersey White clover for their firm. Mr. E. B. Turner, of Barnston Hall, recalls growing what was called Essex Wild White Clover for Hurst's before 1914,

103. R. A. Fry with the Trojan and some oat specimens.

and that, when using this strain, one plant per square yard was enough in the first year of a ley. During the inspection season, Mr. Fry of Hasler's could always be found somewhere across the fields from his parked car, a well-known Trojan.

Mr. F. Smith, who for years worked tirelessly as Secretary to the Essex Seed Growers Association, was known as 'Sockless' because he was never seen wearing this article of clothing. (I leave it to Mrs. Bolt, daughter of F. T. Smith of Tilbury Hall Farm, Tilbury-juxta-Clare, Suffolk, to write the story of this Association from her own memories and her father's papers.) There was also Mr. G. E. Barrow who delighted in his trial plots of clovers

104. Presentation of herbage seed and clover cups in Church's office: Messrs. Hines, 'Sockless' Smith, R. P. Hawkins and W. Brown (senior).

and, at one time, worked with Pertwee; and Mr. R. P. Hawkins of the East Anglian Institute of Agriculture who, on at least one occasion, is said to have been seen 'having a lively time transporting, in the back of his car, a hive of bees to a clover field', and there were many more, no less meritorious for not having been mentioned.

The start of the Essex Seed Zoning Scheme

Over the centuries the climate of Great Britain has experienced considerable and, on occasion, relatively sudden changes (Appendix J). Variable climatic conditions induce excitement in a plant's genetic make-up and when this happens mutations are liable to occur. This has proved particularly true within the Brassica family which is easily excitable as well as adulterous and has, from its wild, loose-leafed beginnings already produced forms which diverge from hardy kales and drum-headed cabbages to savoys, Brussels sprouts and calabrese. In fact, it was probably the cabbage family (*B. oleracea*) that first gave Essex seed growers the idea that a proper isolation and inspection of their crops in the field was essential. Precisely when this happened is not remembered but it was before 1939 that the first recorded Seed Growers' Association was established in north Essex, and out of this self-funding association grew the Essex Herbage Seed Association and the N.F.U. Root, Vegetable and Flower Seed Committee.

For many years previous to 1942 there had been an unwritten law between the established seed growers and merchants regarding the isolation of their various seed crops. After the outbreak of war in 1939, however, conditions necessitated the growing (rather than the importing) of our nation's seed supplies. This not only gave rise to an increase of acreage and therefore an increasing danger of cross-pollination, but seeds were now being grown by those who did not fully appreciate the vital necessity for a proper isolation of these crops. Inevitably much trouble arose and nationally the Seed Production Committee of the N.I.A.B. was made the focal point for all problems relating to home seed production. At the same time the War Agricultural Executive Committee in every seed-growing county in the country made its arrangements for this increased production.

In October 1942, the N.I.A.B. issued the first of its series of leaflets entitled *Seed Notes*, with the promise that, as far as was practicable, similar notes would be sent to all seed growers at no longer than quarterly intervals. These leaflets contained up-to-date information on the various seed crops, from both cultural and marketing points of view and it was suggested that growers should contact their local E.W.A.E.C. for further advice and information. Again, and with the revival of the existing Wild White Clover Certification Scheme farmers, and particularly those tackling this crop for the first time, were urged thoroughly to acquaint themselves with the requirements of the scheme. This would enable all possible precautions to be taken to avoid rejection of their crop when the time came for its certification.

It is evident that a concerted attempt was being made by scientists, forward-thinking merchants, the farming community and technical officers of the E.W.A.E.C. to bring law and order into the hitherto somewhat neglected and very secretive world of seeds. Patiently, members of the N.I.A.B. Seed Production Committee gradually convinced all concerned that they had a common interest in the production of reliable top grade seeds. As one seedsman has told me, 'It is the only time, that I know of, that the trade has voluntarily put shackles on itself!'

Essex, as a seed-growing county of major importance, was much concerned by these moves and in the autumn of 1942 the E.W.A.E.C. held a Seed Production Conference at the then Essex Institute of Agriculture, Writtle. On this occasion it was agreed that a Seed Zoning Scheme should be formulated and brought into operation in the county. By some time in 1943 the E.W.A.E.C. (Seed Production Committee) issued a note giving details of the Seed Zoning Scheme; the opening paragraph under a map which showed the zones stated that:

> The Essex War Agricultural Executive Committee, the Essex Seed Growers Association, and Representatives of Seed Merchants have jointly agreed that in order to prevent damage to farm and vegetable crops through undesirable cross-pollination, a zoning scheme shall be brought into operation for the 1944 harvest, and thereafter. The zoning scheme provides that except with the written consent of the Committee, no seed crop of the kind prohibited in any of the undermentioned zones may be grown in that zone.

There followed a detailed description of the exact location of zones A, B, C and D, and a statement that,

> The Essex War Agricultural Executive Committee, the Essex Seed Growers' Association and Representatives of Seed Merchants acting jointly, reserve the right to alter the Zoning Scheme at any time.

On 20 February 1945, a 'Seed Growers' Conference' was held in the Public Hall, Witham, at which Mr. O. G. Dorey (E.W.A.E.C. Horticultural Officer) reported upon the progress of the Zoning Scheme, in substance as follows:

> The Essex Seed Zoning Committee, which consisted of four growers, four merchants, one merchant grower and a Technical Officer from the E.W.A.E.C. Seed Production Committee had since its formation in 1942 worked reasonably well during its first year [1943]. Of the crop registration forms sent out 80% had been returned to the Committee; every field had been scheduled and plotted on a map and this had shown areas in which crops tended to be grown so that, in 1944, 12 areas were zoned and maps, showing where these were, had been sent to seedsmen, district committees [E.W.A.E.C.] and others with a direct interest.

The report continued, that zoning by means of colour had also been looked into for mangels but the results were not clear cut and of the 700 acres notified only 450 appeared in the right zone. Therefore there were 250 acres which were at risk to themselves and a danger to others. It was then stated that where mangel crops were found to be in the wrong zone and too close to any other varieties, the grower with the unscheduled crop should be the one to be asked to prevent his crop from flowering.

The scheme had no statutory teeth and, although the more far-seeing seedsmen and growers were sympathetic towards its aims, it is clear that not all was plain sailing. For instance, the opening remarks by the chairman of the conference, Mr. Hollis Clayton, contained the sentence that 'the Committee did not want criticism of a negative character [such as the abolition of the scheme and finding jobs for officials] but suggestions that would prove helpful in maintaining the high standard of Essex seeds'. To which Mr. L. D. C. McLees, then Executive Officer of the E.W.A.E.C., added that 'the two chief causes of trouble were ignorance and cussedness', by which time, one imagines, everyone knew what was expected of them! In 1947 the E.W.A.E.C. sent out a further two foolscap pages of information on the Seed Zoning Scheme. This clearly defined in which zone or part of a zone each crop and each variety of that crop was allowed to be grown.

By 1968 the Essex Seed Zoning Committee had become an offshoot of the National Farmers' Union, Root Vegetable and Flower Seed Committee and in this year appointed a Registration Officer, Mr. G. B. Black, the retiring principal of the Fordson Institute of Agriculture at Boreham, Essex. He was followed in 1974 by Mr. J. R. Keyworth, the retired County Agricultural Officer of Essex, who currently holds this tact-demanding post amidst acres and acres of the oil-seed rape crop.

Difficult cases continued to arise and statutory powers became more and more necessary. To this the N.F.U. gave its backing, but it was not until 1968 that any Government support was given and, at last, an addition to The Plant Varieties Seeds Act of 1964 appeared on the statute book as The Protection of Seed Crops (North Essex) Order, 1968.

One seedsman, L. A. W. Prior, has memories of a very skilled grower, Mr. John Rogers of Easthorpe, who was also somewhat eccentric and extremely anti-officialdom. He once walked from his holding at Easthorpe to Witham (presumably to attend the 1945 conference) where he told the Essex War Agricultural Committee that he had absolutely no intention of complying with their proposed Zoning Committee's rules. It was also recalled that he never paid any rates because his bungalow, which was mounted on wheels, was moved a few yards each year. Nevertheless, he was looked upon by some of the best seed houses as one of their top growers and one who had a quite remarkable eye for plants that were not quite right. If you were in his favour, you might be given a pheasant to take home. In this case it would never show a shot wound! Lastly, incredible as it may now seem, the soil of this nine-acre holding was turned over by him each year, using nothing more mechanical than a good sharp spade.

Chapter Thirteen

Hybridisation Opens Up New Possibilities In Plant Breedings

Our gardeners moderate her [nature's] course on things as if they were her superior.
The Reverend William Harrison (1534-93)

The above somewhat testy remark by the Dean of Windsor indicates that, by at least the latter part of the 16th century, some practical experimentalists were attempting to bring about changes in their plants such as those which had occasionally occurred, by chance, in nature. Perhaps the intuition and keen observation of a few was even then leading them to wonder if these 'sports' were the result of cross-pollination between species of the same genus. Miles Hadfield[1] writes that 'the science of genetics [was] quite unnoticed by the scientific world until 1900'.

In an attempt to provide a differently-coloured or a double bloom, a larger leaf, or a longer root, most nurserymen continued to select by eye and with no inkling of the laws of heredity. Gradually, as they blundered doggedly on, a few began to suspect the existence of genetic laws, that it might matter which plant was chosen to be the male parent, and that some characteristics would dominate and others recede.

The first Englishman who is known to have experimented with deliberate hybridisation is Thomas Fairchild (1667-1729). He had a nursery at the far end of Hoxton in Middlesex and in 1715 he put pollen from the stamens of sweet william plants on to the stigmas of carnations. (Authorities differ as to this date. I have used that given by Richard Gorer in his article for *The Garden*, pp. 52-5, published for the Victoria and Albert Museum Exhibition of 1979.) The result was sterile offspring which differed from both their parents. Labelled 'Mr. Fairchild's Mule', a dried specimen of one of these hybrids may still be seen in the herbarium of the Botanical Department at Oxford.

Another pioneer was Thomas Andrew Knight (1759-1838) who, although he suspected the existence of genetic laws, was unable to discover the principles upon which they were based. He was nevertheless one of the first to recognise the tremendous potential of hybridisation and before he died had come to the conclusion that, in order to produce a new plant, selection and cross-pollination had to be repeated until a stable species was achieved. Therefore in the modern sense and so far as is known, he was the first systematic plant breeder. Dessert fruits, potatoes and cabbages were all improved by his work and, during his 27 years as President of the Horticultural Society of London, he was able to exert a considerable influence on the acceptance of the then new concept of horticulture as a practical science.[2]

As the 19th century progressed, knowledge of plant breeding increased.[3] For instance, the Honourable Reverend William Herbert began to be active in the field of flower hybrids in 1808, and while he was attempting improvement in the winter hardiness of his plants by way of cross-pollination, he discovered that the F1 hybrids were intermediate between their parents in this respect.[4]

In Scotland, a country gentleman named Patrick Sheriff was trying to improve varieties of wheat. By 1819 he had more than 70 individual selections in his trials which, by 1860, had extended to over 12 acres. After working for some 25 years, this persistent individual realised that he was getting nowhere. Then, probably after having read or heard of the work of Thomas Andrew Knight, he realised that he must cross-pollinate his wheat varieties before he made a further selection of individual plants.

John Goss of Devonshire was, by 1820, crossing varieties of peas with a view to finding new types which would be of more value to the grower. He also observed, after crossing a white and a blue variety of pea, that there was a segregation of types in the F1 generation, but he did not realise that this segregation followed a numerical pattern.

As a plant breeder, Russet Burbank of the United States of America was undoubtedly ahead of his time. He gained fame for his work with potatoes, plums, raspberries, blackberries and grasses for lawns. In his breeding he wittingly selected plums for their tolerance towards transport, and he discovered that certain characteristics of the young plant gave a reliable indication as to its character when mature. By making use of these 'guiding characters' he was able to work through more than 300,000 plum seedlings over a period of only 20 years. Furthermore, having successfully produced species hybrids, his genius soon found that repeated back-crossing was required in order to 'fix' a reasonably stable level of production and quality.

During the 1840s, in almost every house there was at least one tenderly nurtured fern. Hybrid varieties proliferated so that in 1866 one seedsman's catalogue was able to list 55 variants of the Hart's Tongue type.

The time was ripe for a conference and in 1899 the Royal Horticultural Society arranged the International Hybridisation Conference to which they invited not only scientists but also practical plant breeders — a daring innovation for those times!

On the continent in 1843, the Austro-Silesian Gregor Johann Mendel (1822-84) entered the Augustinian monastery at Brün. He became abbot in 1860 and carried out experiments there which were at last to provide proof that the phenomena of inheritance are not haphazard but subject to certain laws. His findings were published in 1885, but were not recognised as a 'breakthrough' until they came into the hands of William Bateson in 1899.

Bateson was a scientist studying hybridisation by means of statistics and he had been asked to speak at the R.H.S. 1899 Conference. Before he left home that morning, the postman arrived with a letter from the Dutch botanist and scientist, Hugo de Vries. This contained a copy of Mendel's paper of 1885 which Bateson took with him to read on the journey and, as he read, he recognised that here was something of great significance. In fact, it was the missing link which would provide the key by which future hybridists would be enabled to plan their work and to produce results with far greater certainty. Yet, even today when we have learnt so much more about the application of Mendel's laws, breeding is still not a mechanical application of what the book says, but an art in which only a few individuals are really gifted. Good hybridists are born, not made. It is by no means everyone who, even after training, can select varietal 'parents' for crossing which will produce a worthwhile result. Sometimes, even after a variety has been brought out and admired, it is found to be commercially non-viable because of some difficulty such as a failure to produce a good weight of seed. This has happened with the sweet pea 'Mary Malcolm' and the antirrhinum 'Coral'.

Considering the many Essex seedsmen who were early in the field of hybridisation it is surprising that J. K. King seems to have stuck to the old-fashioned method of selecting plants from an existing stock. Certainly before 1847, Charles Baron was experimenting with hybrid hollyhocks and his work was continued by Chater, who also improved the ageratum. Perhaps in J. K. K.'s time, this was yet another closely-guarded secret.

Between the two world wars, the firm of Clucas of Ormskirk, Lancashire, was actively seeking farmers in Essex who might be considered as suitable growers for their brassica seeds. They were early producers of the hybrid types some of which were grown by Ted Cranmer on East Gores Farm, Little Tey. Ted's daughter still has vivid memories of Tom

Clucas's visits to their farm to inspect his firm's seed crops. This jolly young man, 'with wild red hair', was liable to seize the handle of her pushchair and to rush up and down their drive at break-neck speed, while she 'hung on for dear life', both scared and delighted.

From this time on it became general knowledge that the way ahead was through the breeding of suitable hybrids. Hybridists were employed by almost every seed-producing firm of any size and even the more modest establishments tended to have at least one member of the family who had become familiar with this art and was attempting their own improvements. By 1947 the first stream of hybrids had become, as a result of large-scale scientific breeding, a flood of flower and vegetable varieties of a completely new standard of excellence.

Today breeding methods are immensely complicated. It is already possible to manipulate genes within plant cells and a further aid to breeding is the use of the meristem: the minute (0.1 mm.) innermost growing point of the shoot (see Appendix J for some amplification).

The science fiction aspect of this work emerges with the suggestion that at some future time it might be possible to make crosses not only within the same species, but also between different species. Nevertheless, the future could hold great hope for the starving millions in the world, and there is little doubt that, when we are in danger of over-stepping ourselves, the indefinable force referred to as Mother Nature will step in and prevent us from achieving anything too disastrous.

David Fenwick, M.A., flower seed specialist, By-pass Nurseries, Colchester and Marks Tey

'When my father came down from Oxford in 1936, having studied law, he could not decide what to do with the rest of his life and, to amuse himself, began pottering about in a tumble-down greenhouse on a small patch of land at Stratford St Mary on the Suffolk border'.[5] This young graduate must have become fascinated by what he could achieve under glass for, from that time until his death in 1982, David Fenwick pursued a seemingly unquenchable ambition and became something of a legend in the world of seeds.

As soon as he realised the huge potential then opening up for the production of first-class pot plants, garden centres, cut flowers, and container plants for instant garden displays, he foresaw a market for seeds which had been grown, harvested and cleaned under close supervision by an elite class of contract growers. It very soon became apparent that if plants were to be produced early in the season they would need to be started under glass and later transplanted into the field or repotted and taken through to seeding in a greenhouse. The seed industry has always kept its expertise within the 'family' and so, although by 1966 David Fenwick had become the largest contract grower of glasshouse flower seeds in Great Britain, very few people would have heard of him.[6] Yet, on less than 100 acres of land and about one acre under glass he had world-wide connections, and almost all British flower seed growers would, at some time, have grown seed produced by him.

In his paper 'The Production and Distribution of Flower Seeds', Mr. Fenwick stated that by 1966 almost all the contract flower seed growers in England had concentrated themselves into an area some 20 miles long and rather less wide between Witham and Colchester. Their number was rapidly decreasing and he estimated that there were no more than 25, of which many grew only a very small acreage. These few were responsible for maintaining supplies of the highest class stock seeds and of certain seeds, such as salvia, which need to be grown in this country in order to meet a special requirement of our market.

Some flowers must be very skilfully rogued in order to maintain the correct characteristics for their variety or a good colour balance in mixtures of their seeds. The modern highly-bred varieties of antirrhinums require constant roguing and continual supervision to remove off-types. This roguing is very skilled and only a handful of men in the country can make

105. David Fenwick (fourth from the left) with his staff at Wolverstone Hall, Suffolk, *c.*1944. Many of the girls were members of the Land Army.

a good job of it. Anyone can remove the odd pink plant which comes in a bed of red. Contract growers do this as a matter of course, but they would not presume to rogue an antirrhinum crop for one of these experts, who seem to work to an ideal in their minds. It is impossible to predict which plants they will pull out — often one in ten. The florets may be too far apart, the habit too tall, too short, too bushy, or the colour not the shade at which they are aiming. Most of the quality English firms grow their antirrhinums in Essex. The most skilled job of all is the roguing of a mixture where some of the colours are not completely set. Great experience and knowledge is required to preserve the colour balance as some varieties seed more freely than others, so that several different visits will have to be made and the selection of 30 or so plants for stock may well take many hours.

Lobelia quickly deteriorates in habit of growth and some firms still like to keep their best stocks in Essex, although the bulk of the commercial stocks are now grown in California which has a more reliable climate. Some years ago Mr. David Fenwick had one hundredweight of lobelia seed for a single contract which was worth over £1,000. Some of it would have reached most merchants in due course. When it came to despatching it his foreman was alarmed at the idea of so much money in one sack but he decided that they would put the clean, clearly labelled sack into an old potato bag and send it by ordinary goods train. A hundredweight of lobelia would be as difficult to dispose of as a part of the Crown Jewels.

The international seed business is now so complex and intermingled that it would be tedious to attempt to unravel it in this book. Anyone interested may still gain a good insight into world flower seed distribution by reading pages 24, 25 and 26 of David Fenwick's paper. The complexity of flower seed harvesting and cleaning was also emphasised by him in the following words:

> Flower seed harvesting is roughly divided into two groups, the first where we pick the pods as with Sweet Peas when two or three picks will suffice, or pansy which requires picking every few days for a period of weeks. In this case picking is a high part of the cost. After picking the seeds are relatively easily cleaned. Dahlias are hand-picked but not till after the frost has dried off much of the sap. Helichrysum and annual chrysanthemum have to be picked as soon as dry or the birds will take the crop. Birds can be a great hazard in seed harvesting especially with such crops as cornflower. Some crops like the marigolds are easily picked but need to be dried. In England this means greenhouses or heated driers.
>
> The second group are to my mind the more interesting; here the whole plant has to be cut and dried till it is crisp, it then needs to be thrashed till the whole volume is reduced to dust. We then start the needle in the haystack process. Lobelia is perhaps the finest example. The first process is to sieve away any large pieces and there will not be many of these. The mass then has to be blown on seed dressers to separate as much light matter as possible, this may be done twice and a hundredweight of seed will take a man a week. We are then left with a fine mixture of seed, dust, grit and fine particles of soil. We can then put it again through the dresser and this time with more air so that the seed is blown off and the grit remains. The sample will still not be clean as the minute particles of soil have the same specific gravity as the seed so cannot be separated by air methods. The size is the same so sieves are of no use, so we have to resort to water and the mixture, a small quantity at a time, has to be mixed in buckets of water till the soil dissolves and forms mud which will settle and fall to the bottom, while the seed floats. This then has to be dried quickly so that it does not germinate but the heat must not be too great or ultimate germination will be impaired.
>
> Still the end is not reached; a portion of sand will remain, the same size, the same weight and insoluble, but there is still one difference to exploit. The surface of the seed is more slippery and a skilled man can rye it in a sieve so that the impurities gradually come to the centre when they can be taken off with a knife a few ounces at a time. Some dirt will still remain containing traces of precious seed; these are usually left back till the bad weather gives time to spare when ounce by ounce they can be removed by hand and the dust flicked off with a feather. Lobelia . . . retains its germination for years so there is no hurry to effect delivery.
>
> With flower seeds there is almost infinite variety, conditions will vary from year to year. Some seed is of little value, some of great value, our most expensive is begonia. They all have their problems, some complex, some simple, tagetes for example cannot be put in a sack or if you do you can never clean the sack afterwards and will waste seed as the quills stick in the canvas. We now store the uncleaned seed in dozens of cardboard market flower boxes and the clean seed in paper sacks. Plastic can be dangerous as the seed may sweat and germination will be lost.
>
> Mistakes can be costly if germination is impaired; there is usually only one remedy — the bonfire; equally if two stocks of the same seed become contaminated by error or a badly cleaned dresser or drum, this will be found out by the good merchant on his trial ground and there will be a debit note to the contract grower and the seed returned for destruction.

Seed crops under glass are generally grown on sand-benches which enable the plastic-potted plants to be sub-irrigated.

At the pollination stage glasshouse seed crops have to be most scrupulously protected against any undesirable cross-pollination. For instance, one possible method is to seal a hive of bees into the glasshouse and another is to cross-pollinate by hand, using a paint brush. It is also advisable to know such facts as that the primrose crop pollinates better in

January than April; that bees are not particularly good pollinators of primroses or polyanthus; and that salvias grown for seed in a greenhouse may have to be sprayed with a sugar solution before the bees will work among them.[7]

As the plants come up to seeding they are moved on to a bench covered with a polythene sheet. This is then arranged to form an open box with sides of some eight inches high. Each pot is also provided with a small piece of polythene which covers the compost within. This prevents seeds from dropping on to the compost and so being lost.

The first new horticultural line to be promoted by the National Seed Development Organisation (N.S.D.O.) was hybrid tomatoes. The stock seed of three hybrids had been produced by the Glasshouse Crop Research Institute one at each of their stations. Some of this seed had been multiplied at the N.S.D.O. under strictly controlled conditions and part of the parent seed for the first Kingsley Cross F1 Hybrid seed was entrusted to David Fenwick to be crossed at his nursery. The conditions for growing such seed in order to meet the standards of certification are rigorous. Firstly no other tomatoes except the male and female parents of the cross may be grown on the nursery. Seeds of the two parent lines are sown in March and the resulting plants put out into two separate greenhouses. Stamens from each female parent plant have to be removed from the moment each flower is big enough to handle, otherwise self-fertilisation would occur and cross-fertilised hybrid seed would not result. Four women are responsible for 2,000 plants of the female parent. During the seven weeks before all flowers are set and the plants stopped, they arrange their duty hours so that no flower will escape emasculation. If it does happen that stamen removal does not keep pace with the opening of the flowers, the open flowers must be nipped off, for if any flower becomes self-fertilised and is left to produce seed, it will contaminate the F1 hybrid seed batch.

Pollen from the male parents is collected by a mechanical 'bee' — a piece of metal powered by an electric battery to vibrate over each flower and so shake its pollen into a metal cup. This pollen is then taken to the house containing the female parents and applied to each stigma with the aid of a piece of cane hollowed at one end to take just a few pollen grains. When ripe, the fruit from the male parent is sold for human consumption, and that from the female gathered, crushed, and fermented in a container for 60 hours. By that time scum will have gathered on the surface and can be removed, leaving the seed ready to be washed and sieved six or seven times in plain water before it is dried under a fan at room temperature.

It is at this stage that the seed is officially 'crop approved' by the certifying authority, the N.I.A.B., on the basis of inspections made during the growing season. For the first year the seed is sold as 'crop approved' but, to receive a certificate for 'certified' seed of a named F1 hybrid, this seed must also pass growing-on tests to show that it is true to type and free from disease. A sample of each consignment is retained by the N.I.A.B. for use in the event of any subsequent complaint. Seed of the tomato, if properly stored, will remain in a good condition for several years.

In 1971 the *Gardeners Chronicle*[8] reported on an interview with David Fenwick. It brought out the remarkable foresight of this man and how, by attention to detail in matters of protocol and by correspondence with foreign firms in their own language, he was successfully building up his trade to meet the opportunities of the Common Market. Although, due to their better climates and increasing expertise, foreign countries were wresting the growing of seed crops from England, Mr. Fenwick believed that in the realm of pot-plant seed production we should still be able, so long as a high quality of product and service to the customer was maintained, to compete successfully with the foreign producer.

Primroses, primulas and cinerarias were then this nursery's main lines both for seed production and for sale as pot plants. Mr. Fenwick believed that his firm raised more primroses than any other in Europe, and a mauve cineraria was then selling particularly well to the funeral trade in France.

Before he died, David Fenwick saw the fulfilment of his original belief that there would be a wide demand for first class seed for the pot-plant and container trade. The nursery at Marks Tey, once owned by Dobbies Seeds, is still in use by the firm but all flower seed production is now carried out under glass. Even by 1966 some 20,000 primulas, 4,000 primroses, 6,000 cinerarias and 1,000 begonias were being grown in individual pots on the greenhouse bench for seed. Today, the numbers must be astronomic for the overall size of this business has increased in turnover by more than tenfold. The main seed production is from *Primula acaulis*, *Primula obconica*, *Primula malacoides*, polyanthus, begonia, cyclamen, streptocarpus, cineraria, calceolaria, salvia and coleus. In most cases the seeds produced are F1 hybrids, for which the firm is often involved in pre-production trials.

The vast majority of this firm's production is for export and contracts are currently held with leading seed houses in France, Holland, Switzerland, Germany, Denmark and the United States. A very close co-operation with these customers is maintained and visits from other leading seed breeders are a common occurrence. Furthermore, as a member of Fleuroselect, and as a centre for these trials, the firm is kept fully in touch with all the latest developments in the flower seed trade.

Chapter Fourteen

Seed Testing, Varietal Assessment and Preservation of Varieties

> I doe undoubtedly perswade myself if a true accompt might bee had thereof, those that doe willingly deceive others by false seedes, doe rob the common wealth of a greater summe then all others the robbing theeves of this whole land doe by much . . .
>
> Richard Gardiner (1603)[1]

The post-war public and political climate

The majority of this island's population, except when in imminent danger of suffering from hunger, quickly forgets that its ultimate survival is dependent not upon the business of our cities but upon a constant supply of food. The result is that our agriculture, time and again, has been subjected to a 'stop-go' policy excused on the grounds of political expediency.

During the Second World War, food imports to Great Britain almost ceased and home producers, who had suffered years of neglect, once more gamely rallied to try to fill the gap. After this war, the fear of starvation was remembered for a while and for the first time in our history the Government, industry, research institutions, merchants and growers made a concerted effort to ensure that such a state of affairs would never happen again.

It was in these post-war years that institutions such as the Official Seed Testing Station and the National Institute of Agricultural Botany banded together with more recently established bodies such as the National Vegetable Research Station, the Grassland Research Institute, the Pea Grower's Research Organisation, the National Agricultural Advisory Service and many others, to provide the scientific and technical back-up that was needed. Their work, coupled with the practical skills of our farmers and growers in its application, has produced results that are no less than phenomenal. It is to be hoped that today's and future generations of townsfolk, before complaining of the cost, will acquaint themselves with the true worth of this investment in agriculture; that they will not mistake neglect for conservation, and will support every effort to ensure that, even though the pressure to produce may need to be relaxed for a while, our farmland and our knowledge of how to increase yields remains in a state from which, when needed, it can be readily returned to at least the level of food production that was achieved in the early 1980s.

Seed care and improvement are of particular concern to the O.S.T.S., the N.I.A.B. and the N.V.R.S., and therefore there follow some short notes on these institutions as well as some facets of this section of their work.

The Board of Agriculture's Official Seed Testing Station

Early seed testing

The Adulteration of Seeds Act was passed by Parliament on 11 August 1869. Also in 1869, Professor Nobbe of Tharandt, near Dresden, Saxony, set up what has been recognised as the first laboratory expressedly for the testing of seeds. Similar institutions quickly followed throughout Germany, France, Austria, Switzerland, Italy, Denmark and, between 1877 and 1900, in many American states, Vienna, Budapest, Zurich and Paris.[2]

In England, although some of the more progressive seed houses recognised the benefit of such testing, there were many merchants, growers and other sellers of seeds such as ironmongers, grocers, corn chandlers and apothecaries who, through ignorance, vested interest or sheer dislike of change, were bitterly opposed to any such innovation. That seed may vary in quality has probably been recognised almost from the time that agriculture began but, until quite recently, very little was understood as to what actually constituted this quality. In fact it was not until the advent of high-powered microscopes that it was even suspected that a germination test needed to be anything more than arbitrary tests of sight, taste and smell. For generations it was not realised that seeds might pass these tests and even win prizes at shows, and yet be quite unsuitable for sowing because of the presence of a disease virus, bacteria, or spore within or on their walls. (Appendix K)

Those seed houses who wished to maintain their reputation of trust and respectability attempted, within the knowledge of their day, to supply a good quality product. As the trade grew and then boomed, it was inevitable that others, seeing the chance to make a quick penny, sold seed from any source, of any age and very doubtful quality and, before it was harvested, moved on to peddle their wares and con an ever gullible public elsewhere. For 32 years following the Act of 1869, those having more knowledge, foresight and thought for the public good continued to fight for better seeds and, in the summer of 1900, a departmental committee[3] was appointed by the Board of Agriculture to enquire into conditions under which agricultural seeds were sold in this country.

Amongst the 15 seed merchants, seven farmers and six scientific experts called to present evidence, were two from Essex: Nathaniel Sherwood, representing Messrs. Hurst and Company, and J. W. Moss, who described himself as a farmer who grew seeds for the trade. Several of these witnesses gave instances of seed adulteration which had occurred in the past and, although barely admitted, it seems clear that the practice was still not unknown.

An instance is given for the year 1859, when dearer seeds were reported to have been bulked up with similar-looking seeds of lesser value. These latter had been 'killed' to prevent detection. Again, in 1860, a reputable seed house had been offered for £2 a machine which would kill seeds for adding to the bulk. The Commissioners, of course, were assured that this offer had been refused. On 27 November 1877, it was reported in *The Times* newspaper that seven sacks of charlock seed (a troublesome agricultural weed) had been offered on Mark Lane for admixture (with similar-looking cruciferous seeds) and on 29 November this was followed by a report that a Mile End seed merchant had been summoned to the Mansion House, to appear before the Lord Mayor for infringement of the Adulteration of Seeds Act of 1869.

Messrs. Sutton and Sons' witness advised against the buying of cheap seeds as these were 'almost certain to have been adulterated either by similar seeds which had lost vitality by age or had been boiled or kiln dried'. Again, there were cases when the seed, and particularly grass seeds, had been so improperly cleaned that the sample, when analysed, was found to contain as much as 50 per cent trash. Some seeds were even dyed to improve their appearance and clovers were found bulked out with dyed sand grains of similar size to the seeds.

In 1901 the Commission issued its report. A summary of it appears in an article[4] describing the Aynsome Agricultural Station's seed-testing laboratory at Grange-over-Sands, Lancashire, where, immediately after the publishing of the report, the Director had decided to establish a seed-testing station on the most modern lines which were then known. (This station was providing tests on a commercial basis by 1903.)

Up to 1903 almost the only seed testing done in this country was carried out by the respective botanists in the two leading Agricultural Societies. This was almost entirely limited to their members whose use of the facility was rare. Gradually as the need and commercial advantages were appreciated by seed merchants, farmers and growers, members of the University, College and Farm Institute staffs were asked to perform these tests.

By 1917 it was obvious that, to be of any real value, rules and standards which were enforceable by law, and improvements to and standardisation of the testing methods, were essential. For admirable as the attempts to provide better seeds were in concept, in practice, both here and on the Continent, they lacked any uniformity of methods by which the tests were carried out and so no comparison was possible.

Some 300 years had elapsed since Richard Gardiner's outburst, but it is clear from the following paragraph from the Aynsome Agricultural Station's report that little had been done to remedy the matter during the intervening years.

> Unless the seed used by the farmer be genuine, or true to name — comparatively pure, or free from weed seeds and dangerous fungi inimical to healthy growth — and the bulk of the seed respond readily to the germination test, the crop must fail to remunerate the sower.

On 12 November 1917, the first Testing of Seeds Order (no.1156) came into force in Great Britain. This was immediately followed by the opening on 14 November of the Official Seed Testing Station (O.S.T.S.) at the Food Production Department of the Board of Agriculture, 72 Victoria Street, Westminster, S.W.1.

The O.S.T.S. Report of 1918[5] shows that 7,744 seed samples had been received for analysis. Of these 5,676 had been sent in by 492 seedsmen; 1,553 by 772 farmers, landowners and allotment holders, and 515 which were tested for the Board of Agriculture and other public departments. The tests highlighted the problems ahead, for six per cent of the wheat samples had a germination capability of less than 50 per cent: perennial rye grass samples might contain as much as 10 per cent of Yorkshire fog and soft brome grass seeds, and the parasite dodder (*Cuscuta species*) was found in just under a quarter of the red clover samples. The report continues that with the necessity to perform these tests promptly the staff of the O.S.T.S. came under such pressure that assistance had had to be sought from staff within the other agricultural departments and from college authorities. It is here that a connection is seen with another Essex character, still remembered with amusement and affection by many former students who were trained at the East Anglian Institute of Agriculture, Market Road, Chelmsford. Mr. Robson, a man of great character and integrity, whose teaching methods and mechanical inventions were far ahead of his time, was one of those released to help with the volume of seed testing which according to the report extended 'over and above the University vacations'. (Before 1930 he had constructed a machine on the principle of a vacuum cleaner, which successfully removed Frit Fly from an oat crop.[6])

The forerunners of today's M.A.F.F. leaflets began to be issued in 1894. They are constantly being up-dated and have remained among the most reliable and easily understood sources of information for farmers and allied trades. The first of a series prepared by the O.S.T.S. was *Food Production Leaflet, No. 47* and was expressly for the guidance of seed-growing farmers. At the same time the O.S.T.S. released the eighth in its own Seed Testing Series (S.T.S.), *Notice to Seedsmen.*

Because conditions were extremely cramped in Victoria Street, during 1919 the station moved to 18 Leighton Court Road, Streatham Hill, S.W.16. Here there was more accommodation together with a small garden and glasshouse.[7] It is just possible that this was Nathaniel Sherwood's former home (see p.104) — his grandson believes that the property was sold by the family at this time.

Sir George Stapleton will always be remembered for his work on pasture grasses and the production of the 'S' strains. It is less well-known that he was the first Director of the O.S.T.S. where, in 1917, before he left to take up the Chair of Agricultural Botany at the University College of Aberystwyth, he had already initiated an ambitious project on the behaviour of seeds during storage.

Seed samples submitted for the year ending 31 July 1919 had greatly increased in number. There had been:

23,604 samples from 808 seed firms
4,541 samples from 2,467 farmers (only 65 samples from Essex)
5,113 samples from Public Departments.

The increase in samples from Public Departments was largely accounted for by 2,000 samples of oats tested before shipment to our cavalry in France, and by an increased number of 'control' samples.

That year (1918-19) was the first in which seeds of forest trees were tested, a task which has now been transferred to the Forestry Commission's Research Station at Alice Holt, near Farnham in Surrey. Miles Hadfield[8] writes that in the 1790s,

> From the Marquis of Buckingham's woods at Gosfield Hall, (near) Braintree, were procured 'most sorts of fir-tree seeds' that were sown in England.

Today, Essex provides seeds of the Sessile oak for use by the Forestry Commission. They come from Bovingdon Hall, Braintree. (The Sessile oak has no stalk on the acorn but a stalk on the leaf. The more common oak, to be found in Essex, is the Pedunculate and it has a stalk on the acorn but no stalk on the leaf.)

The first seed regulations in the United Kingdom are embodied in the Seeds Act of 1920. These regulations are administered by the Seeds Branch of the Ministry of Agriculture, Fisheries and Food, and lasted until replaced by the Plant Varieties and Seeds Act of 1964, with an Amendment in 1967. It was after 1964 that a Plant Varieties and Seeds Division was established in London by the Ministry. Today seedsmen have also to abide by the regulations within the European Communities Act of 1972, and there are also International Rules for Seed Testing,[9] and the Seeds National List of Varieties Regulations of 1979.

Before the start of the seed testing year on 1 August 1921, it was decided that the O.S.T.S. should move from Streatham to new accommodation within the complex of the National Institute of Agricultural Botany, Cambridge, of which it then became a branch, and here it remains (1985), grappling with the many problems which continue to arise.

Today the O.S.T.S.s in Great Britain are located in Cambridge, Edinburgh and Belfast: each is responsible to the appropriate Minister for carrying out all official or statutory tests as required by Seeds Acts or Regulations. Private licensed seed testing stations, such as those attached to seed firms, only operate as official satellite stations to one of the three official stations.

National Institute of Agricultural Botany

A faint suggestion that such a body as the National Institute of Agricultural Botany (N.I.A.B.) was needed, was made by Professor T. B. Wood as early as 1912. During the Food Production Campaign of the First World War it became clear to the Board of Agriculture, certain scientists and the more forward-thinking members of the seed trade, that if crop yields were to be improved something more than an Official Seed Testing Station was required. It was also apparent that for the project to be a success there must be agreement between a widely differing collection of people, several of whom were extremely secretive, while others had an underlying fear of being made to look foolish by the scientists or by those with practical expertise.

Many meetings and much patient and honest discussion between all parties, even those who were but remotely concerned, gradually brought about a greater understanding and a will to follow Edward Sherwood's advice to 'co-operate with officials — do not fight them'. At the same time the officials learnt that when dealing with matters affected by such variables as the weather, sometimes, to make things work at all, the rules must be capable of some flexibility and that not every seedsman was 'a rogue and a vagabond'. Even more marked, once they had got on to the same wavelength, was the mutual respect which grew up between those with practical seed-growing and merchanting knowledge and the scientists. Reports from meetings held during this period are models of painstaking firmness and quite extraordinary tact on the part of the N.I.A.B. council and its various committees so that, by 1919, all sides were beginning to understand their interdependence.

To finance this project a Trust Deed was launched and, as Treasurer of the Agricultural Seed Trade Association, Edward Sherwood was made responsible for the collection of donations from its members. The Minutes from a meeting held on 9 December 1918 record contributions from Essex firms as follows:

Cooper, Taber and Company Ltd.90 Southwark Street, S.E.1	£1,000
J. E. N. Sherwood Esq. (Hurst and Son) 152 Houndsditch, E.1	£1,000
Hasler and Company, Dunmow, Essex	£500
T. Cullen and Sons, Witham, Essex	£100
E. W. King and Company, Coggeshall, Essex	£100
J. Ottwell Polley, Ewell Hall, Kelvedon, Essex	£50
Barnard Brothers, Newport, Essex	£25
Thomas Bradbridge and Company, Great Bardfield, Essex	£21
C. B. and A. Sworder, Epping, Essex	£10 10s.
Chas. J. Taylor, Billericay, Essex	£10 10s.

On the early morning of 14 October 1921, the N.I.A.B. staff, in company with that of the O.S.T.S., who by then were also operating from Howe's Place, Huntingdon Road, Cambridge, busily made the final preparations for the official opening by King George V and Queen Mary. The objectives which its Director and Council were entrusted to fulfil were the improvement, introduction and distribution of seeds, plants and crops; the improvement of husbandry methods; the provision of buildings, equipment and trained staff for the purpose; and the encouragement of research, the taking-out of patents and the provision of awards and prizes within the various fields of activity. Furthermore, the results of trials were to be co-ordinated and published each year together with any useful new cultural advice then available for the grower, farmer or seedsman. Anyone who is unfamiliar with just what this entails is encouraged to read Sir Harold Sanders's clear summary of the development, organisation and seemingly endless ramifications of this, by now, world-respected institution.[10]

In order to make a start on the improvement of seed varieties, it was first necessary to gather together, remove the synonyms from, classify and sort into some sort of yield potential the many varieties of seeds available in this country. Only after this has been done is it possible for those varieties showing most promise to be subjected to further tests and trials for qualities such as resistance to disease or suitability for a specific purpose, in order that they may be judged as acceptable or otherwise for inclusion on one or another of the N.I.A.B.'s Recommended Lists ('R.L.s'). In fact, the task has proved so time-consuming that it has only been possible to deal with one type of crop at a time and, even in 1986, there are still many crops for which there is not yet a Recommended List. Furthermore, each year new varieties come on to the market and these must be tested to ensure that they really are new and not re-submissions under another name. If genuinely new, the variety is accepted for inclusion on the United Kingdom's National List and on the sample, as well as tests for quality and disease resistance, the N.I.A.B. conducts unbiased field trials on different types of soil and in different geographical locations throughout England and Wales. The most promising are further tested in N.I.A.B. trials and on selected farms by the Agricultural Development and Advisory Service. Thus every year the Institute can recommend those varieties which are as good as, or better than, the best already on their 'R.L.s'.

Also published annually by the N.I.A.B. is a Classified List of all tested varieties which indicates the main performance characters of all those on the United Kingdom National List.

Each year the publication of the up-dated 'R.L.s' is eagerly awaited by plant breeders, farmers, merchants and advisers for they contain a quantity of easily understood information and have gained and maintained a reputation for reliability and integrity which is recognised far and wide. It was even said that if a plant breeder's new variety failed to gain a place on its appropriate 'R.L.' this was almost tantamount to its death warrant and, remember, this is but one aspect of the work of this most important establishment.

The National Vegetable Research Station, Wellesbourne, Warwickshire

In the mid-1940s the need to reinforce our diet with more vegetables, and particularly vegetable oils and proteins, became apparent. Fortuitously, medical evidence also came forward which strongly suggested that vegetable fats were better for our health than those from animals. This, in its turn, helped to remove the age-old prejudice that vegetable substitutes for meat were only for the financially-poor and underdeveloped communities, and so even when the war was over the idea continued to gain acceptance.

Clearly, if the needs of modern society were to be met, a major reorganisation of our vegetable production had to take place. What happened was that, for all practical purposes, vegetables left our small market and kitchen gardens for the arable fields and commercial glasshouses. At the same time, although there was still a ready market for good quality greengrocery, an increasing tonnage was absorbed for canning, freezing and other processing industries. As has been said, this change, with developments in the field of mechanisation, the use of chemicals and the dissemination of new husbandry technology, all helped to prevent seed wastage and so there was a fall in the quantity of seeds used. However, a supply of seeds of guaranteed growing quality which would give rise to plants bred to suit a particular market became even more necessary.

Many of the hybrid Brussels sprouts and cabbages are bred to mature at almost the same time which is an advantage to the processor and enables the grower to clear his field at one go and to proceed immediately to prepare the land for the next crop. This type of seed is of no advantage to the domestic gardener who usually wants to use his vegetables over a period of time. On the other hand, those hybrid flowers which do not readily go to seed are liked by the gardener but are a bane to the seed-grower.

To appreciate how crucial it is to have reliable seed it is only necessary to be aware that, provided it is good, one ounce of tomato seed costing, say, £2 or less is all that is required to produce enough plants for one third of an acre of glasshouses. The resulting crop can be worth several thousands of pounds.

A survey group, appointed to assess the facilities available for the improvement of vegetables, found these to be inadequate for the task. Even the first sorting of the mass of varieties which accrued from each seedsman was made especially difficult as there were few true synonyms amongst them. This meant that they could not be reduced by the relatively quick Observation Plot method, but would need to be assessed in trials over a number of years. By October 1947 the establishment of a vegetable research station had been recommended and agreed by H.M. Treasury. Its first quarter-century is described in the N.V.R.S. Report for 1974 (repr. 1975)[11] and, therefore, nothing but the station's relationship with the County of Essex and a few words about the gene bank will be given here.

A firm connection with Essex was established from the day after the station's governing body was legally incorporated when, on 29 September 1947, two properties were finally chosen from the 318 which had previously been considered. The main station was to be at Wellesbourne in Warwickshire and there was also a smaller (64 hectare) sub-station at

Paglesham in Essex. Initially the Paglesham site was intended for studies on vegetable growing but subsequently this was found to be impracticable and seed multiplication has become its main function.

Essex growers of Cheltenham Green-Top red beet soon discovered the value of Wellesbourne and, when its Plant Pathology Section was established in 1952, the first disease to be investigated was silvering of red beet. This disease was then becoming a great nuisance to seed-growers on the north bank of the River Blackwater and the outcome of investigations by Dr. J. R. Keyworth was that a very successful control measure was found. Since these early days the station has undertaken research into many other vegetable disease problems, including halo blight of runner and French beans, virus in parsley, alternaria of brassica crops and the likely date of emergence of the pea moth, all of which have great relevance to Essex.

When the N.V.R.S. in 1949 took over the Cambridge Horticultural Research Station a nucleus of seed stocks and other less advanced material was inherited. By 1952 an increase in staff made it possible for a programme of plant breeding and investigation into breeding methods and problems to be initiated. From this work there has resulted the many improved varieties which carry the affix 'Avon' or are named after Shakespearean characters.

In the 1960s there was a particular interest in seed-borne diseases and the N.V.R.S. may take credit for the development of several effective controls by the use of seed-soaking techniques.

The Vegetable Gene Bank

In 1974 there was a Food Conference in Rome at which OXFAM were urged to support the efforts of the United Nations towards increased world food production. Concurrently, OXFAM became aware that, if something was not done to preserve them, many of the genes within our inherited varieties of vegetables were in danger of being lost.

This mattered because although, at first sight, many of these old and wild varieties appeared obsolete, they might carry the genes that could be bred into modern varieties to help them to survive the remarkable shifts, which are already becoming evident, in the climate of our world. To quote from an article written by OXFAM's Director General, Brian W. L. Walker[12] from which much of the information that follows is taken:

> It is bad enough when a wet summer ruins an annual holiday — it is disastrous when the monsoons destroy an entire year's supply of rice in a particular country. Two successively bad harvests in both the U.S.S.R. and North America would plunge the world into disastrous competition for food, the political consequences of which would appear to be more serious than that posed by nuclear warfare.

Furthermore, unless a substitute is found for today's oil-based fertilisers, pesticides and insecticides, there is likely to be a great shortage of these substances in the future. In the Western World, consumer preference for a certain size or shape of vegetable will probably continue to exert strong pressures upon plant breeders and, to meet these demands, it has often been found necessary to breed back by using former wild ancestors. For these reasons it was ultimately recommended that a gene bank, based on a collection of seeds of temperate vegetables but incorporating a small number of seeds of tropical vegetables, should be added to the N.V.R.S. complex at Wellesbourne.

To quote from Mr. Walker once again:

> It comes as a shock to realise that the human family draws its basic food needs from only thirty-five plants. This is a very narrow base, especially when one considers the pressures which are placed upon some of these plants, even to the point of extinction. It is also a concern that world food supplies rarely exceed more than thirty days and, at times, have dropped to the U.S.A. legal minimum of twenty-eight days supply.

> Within the food syndrome the common vegetable plays an important part. Not only is it a vital supplement to the food staples, but certain trace elements essential to human health are often available only from a diet which includes vegetables. For the greater part of the human family, which live below the poverty line in the Third World, the vegetable is doubly important because, provided seeds are available, it can be grown in small plots around people's houses, regardless of complicated questions of land tenure or agrarian reform.

A handout printed for the opening of the Wellesbourne gene bank summarises facts about it under many headings. The following have been chosen as most relevant to this book:

AIM: To collect and preserve seeds of old and wild varieties of vegetables, so making them available to breeders.

VEGETABLES TO BE STORED:

Storage and regeneration: up to 1 litre of seed of approximately 9,000 varieties

Cabbage	Phaseolus beans	Parsnips
Brussels sprouts	Onions	Celery
Calabrese	Turnips	Rhubarb
Cauliflower	Swedes	Leeks
Carrots	Vicia beans	Tomatoes
Lettuce	Beetroot	

Storage only: smaller quantities of approximately 3,000 varieties of tropical species and minor crops such as amaranthus, pumpkins, peppers, melons, okra and egg plant.

REGENERATION AND ASSESSMENT:

Small quantities from the stores seed will be grown to regenerate seeds (for further storage and distribution) and to assess potentially important economic characters.

SEED AVAILABILITY

Small quantities of seed will be available, free of charge, to plant breeders anywhere in the world.

DONATIONS OF SEED:

Offers of donations of old and wild varieties of vegetable seeds, together with as much information as possible, should be sent to

The Vegetable Gene Bank
National Vegetable Research Station
Wellesbourne
Warwick CV35 9EF

Chapter Fifteen

The Problems of Great Britain's Seed Growers and Merchants After 1945

Contained within the Second Statute of Westminster (1285) is a decree that the eldest son should inherit the family estate and broadly speaking this has saved England from a fragmentation of the ownership of her land. This fragmentation problem still besets other members of the European Economic Community but, so long as it provides them and other exporting countries with a supply of cheap family labour, these countries will have an advantage over us.

After the Second World War, Great Britain's seed industry was not able to be one of our Government's first priorities. Certain continental countries, although occupied by the enemy, had been encouraged by them to keep their seed industries in good shape and, when the war was over, their governments provided financial aid. Thus they were immediately able to go into production, and to send out their catalogues, already advertising several new lines, and many of them had the advantage of a warmer, more sunny and reliable climate.

Faced with this, our seed industry had to re-think its policy. The situation was one of high and ever-rising costs that had to be reconciled with the demand for a smaller quantity of seed to sow each acre. On top of this were the restraints of uncertain climate; of what was known as 'colonial preference'; and the fact that many of our industrial goods are bought by countries who are only able to pay with agricultural produce that has cost less to produce than our own.

Cattle foods, in the shape of imported by-product oil-seed cakes from the vegetable oil industry, greatly rose in price and were by then needed in their country of origin. This led to a search for more home-grown and particularly protein-rich foods (which extended into vegetable meat-replacements for humans), and a tremendous programme of research and development connected with crops such as grass, clover, lucerne, peas and beans. A demand for more of these seeds was thus created although much is now grown outside the country.

Since the 1950s increasing quantities of fresh greengrocery and fruit have been flown or trucked in refrigerated containers into this country from abroad, and are on sale in our shops within a short time of having been gathered. This also has reduced home seed requirements.

After the war, farmers were seeking remunerative change crops and vegetables looked promising. Not, this time, for the London markets or for seed but to supply the demands of the food processors.

The first food in tin cans came onto the market around 1910, and by 1945 tinned and, a little later, quick frozen vegetables were making inroads into the fresh market. Both were liked by the working housewives and flat dwellers who constituted a large proportion of post-war society. 'Convenience food' is now commonplace and, although much of it and the seed necessary for its growth is grown elsewhere, most of our 'mother seed' is still produced in this country. Furthermore, although much of our merchants' stock of first and second generation seed is grown for them outside Great Britain, a careful watch is kept to see that the quality is maintained. Every year merchants' officially-trained inspectors go abroad to examine their crops and, after harvest, samples of seed from them come back for trial and comparison with the original seed stock. In this way any deterioration is quickly discovered and appropriate action can be taken to maintain the reputation for quality that our leading seedsmen have built up over the generations.

By 1946, a few growers were experimenting with the oil seed poppy crop, but this did not develop to any great extent. The first stream of F1 hybrid plants and seeds had become a flood by 1947. These F1 hybrids are produced very differently from the new varieties in seedsmen's early catalogues for they were selected only for their outward appearance. Loosely, it may be said that up to 1914 breeding was a simple matter of selecting promising plants. This was followed by the cross-breeding of selected plants and finally, after 1945, by a selection which included that for particular characters carried by the genes within the parent plants.

By the time of the United Kingdom's accession to the European Economic Community in 1974, our cereal seeds were in a good state to comply with the E.E.C. directives. This was because from 1942 onwards to 1975, various voluntary schemes for the upgrading of cereal seeds had operated between the merchants and growers of Great Britain. In fact, in many respects, our schemes demanded a higher standard than did those of the directives. Nevertheless, until a really effective selective herbicide was found (in the early 1970s) which would kill wild oats in wheat crops, there was some difficulty in complying with E.E.C. standards for this impurity.

By 1950, wheat yields were showing promise of the dramatic increase that took place in the 1970s. In 1955 our Government lifted its ban on foreign seed imports and after 1958 all kinds of new varieties of seeds were coming on to our market from overseas merchants. Some 1,500 acres of runner bean seed were still grown in Essex in 1959, after which date the acreage declined to about 200 acres in 1969. This fall was partly due to fewer fresh green beans being required on the London market and partly to the popularity of the canned and frozen stringless French beans. Possibly, the acreage also fell because many runner bean crops carry 'halo blight' disease which, in most seasons, has little deleterious effect upon the runner crop but is fatally infectious to any French bean within the vicinity.

The 1945/6 report of the Essex and Hertfordshire Seeds Trade Association shows that this body then represented 32 independent firms. During the 1960s these once thriving little businesses were having to close down, to amalgamate with one another, or to suffer absorption into large consortiums of, at best, allied but frequently very differing trades. This continued through the 1970s by which time developments in plant breeding and cultivation had become so sophisticated that seed houses were forced to employ even more technically-qualified staff. This, at a time of ever-escalating costs, caused many good but undercapitalised firms to go out of business.

The precision drill came into use in the 1960s. It was said of this tool that 'it was the farmer's friend and the seedsman's enemy', for it still further reduced the seed required to sow an acre.

From 1945 until well into the 1960s herbage seed crops proliferated. A lesser acreage is still produced in this country, including those varieties now required for the amenity and sports trade. From about 1965, to the consternation of the more far-sighted brassica growers, the acreage of oil seed rape rapidly increased. It is a widespread belief that outbreaks of alternaria disease, which continue to cause trouble in both brassica flower and vegetable crops, date from this time.

In 1970, the acreage of flower and vegetable seeds grown in Essex was estimated to be but some 2,000 acres. In 1985, it was doubtful if 500 acres were to be found.

For several centuries breeders have been interested in producing better varieties of peas. Since 1945, their efforts in this direction have been prodigious as they have attempted to meet the requirements of the various kinds of processors. One variety of pea seldom, if ever, suits them all: for the needs of the canning, freezing, drying and, today, the high-protein pea industry are very different. Our individual breeders and such bodies as the National Vegetable Research Station and the Processors and Growers Research Organisation (formerly the Pea Growers Research Organisation) have all played their part.

Finally in 1985, there is a market for seeds of wild flowers and the swing back to the growing of field scale herbs and their seeds continues. They will be used to produce herb plants for patios, window sills and gardens; for flavourings; sweet-smelling and sleep-inducing pillows and cushions; as garnishes for food; in salads; and for use as medicines.

Medically the current interest seems to have passed from fenugreek to evening primrose and even more recently it is reported that J. K. King and Sons Ltd. of Coggeshall has formed a new company with Bio-Oil Research, of Crewe, to produce and market borage, the oil from which is said to be a richer source of gamma-linolenic acid than is evening primrose, and the pace of modern development continues.

Final Thought

As to the future, plants started it all and have continued to adapt their seeds to meet every circumstance. If man's intelligence does not keep pace with his inventions it may be the plant, and not the animal kingdom, that continues life on earth.

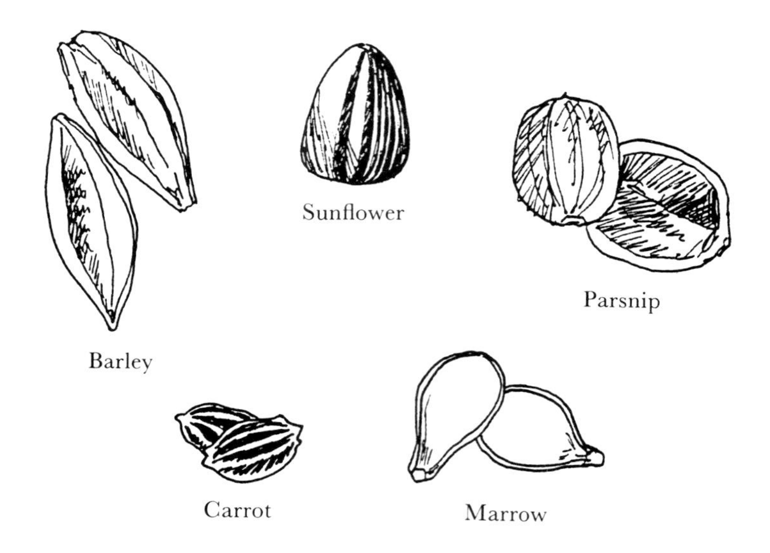

Chronology Of Events which have had an Influence on the Essex Seed Trade from 1750 to 1985

The 18th century — During which agriculture and all that this word embraces became a proper interest for a gentleman

In Essex, vegetable and herb seeds were firmly established as field scale crops from the mid-18th century. It is also evident that some had been grown here during at least the previous 100 years. Comings and goings between Great Britain and America were increasingly noticeable in the plant and seed world.

1730s	Seed firms were starting to move out of London and the large estates were transferring their seed orders from the City to more local establishments. Bulb imports increased. There are references to turnips being grown to feed sheep.
***c*.1750**	Printed broadsheets of firms' goods showed prices written in, in ink. This indicates the growth of the middle-class custom.
1755	An improved swede was introduced from Holland, as food for cattle.
By 1764	The Society for the Encouragement of the Arts Manufactures and Commerce was astonished to find that agriculture overshadowed all its other activities.
1770-1790	Canals were constructed in Great Britain. In Eastern England the canalisation of existing rivers increased from the early 18th century. It preceded and was analagous to the systems of true canals which developed in the more industrialised regions.[1]
1770-1813	The revolution that had already taken place in garden flora and cultivations by 1736 gave rise to a tremendous interest in the production of new varieties of plants.
***c*.1775**	Priced seedsmen's catalogues, in book form, began to be produced in Great Britain. Mangel seed was introduced into this country in mistake for that of beetroot.
1785	Robert Ransome invented his tempered steel plough shares.
1 February 1787	The first edition of the *Botanical Magazine* was published — it was the first periodical devoted to scientific horticulture and was edited by William Curtis.[2] From this time many nurserymen entered the field of garden journalism.
1793	John (K.) King founded his seed firm. There are imports of South African seeds and plants.
Between 1780 and 1800	In Essex, the cloth industry collapsed. Many of those then unemployed found work in the seed fields and iron foundries. The growing of crops to provide winter feed for livestock led to an increase in this country's agricultural seed production and export trade.

The 19th century — a restless and confusing period. The urban population rose to hitherto undreamt of heights. By the end of this century the seed trade had reached its zenith.

After 1800	Mangels were fairly extensively grown by early in this century. John (K.) King was supplying root seeds to the Sandringham Estates by at least 1850.
1804	Guano fertiliser was being imported from Peru.
1815	The first Corn Law was passed and, although it provided a fair farm price, it resulted in dearer priced bread and much hardship for the poorer classes. Sulphate of Ammonia first reported as being manufactured in Great Britain.
1826	The first modern strawberry was introduced.

	Drain pipes were exempted from tax, but they had to have the word 'drain' impressed upon them before being baked.
1830 (approx.)	Nitrate of Soda imported from Chile and Peru.
1832	In Essex, the first beet-sugar was produced by Marriage, Read & Marriage, at Ulting.
1833	Italian rye-grass was introduced.
1837	When Queen Victoria came to the throne reaping machines were still practically unknown. Corn was cut by scythe, fagging-hook or sickle. When cut by scythe the labour consisted of gangs of five: one man to cut, followed by a gatherer and a sheaf binder, a thraver (colloquially in Essex, a traver) and a raker. Led by a good scythesman this gang would easily complete two acres in a day.
By 1839	Corn Exchanges were being built in the larger market towns.
1840s	These years represent the last time that there was near famine in Great Britain.
	Railways were extended into Essex; to Colchester in 1843, and to Sudbury and Harwich in 1854.
1842	Superphosphate fertiliser began to be manufactured.
	First recorded appearance of a portable steam engine and thrashing machine was that of J. R. and A. Ransome of Ipswich.
1846	The Corn Laws were repealed.
	The Electric Telegraph Company was formed.
	Around this time the window tax and other related taxes on bricks, tiles and timber were abolished. This resulted in more glasshouses.
	Arable farmers began to take an interest in growing market garden crops on a field scale. By mid-century market gardening and fruit growing had become major industries.
	Although new types of farm machinery continued to be invented throughout this century, its adoption was delayed by a general lack of farming capital and by the readily available supply of cheap labour.
1850s	Most established seed firms were striving to produce a good quality product. But with very little technical knowledge at their disposal the quality of seeds sold remained extremely variable and there was no legislation to curb the unscrupulous.
1859	There was a Government loan scheme for land drainage.
	Fowler's mole-draining system was exhibited at the Warwick Show.[3]
1865	A. W. Eddington, of Chelmsford, was marketing a machine for laying land drains which refilled the trench it had dug.[4]
1869	The Adulteration of Seeds Act was passed.
	Cut flower trade increasing.
***c*.1870**	Corn prices reached a very high peak but, within the next decade, there was a catastrophic fall.
	At the same time Great Britain suffered a succession of poor harvests.
1875	The 'Self Binder', a machine for cutting and binding corn in one operation, was invented.
1885	Gregor Mendel published his paper on genetic laws which, at the time, passed almost unnoticed.
***c*.1887**	The bigger American seed firms were now beginning to grow their own supplies of seeds.
1880-1912	Particularly in respect of flower, vegetable and root seeds, these years represent the peak period of the seed trade in Essex.
1881-1901	Great Britain's wheat acreage fell to less than half. This was due to imports of cheap 'prairie wheat' from Canada and North America. As a result many inland flour mills went out of business or, if they had the capital, developed along new lines.
	These years also represent twenty years of low corn prices. Wheat was below 40s. a quarter, barley even less and oats below 20s. for most of this period.
***c*.1897**	There were developments in local authority gardening and in the use of glass for market gardening. The less affluent growers turned to 'French gardening' (cloche and frames) rather than glasshouses.

Early in the 19th century, pineapples, melons, currants, oranges and lemons were being brought from as far away as the West Indies by small, fast merchant schooners. The first shipload of refrigerated green beans and pears arrived from Italy before 1897 and soon afterwards refrigerated ships full of fruit came in from Australia. The zenith of the barge trade is said to have been reached by 1898 and there was no obvious decline until 1918. By 1930, some thousand trading barges remained in service which, by 1939, had dwindled to six hundred and by 1950 their use for trading had virtually ceased.

1899 An International Hybridisation Conference was convened by the Royal Horticultural Society at which Gregor Mendel's paper of 1885 was recognised as the breakthrough for which plant breeders had been searching.

The 20th century — the many happenings in the seed trade during this century are clarified if it is separated into three phases.

Phase I — 1900-1914

These years were substantially a continuation of the 19th century, although showing signs of advances and changes that were soon to come.

1900 Most of the well-known seed houses were already established.
The Sweet Pea Society was founded.

1901 A Departmental Committee of the Board of Agriculture reported upon the quality of seeds sold in Great Britain.
A variety of sweet pea mutated and produced large frilled petals.

1912 The culinary runner bean and green pea trade was booming.
John (K.) King of Coggeshall was exporting his seeds to India, Australia, New Zealand and South Africa.

1900-1914 During this phase, railways continued to replace waterways for inland transport; bicycles developed from the 'penny-farthing' model to something which, even though for a time it had solid tyres, was both safer and more practical; and the internal combustion engine was ousting the dray horse, as well as coming into use for public transport.
In August 1914 the Great War began.

Phase II — 1915-1940

A period of rapid transition from one way of life to another. The country and most of the population suffered from very reduced circumstances.

1917 The Corn Production Act (1917) not only set up an Agricultural Wages Board but guaranteed a minimum agricultural wage of 25s. a week.
The Testing of Seeds Order (No.1156) came into force.
The Official Seed Testing Station was opened in London.
The corn and agricultural merchants formed themselves into a National Association (N.A.C.A.M.)

After peace 1918 Educational opportunities were opening up for the working classes. It was in 1912 that the Essex County Technical Laboratories became the East Anglian Institute of Agriculture, the origins of which can be traced back to 1893.
The Americans imposed a duty of 6d. a pound on all seeds imported into their country.
Seed export opportunities opened up with our colonies, New Zealand and Australia in particular.

1920 The Corn Production Act (1920) was passed. This attempted to regulate corn prices but, as in 1815, there followed an outcry about the price of bread and the Government repealed this Act in 1921.

1921 The National Institute of Agricultural Botany was officially opened in Cambridge. It was given the formidable task of looking into all aspects of seed production.

The Official Seeds Testing Station moved from London to Cambridge.
There was a most disastrous drought.
Wheat, which in 1920 has sold for 80s. a quarter, fell to 40s. 10d. by 1921. There followed some 10 years of agricultural depression.

***c*.1925** The production of sugar from home-grown sugar beet was, for the first time, seriously considered by the Government of this country.
Greater quantities of chemical fertilisers were becoming available.
By this time, trade with the Thames-side quays was declining in favour of our smaller coastal ports.

1933 Essex seed growers formed themselves into an association which, shortly afterwards, changed its name to the Essex Herbage Seed Growers' Association. From this body there originated the idea that was to develop into the Official Seed Certification Schemes.

1934 Sugar beet seed production — to breed a variety to suit our climate — began at Woodham Mortimer.

By 1939 Plant hunters were able to send their plants and seeds home speedily, by air. At this time they were being sent from the Himalayan area.
Mendel's Laws were becoming more widely known and were better understood. To maintain their standing seed houses were finding it necessary to employ greater numbers of more technically trained staff.
Hybridisation, although still at the simple cross-breeding stage, was advancing by leaps and bounds.
The culinary green pea and bean trade, with ups and downs of glut and shortage, continued between the wars and, in 1939, there were few people who then realised that, in a few years, this trade would have almost faded away.

September 1939 On 1 September 1939, the Second World War was declared. The country was confronted by the consequences of a policy which had aimed to provide a supply of cheap food (produced below the true cost of production) rather than to ensure fair prices for the producers.

Phase III — 1940-1985

During the depression between the wars thousands of once productive acres had deteriorated into scrub-bush land, lacking in fertility and with their drainage systems silted up. All had to be brought back into cultivation as quickly as possible and at almost any cost.

The war years Initially, the seed trade was responsible for 'conjuring up from somewhere' the whole of this country's seed requirements. It had been abruptly cut-off from European seed sources and by the time America augmented our scanty supplies by mean of the Lease Lend agreement (the American Congress passed the Lease Lend Act in 1941), it may be said that our considerable seed export trade with that country had been completely reversed.
The flower seed acreage was cut to a minimum in order to augment that for food crops.
A run of very good harvests produced gluts — particularly of onion seeds. This had dire results for some merchants and produced difficulties for all.
In 1942 the N.I.A.B. produced its first Recommended List of Varieties. It was for wheats and in the same year it introduced the original Cereal Seed Crop Inspection Scheme.
By 1943 Essex seed growers realised that there must be some official isolation of brassica crops and, with the help of the Essex War Agricultural Executive Committee, instituted the first Seed Zoning Scheme in this country.

After the war 1945-1985 In 1945, both seed growers and the trade were confronted with increasing costs; immediate foreign competition; lack of capital for technical expansion; an overall need for less seed; changes in lifestyle of the population; the availability of 'convenience foods'; and greatly increasing fresh vegetable imports.

1947	The National Vegetable Research Station was set up. The N.I.A.B. began to sort out the problem of crop synonyms. The first stream of F1 hybrids now became a flood.
	The pot-plant trade was increasing.
	In the late 1940s there were great developments in canning and freezing of foods.
By 1950	Wheat yields had begun their rapid escalation.
1952	The N.V.R.S. began breeding its own vegetable varieties.
1955	Our Government lifted the ban on foreign seed imports.
1956	A cereal Field Approval Scheme operated by the N.I.A.B. in England and Wales from 1956 to 1967.
1957	Great Britain won the World Wheat Championship in Ottawa with seed from an Essex farm.
1958	Herbage seed growing was booming in this country.
1959	In the next 10 years the runner bean acreage fell significantly.
	Further substantial improvements were made in our varieties of cereals.
By 1960	There was considerable interest in seed-borne diseases.
	The country's flower seed acreage decreased substantially as seed merchants placed their contracts abroad. From some 2,000 acres in 1970, flower seeds have fallen to about 200 acres in 1985.
1961	The Seeds Act (1920) and its amendments were consolidated into Seeds Regulations 1961.
1964	The Plant Varieties and Seeds Act was passed — at last plant breeders had some protection of their rights.
	Around this date the 'Stanhay' Precision Drill came onto the market.
1965	The Ministry of Agriculture established its Plant Varieties and Seeds Division.
	The Home Grown Cereals Authority came into being.
1966	The European Economic Community issued Directives related to Seed Production and Marketing (Brussels 4/4/1966.R/326/66 [AGRI]).
	The oil seed rape acreage greatly increased and altenaria disease of brassica crops spread.
1968	The British Cereal Seed Scheme was introduced by the N.I.A.B.; the Department of Agriculture for Scotland and the Department of Agriculture Northern Ireland. It was operated on a *voluntary* basis by seed companies and seed growers' organisations.
	Animal protein replacements from vegetable sources were coming to the fore.
1972	The British Association of Seed and Agricultural Merchants (B.A.S.A.M.) was established from the amalgamation of the N.A.C.A.M. and the Seed Trade Association.
1974	Cereal Seed Regulations (1974) were introduced to bring the United Kingdom seed legislation into line with the E.E.C. Directives.
	There was a Food Conference in Rome at which OXFAM made a case for Seed Gene Banks.
	International Rules for seed testing came into force.
1976	The 1974 Cereal Seeds Regulations were modified, amended and updated.
1977	The United Kingdom Agricultural Supply Trade Association (U.K.A.S.T.A.) was formed by a merger of B.A.S.A.M. and the Compound Animal Food Manufacturers' Association (C.A.F.M.A.). It continues the role of B.A.S.A.M. with the interests of the animal feed producers.
By 1980s	There is a great interest in homeopathy and vegetarian food.
	Herbs from abroad have become expensive and there is a renewed interest in growing them in this country.
	Conservationists and the advocates of so-called natural foods are having an effect upon the seed trade.
	There is a trade in seeds of wild flowers.
1986	In view of the economic conditions, engendered by food 'mountains' and 'lakes', our producers are no longer being encouraged to increase food supplies. Plant breeders

now search for varieties which are able to give economic returns at a lower yield, because producers can no longer afford to use the level of sprays and fertilisers demanded by the highest yielding varieties.

Some useful money conversions

Henry VIII (1509-1547) to 1972 prices = x 50 for a rough comparison.
George III (1760-1820) to 1972 prices = x 11 for a rough comparison
(for the year 1775; it varies between x 10 and x 12)

Appendix A

J. L. Fisher's Unpublished 'Introduction' to his *A Medieval Farming Glossary* (E.R.O., T/Z 35)

In 1300 A.D. at Brightlingsea in Essex:
Geoffrey Snow holds a certain native tenement . . . called Snowes, and for the same will plough 2a. at the rye sowing, 2a. at the second ploughing, and 2a. at the oat sowing: he shall have two works allowed for the ploughing of each acre if he has done it if not he shall give to the lord for the ploughing of each acre 6d. Every week he shall do 2½ works, worth ½d. a work, except in the fortnight after Christmas and the octaves of Easter and Pentecost. He shall thresh and winnow for his work 3 bushels of wheat, or 4 of rye or barley by strike measure, or one quarter of oats by heaped measure. If he shall work at small tasks such as fencing, tedding hay, bundling straw, carrying water for thatching or cresting, or hoeing, one work shall be allowed for half a day, or two works for a whole day. He shall come to the manor with cart, horse and man to carry the lord's manure to the field with the other *customarii*, when summoned by the bailiff or other servant, and he shall be allowed one work for half a day. He shall reap in autumn 2a. of wheat or 2a. of oats called a 'gavelrep' without any allowance for the same, and besides he shall reap all autumn while the lord has corn to reap on the demesne every workday ½a. of wheat or oats, if the bailiff or other servant summon him to do so, and for every acre reaped he shall have two works allowed. He shall mow in certain demesne meadows, viz. in Newemad, Melnemad, and Herboldmad, whenever the lord chooses, without allowance of works, with the other *customarii* of the same *tenura*, but not otherwise or elsewhere, and it is to be known that all who mow the same meadows of the lord shall have for their mowing at the same time the second best sheep from the lord's fold and the second best cheese from the dairy without any payment; also they shall have for the said mowing a cartload of brushwood, and as much salt as will fill the mould in which the said cheese was made. And the said Geoffrey shall do carrying service with horse and man every Sunday of the year if required from the manor to Colchester Abbey, Greenstead or Weeley with 3 bushels of wheat, 4 of rye or barley, or 6 of oats, of corn grown on the demesne of this manor and not otherwise, and for each journey he shall have for breakfast ordinary bread, a cooked dish, and sufficient ale. He shall pay every year 4 bushels of oats called 'foddercorn' at the feast of the Purification, 25 eggs at Easter and 8s. by equal portions at the four usual terms.

Sometimes the villeins had to provide seed from their own stock:
Besides manual works and rents in money and kind, in early days the villeins owed gafol, apparently a kind of food tribute. On some manors notably those belonging to Waltham Abbey, certain villeins were expected as gafol to plough an acre with their own teams and sow it with their own seed. After ploughing and the *rebinacio*, or second and third ploughing, the seed was broadcast and harrowed in, a task at which every villein who possessed a horse was bidden to help. The sown fields were then fenced in with brushwood bound to stakes with long flexible branches of hazel or similar material.

Appendix B

Major Climatic Changes in Great Britain from the Middle Ages

John Harvey writes that the Middle Ages are generally considered to extend from the death of the last Western European Emperor, Romulus Augustulus, in A.D. 476 until the year A.D. 1500. This period is, for convenience, sub-divided into the Dark Ages, which cover the period to A.D. 1000, and the Middle Ages are restricted to the second five centuries.

Probably the 6th century was the warmest of this period and it is thought that the growing season at this time extended for a month longer than in 1900. With some fluctuations, these warm temperatures lasted until after 1300.

In his book *The History of British Flora*, Sir Harry Godwin considers that, in round figures, the dates 1150-1300 cover an early-medieval Warm Epoch and 1550-1700 a Little Ice Age. However, Sir J. C. Russel considers that this chilly period had already begun by just after 1300 because, as he points out, the Baltic froze to its southern limits in 1303 and again in 1306-7.

Appendix C

Chronological List of Essex Seedsmen and Allied Trades

I am conscious that this list is incomplete. There may be many more examples of early seedsmen from those parts of the county, now built upon, which were formerly agricultural land. No doubt others have slipped through the net. This list is a beginning.

1686	**Daniel Dale**, — Apothecary, Braintree. Shared and perhaps distributed seeds collected for Bishop Compton by Mark Catesby
1686	**John Ray**, Black Notley — botanist
By 1724	**Cant's** of Colchester
1768	**John Stow**, Lexden, near Colchester
1772	**Edward and Thomas Evans**, Coggeshall
** 1780 (?1742)	**Thomas Moss**, Pear Tree Farm, Coggeshall
By 1793	**Mears and Sorrel**, Chelmsford
1793	**John K. King**, Coggeshall
1799	**Brooks (Mistley) Limited**
* 1819	**Bunting and Sons**, Colchester
1824	**Robert Hunt**, Atlas Works, Earls Colne
*pre-1832	**Robert Tansley**, Great Coggeshall — gardener and seedsman (ref. his will of 1832 ER.D/DBM-B36)
By 1839 (?1824)	**William Chater**, Saffron Walden
By 1839	**William King**, East Street, Coggeshall
1840	**E. Marriage and Son**, Colchester — corn miller
1850	**Hurst & Son**, 6 Leadenhall Street, London — first trial grounds at Boreham, Essex
* 1851	**Richard Abbot**, Kelvedon
1860	**James Carter and Company**, High Holborn, London (established 1804) — Essex connection
1861	**George Taber**, Rivenhall
1863	**Hasler and Company**, Dunmow
* 1864	**Barnard Brothers Limited**, Newport
1870	**Isaac Brazier and Sons**, The Eastern Counties and Halstead Wire Works, Head Street, Halstead
1888	**E. W. King**, Coggeshall
1889	**E. P. Brown and Son**, Coggeshall
* 1890	**Thomas Plumstead**, Tilkey Road, Coggeshall — seedgrower and baker
1892	**William Deal and Sons Limited**, Park Farm, Inworth
1894	**Thomas Cullen and Sons**, Witham
*c.*1895	**Frank Folkard and Sons Limited**, Marks Tey
1899	**Frank Pertwee and Sons Limited**, Colchester
Before 1900	**Bertrand W. Deal**, Brooklands, Feering
,,	**Edwin J. Cranmer**, Bridgefoot, Kelvedon
,,	**J. Polley**, Highfields Farm, Kelvedon

1902	**Church** of Bures
1907	**Robert Bolton**, Warton, near Carnforth, Lancashire (established *c.*1900) — land in Essex
*c.*1936	**David Fenwick**, By-Pass Nurseries, Colchester and Marks Tey

* Not mentioned in text
** Not involved in marketing

Appendix D

Copy of certificate presented to JOHN BARRINGTON TRAPNELL CHEVALLIER to commemorate the centenary of the introduction of CHEVALLIER BARLEY by the REVEREND JOHN CHEVALLIER, R.J., M.D., of ASPALL HALL, DEBENHAM, SUFFOLK, 1831

CHEVALLIER BARLEY

In the year 1831 the Reverend John Chevallier, J.P., M.D., of Aspall Hall, who was Perpetual Curate of Aspall for 30 years and who, in addition to practising medicine in his immediate neighbourhood, farmed the Aspall estate, introduced the barley which is known throughout the world by his name.

The origin of the barley is stated to be as follows:

> About the year 1820, John Andrews, a labourer of Mr. Edward Dove of Ulvereton Hall, Debenham, had been threshing barley, and on his return home complained of his feet being uneasy, and on taking off his shoes, he discovered in one of them part of a very fine ear of barley — it struck him as being particularly so — and he was careful to have it preserved. He afterwards planted the few grains from it in his garden, and the following year Doctor and Mr. Charles Chevallier, coming to Andrews' dwelling to inspect some repairs going on (the cottage belonged to the Doctor), saw three or four ears of the barley growing. He requested it might be kept for him when ripe. The Doctor sowed a small ridge with the produce thus obtained, and kept it by itself until he grew sufficient to plant an acre, and from this acre the produce was eleven and a half coombs (about the year 1825 or 1826). This was again planted, and from the increase thence arising, he began to dispose of it, and from that time it has been gradually getting into repute. It is now well-known in most of the Corn Markets in the kingdom and also in many parts of the Continent, America, etc. and is called the Chevallier barley.
>
> (Extract from MS. History of Debenham, 1845, in possession of Mrs. Lock of Debenham.)

Chevallier is a narrow-eared type of barley of fine malting quality. After its introduction it rapidly became the leading variety in the British Isles and other countries, and its deservedly high reputation for yield of grain and for malting quality is still maintained.

Appendix E

The Testing of Seeds by the State

With reference to the suggestions made to the Minister of Agriculture as to the desirability for the establishment of properly equipped stations, at which Farm Seeds can be tested as to their quality and vitality, I presume, at the expense of the State, let me at once say, as one of the largest Seed Growers in the United Kingdom, that I should welcome the formation of such stations, as there can be no question as to the importance of Farmers and Landowners sowing only Seeds of the highest possible germination. At the same time I think it is almost unreasonable to expect the State to do what certainly should be done by every Seed Merchant.

It is some few years since that the Royal Agricultural Society of England recommended that no Seeds should be purchased without a guarantee of their germination and purity; and if Farmers would only act on this recommendation there would be no necessity for the establishment of Seed-testing stations.

But the recommendations of the Royal Agricultural Society, while adopted by some Seedsmen, have been deliberately ignored by others; hence, without doubt, there are large quantities of Seeds sown every year which are of very low germinating power.

Until the great bulk of Farmers fully realize the absolute necessity of sowing only Seeds of the highest germination, and are prepared to pay a reasonable price for them, it will, I fear, be useless to erect costly Seed-testing stations, as only a few would trouble to use them.

Personally, I believe that if Farmers would appreciate such stations it would prevent the sowing of an immense quantity of low-priced foreign Seed of poor vitality; yet on the other hand the State is not of necessity called on to spend money in this direction, when the actual remedy lies in the Farmer's hands, if he will only use it.

Let every Farmer and Landowner insist that the Seeds he purchases shall be of guaranteed germination, according to the recent recommendations of the Royal Agricultural Society of England. It is a demand they have a perfect right to enforce.

So far as I am personally concerned, long before the Royal Agricultural Society of England recommended that no Seeds should be purchased unless their germination was guaranteed, I had my own Seed-testing houses arranged on the most scientific principles, and my customers could always be provided with the percentage of growth of the Seeds I supplied them with.

In a pamphlet published last Spring, entitled 'A Great Seed-Growing Industry', are the following extracts from my Seed-Testing Book of Trials of bulks before being sent to my customers:

	Germination, per cent		
MANGEL WURZEL	160	to	180
CLOVERS	96	to	98
CABBAGE	90	to	98
SWEDE and TURNIP	98	to	100
FIORIN			90
MEADOW FOXTAIL	70	to	80
CRESTED DOGSTAIL	90	to	95
COCKSFOOT	85	to	90
SHEEP'S FESCUE	85	to	95
TALL FESCUE	90	to	95
HARD FESCUE	85	to	95
MEADOW FESCUE	90	to	95
TIMOTHY	95	to	100
SMOOTH-STALKED MEADOW GRASS	70	to	80
ROUGH-STALKED MEADOW GRASS	80	to	90
PACEY'S PERENNIAL RYE GRASS	95	to	100
ITALIAN RYE GRASS	90	to	95

It is only to be supposed that the creating of Seed-testing or Seed-control stations in this country will be strenuously opposed in some quarters, but those Seed Merchants who have gained a reputation by always supplying Seeds of the highest germinating power will regard any measure with satisfaction, if it will prevent the distribution of the immense quantities of practically worthless Seeds which are sown every year.

JOHN K. KING

Appendix F

Number of Seeds in One Ounce

Name	*Number of seeds to the ounce (approx.)*
Achillae (The Pearl)	200,000
Ageratum	225,000
Alyssum	60,000
Aster	12,000
Chrysanthemum (Single Annual)	10,000
Cineraria	100,000
Clarkia	100,000
Coleus	115,000
Dahlia	3,000
Delphinium	15,000
Eschscholtzia	15,000
Godetia	100,000
Lavender	30,000
Lobelia	750,0000
Lupin	1,800
Mimulus	1,000,000
Nemesia	100,000
Petunia	152,000
Wallflower	15,000
Field beans	44
Barley	612
Beet	187
Cabbage, vars.	6,875
Carrot	18,750
Celery	93,750
Wild white clover	56,250
Red clover	14,375
Coltsfoot grass	28,125
Timothy grass	75,000
Vetch	531
Kidney vetch	9,375
Wheat	625
Turnip	9,375

Appendix G

When George and Alan Percival grew mangel seed they used the steckling bed method and work proceeded on the crop as follows:

Sequence of work

End July/beginning August — seed sown in plant bed.

During this autumn — into the field intended for the seed crop (usually one which had just grown clover) was ploughed a good dressing of farmyard manure.

The following spring — as early as possible (usually March) the stecklings were lifted from the bed by sliding a spade, at an angle, under the plants so as to cut through their roots to leave about two and a half inches on each plant.

The plants were then pulled from the bed, shaken free of soil and placed into an apron-like dropping bag ready for debbing in. The plants were rolled firmly into the ground after they were set out, and when they had got a good hold, were top dressed with sulphate of ammonia.

Mid-May — the tops of the plants were usually ready to pinch out.

If they were left too long the plants blew over.

After pinching out the crop was hoed twice to keep it free of weeds.

By mid-August the crop was usually ready to cut[1] and, although it was still quite green, a start was made.

The stems were left to wilt for about two days and then stood up four-square and not tied at the top. When they were dry they were carted home.

Other information relevant to the sequence

This ensured that there were no long roots which might turn upwards and spoil the growth when they were planted. Watch out for hares at this stage as they are very fond of mangels.

This was 'pinched in' at a rate of one heaped teaspoonful to a plant (about one to one and a half hundredweight an acre)

The labour required for planting was one dropper to three debbers for each stetch of three rows (their stetch was 7 feet 2 inches wide).

A knife or fingers were used.

Someone did once try using a lawn mower. It proved rather a hit and miss method and was not recommended as 'mangels are easily upset if knocked about'!

In those days Blackfly was a great plague at this stage.

It was cut with a saw-edged sickle. This tool has to be used with a drawing action as distinct from chopping when using a hook. As they cut they bore down upon the stems with their left hand and arm and then lay the cut stems, from all three rows, across the hump of the stetch. The cut plants from two stetches (six rows) had to be laid to face each other.

The carting — small, unroped loads were necessary, for the pressure from roping a load causes undue seed loss. Either two-wheeled seed carts, or wagons were used. The floors and ladders were covered by a cloth to catch any shed seed. To keep the man

The stack was thatched and left to mature until the following February/March. Then the seed stems were put through the Prestney and Blackwall thrasher.

on the stack busy three wagons were required, each with its loader on the wagon ready to receive the produce of four stetches from his pitcher. (The pitcher needed a long-handled and wide-tined (at least 12-inch) fork for this job.) On reaching the stack the pitcher went onto the stack to pass the seed to the stacker. Shed seed was poured from the cloths into a sack which was buried into the stack as this was being built. Each stack was started on a straw base covered by a hessian cloth supplied by Firmin and Company, Handford Road, Ipswich, who also supplied sacks, bags and vegetable nets. Each stack was made twice as long as it was wide — usually four paces by eight.

Thrashing was described as 'a slow old job'. An average yield was 20 cwt an acre, but Mr. Dann says that 25 cwt was quite possible.

Appendix H

English Red Clover Seed Crop

Year	*Yield per acre*	*Price per bushel*
1914	Good — 5 to 9 bushels	35s. to 40s.
1915	Fair — 2 to 4 bushels	45s.
1916	Very little seed — no record	
1917	,, ,, ,, ,,	
1918	,, ,, ,, ,,	
1919	,, ,, ,, ,,	
1920	Small crop — 1 to 2 bushels	90s. to 110s.
1921	,, ,, — 2 bushels	80s. to 90s.
1922	Bad	15s. to 30s.
1923	Good crop — 5 to 8 bushels	35s. to 50s.
1924	Very little seed — no record	
1925	,, ,, ,, ,,	
1926	,, ,, ,, ,,	
1927	,, ,, ,, ,,	
1928	Biggest crop on record — 6 to 14 bushels	25s. to 45s.
1929	Fair crop — 2 to 5 bushels	25s. to 40s.
1930	Bad — 1 to 2 bushels	20s.
1931	Bad	
1932	Fair — 3 bushels	30s. to 40s.
1933	Good — 4 to 5 bushels	35s. to 50s.
1934	Good — 3 to 5 bushels	30s. to 45s.
1935	Fair — 3 bushels	30s. to 40s.
1936	Fair — 2 to 3 bushels	40s. to 45s.
1937	Good crop ordinary seed — 3 to 7 bushels	15s. to 35s.
1938	Bad crop	25s. to 35s.
1939		
1940	Fair crop — 3 to 4 bushels	55s.
1941	Poor	
1942	Fair crop — 3 to 4 bushels	100s.
1943	Poor crop — 2 to 4 bushels	70s. to 100s.
1944	Small crop	£9 to £10
1945	Good crop — 4 to 5 bushels	£7 to £8
1946	Small crop	£12 to £14
1947	Good crop — 4 to 6 bushels (best quality to date)	£5
1948		
1949	Large acreage — best quality on record	£6 to £7 10s.
1950	Poor crop — bad quality — 2 to 3 bushels	£5 to £6
1951	Better yield than was expected, seed poor quality — 3 bushels	started at £7

1952	Good quality crop in Essex and Suffolk — yields vary from 1 bushel to 2 sacks	started £7 to £3
1953	Small crop, only fair quality — 2 to 3 bushels	£8 to £9 average
1954	Very small crop — 1 to 2 bushels	started at £14 up to £17 to £20
1955	Good crop, beautiful seed	90s. to 105s.
1956	Hardly any seed, brown and poor quality	£3 to £5
1957	Fair crop, only medium quality — 2 to 3 bushels	£5 to £6
1958	Failure, only few acres	£9 to £12
1959	Very good crop — 8 to 10 bushels	£6 to £6 10s.
1960	Failure, poor quality	60s. to 70s.
1961	Good crop, some useful seed but a lot of medium quality	70s.
1962	Small crop, poor quality	£7 to £8
1963	Small crop, very little seed except in East Anglia. Few good, but mainly poor quality	£10 to £10 10s.

Appendix I

Eastern Region Local Clover Varieties

Section 1 History and origin of varieties

In the year 1933 it was recognised that there were in the County of Essex, and in Counties adjacent, certain local varieties of Broad Red and Single Cut Clovers which had, from time immemorial, been produced on the same farms. These strains mostly bore the name of the farming family who had both safeguarded and perpetuated them (i.e., Christy's, etc.). At that time there were large imports of clover seed from various countries and a grave risk existed that these indigenous local varieties might be lost by the intermixture of foreign sources and also by the intermixture of Single Cut and Broad Red.

During 1933 a body of farmers in co-operation with trade sources backed by technical advice formed the Essex Seed Growers Association with the prime object of certifying the authenticity of the remaining true stocks of Essex Single Cut and Broad Red and thereafter maintaining them true to type. An article on the Association's work and recognising its value, appeared in the *Journal of the Ministry of Agriculture* as long ago as February 1938. From 1935 when they became available, the Essex Seed Growers Association also pioneered the introduction and seed production of the now well-known Welsh Plant Breeding Station strains in the Eastern Counties until the National Comprehensive Certification Scheme for Herbage Seeds was introduced by the National Institute of Agricultural Botany in 1956. From that year the organisation changed its name to the Essex Herbage Seeds Association and reverted solely to its initial purpose of safeguarding the interests of Essex Clover Varieties.

Some years prior to this a Suffolk Farmer (Mr. Partridge) of Kersey had found and propagated to commercial quantities a local variety of white clover and with his approval this White Clover, now well known and established under the name Kersey White, was added with great success to the Association's sphere of activity.

The area in which these local varieties of clover were grown continued to expand so that they became associated with a region of similar climate and soil type in the Eastern Counties rather than with mere county geographical boundaries. This situation tended to result in name confusion between the county of origin and the clover variety. Furthermore certain countries abroad had begun to list and compile catalogues of varieties in which only one variety name of an identical type could be included. The Essex Association took the necessary provisional steps to get its varieties recognised. By consultation and investigation with the National Institute of Agricultural Botany it was established that an area east of the Great North Road (A.1) as far as the Wash and bounded in the south by the Thames and elsewhere by the North Sea, produced clovers in which the botanical characteristics were indistinguishable. Negotiations between merchants and growers representing geographical counties within the defined area took place under guidance and advice from the National Institute of Agricultural Botany during 1963 and 1964. The result was the formation of the Eastern Region Clover Association to supervise the development of the three clover varieties under their officially designated names, given above, throughout the Eastern Region defined above, and all seed for further multiplication must be grown within that region and be certified by the National Certifying Authority for Herbage Seeds for this purpose.

Section 2 Varieties of Red and White Clover grown under the auspices of the Association

A full description has been published by R. P. Hawkins in the following papers:

Investigations on local varieties of herbage plants.

1953	**II**	'Types of red clover and their identification', *J. Brit. Grassl. Soc.* 8. 213-238.
1954	**III**	Strains of doublecut red clover and their identification. *J. Brit. Grassl. Soc.* 9. 221-238.
1960	**IV**	White clover. *J. Brit. Grassl. Soc.* 15. 28-33.

The description may be summarised:

Essex Broad Red Clover

This variety like other varieties of broad red clover produces spring growth for grazing in the milder districts, a crop of hay or silage in May-June and a second crop of hay, silage or grazing in August. The August crop may be left to produce seed in suitable districts.

Essex Broad Red Clover can be distinguished from singlecut and late-flowering varieties by its seasonal growth as described above, by time of flowering and by the number of internodes on the main stem when in flower.

English Singlecut (Essex)

English Singlecut, like other varieties of singlecut, is later than broad red clover varieties in starting growth in spring but is earlier than late flowering varieties. It produces a very heavy crop of hay or silage in June but relatively little aftermath and does not persist to more than 50 per cent or so into the following year. English singlecut can be grown successfully on the poorer types of land. It is relatively resistant to eelworm attack and to loss of crop from sclerotinia and scorch. It is essentially a variety for use in a one year ley or in a ley of longer duration to be cut for hay in the first year and followed by two or more years grazing.

English Singlecut flowers 7-10 days later than broad red clover and 7-10 days earlier than late flowering clover. There are more internodes on the main stem when in flower than on broad red clover varieties.

Kersey White Clover

This is a medium-large leaved variety of white clover suitable for hay, silage or grazing when sown alone or included in seeds mixtures. It produces heavy yields of fodder. When sown in seeds mixtures, Kersey White Clover is perhaps best suited to land of average fertility and to districts of lower rainfall where its vigorous growth does not unduly suppress the grass. It will persist for a number of years.

Section 3 Present organisation

The Eastern Region Clover Association is managed by an Executive Committee drawn from the pioneers of Essex Clover Certification over many years. The Executive Officer of the National Certifying Authority for Herbage Seeds at the National Institute of Agricultural Botany is automatically an advisory member of this Committee, and a Fellow of the N.I.A.B. acts as Technical Consultant. There are two joint secretaries one of whom is in Norfolk and the other in Essex. The clover certification scheme is open to Seed Firms within the Eastern Region previously defined in Section 1, who are approved by the Committee, and are approved processors under the National Certifying Authority rules.

This leaflet is intended to be an outline for guidance of clover seed growers and merchants or farmers buying or using Clovers certified under the scheme, or anyone else interested in the value of these Clover varieties. The leaflet itself is published by the Eastern Region Clover Association and supplied to seed firms and farmers organisations already operating within the scheme and therefore where further information is sought approach should be in the first instance to the organisation or merchant whose stamp is affixed below and who will be pleased to supply any further information desired. Alternately the Chairman of the Herbage Seed Committee of any County Branch of the National Farmers' Union within the Eastern Region has direct access to the Executive Committee of the Association and can represent the views of his members thereon.

Appendix J

Cell Cultures

It is already possible to manipulate genes within plant cells. From a cultured suspension of such cells, a number of individuals might multiply to form clumps of undifferentiated cells (callus masses). These, in turn, may be induced to give rise to shoots by 'planting out' on to a medium containing suitable concentrations of hormones. By altering the rooting hormone (auxin) content, roots may be induced on the shoots and thereafter these may be grown on to determine which have desirable characteristics. Large numbers of suitable clones may then be produced by micropropagation in a short space of time.

The meristem is the minute (0.1 mm.) innermost growing point of the shoot. It is made up of rapidly dividing cells from which original leaf structures are formed. A great advantage in this method is that the meristems of a plant infected with virus are often virus-free. By culturing the meristems of chosen lines on an appropriate medium, virus-free plantlets of those lines may be quickly obtained in a micropropagation system. Some, but not all, virus-free potato stocks may be obtained in this way. Some of the earliest commercial work in this field reduced the price of once-costly orchid plants when virus-free meristem cultures were bulked-up far more rapidly than could be achieved by conventional propagation methods.

Appendix K

Loss From 'Bunt' in Corn

From the 1903 report upon the Aynsome Agricultural Station:

> In the publications of the U.S. Department of Agriculture, the annual loss to that country, from the presence of Bunt and Smut [spores] in the corn crop, is estimated at $18,000,000. The loss in our own country from the same cause is, so far as is known, not gauged or estimated, but it is without doubt very considerable. Samples of malting barley have been examined possessing all the qualifications of maturity, colour and size of grain which enabled them to occupy a premier position in the prize-list at an exhibition yet, when microscopically analysed, were found to be utterly unfit for sowing purposes.

Select Bibliography

Booker, J., *Essex and the Industrial Revolution*, E.R.O. No. 66 (1964)
Brown, A. F. J., *Essex at Work*, E.C.C. No. 49 (1969)
Buckley, D. G. (ed.), Archaeology in Essex to 1500, Council for British Archaeology Research Report, No. 34 (1980)
Drummond, J. C. and Wilbraham, Anne, *The Englishman's Food* (1959)
Grieve, H., *A Transatlantic Gardening Friendship 1694-1777*, Historical Association, Essex Branch (1981)
Hadfield, Miles, *A History of British Gardening* (1978)
Harvey, John H., *Medieval Gardens* (1981)
Early Gardening Catalogues (1972)
Early Nurserymen (1974)
'Vegetables in the Middle Ages', *Journal of the Garden History Society* (1985)
'The First English Garden Book — Mayster Jon Gardener's Treatise and its Background', *Journal of Garden History Society* (1985)
Huxley, A. J., *Illustrated History of Gardening* (1978)
Rohde, Eleanour S., *A Garden of Herbs* (1969)
Taylor, George, *British Herbs and Vegetables* (1947)
Thirsk, Joan (gen. ed.), *The Agrarian History of England and Wales*, vol. 1, Part I (1981), Part 2 (1972), vol. 5, Parts 1 and 2 (1985)
Trevelyan, G. M., *English Social History* (1944)
Victoria and Albert Museum Exhibition Catalogue, 'The Garden — a Celebration of One Thousand Years of British Gardening'(1979)
Victoria History of the Counties of England — Essex, vol. 2 (1907)
Webber, R., *The Early Horticulturists* (1959)

References

Abbreviations used in the references

E.R.O.	Essex Record Office
V.C.H.	*Victoria History of the Counties of England – Essex*, vol. 2 (1907)

Glossary

1. Theresa McLean, *Mediaeval English Gardens.*
2. John H. Harvey, *Mediaeval Gardens* (1981), p. 82.

Chapter 1

1. Hugh Johnson, 'The Origin of Plants No. 1 – The Seeds of Adventure' in *Telegraph Sunday Magazine*, 17 May 1981, p. 36.
2. J. J. Wymer, 'The Palaeolithic in Essex', in D. G. Buckley (ed.), *Archaeology in Essex to 1500*, Council for British Archaeology Research Report No. 34 (1980).
3. Richard Bradley, *The Prehistoric Settlement of Britain* (1978), p. 29.
4. Peter Murphy, 'Environmental Archaeology in East Anglia', in *Department of Environment Regional Review* (1984), p. 23.
5. *Ibid.*
6. Barry Cunliffe, *Iron Age Communities in Britain*, rev. edn. (1978), p. 330.
7. George M. Taylor, *British Herbs and Vegetables* (1947), p. 29.
8. Herbal of the Abbey of Bury St Edmunds, *c.*1120 (MS Bodley 130, f.23v).
9. John H. Harvey, *Mediaeval Gardens* (1981), p. 121.
10. C. R. Wright, 'An Introduction to Social History', in *Agriculture and Industry, Book II* (1961), p. 23.
11. John Percival, *Wheat in Great Britain*, 2nd rev. edn. (1934), p. 50.
12. *Ibid.*
13. Vanessa Straker, correspondence with Department of Urban Archaeology, Museum of London, London Wall, EC2Y 5HN.
14. John Percival, *op. cit.*, p. 50, quoting Egelsaga – CAP 17 & 19.
15. Eleanour Sinclair Rohde, *A Garden of Herbs* (New York 1969), p. 10.
16. John H. Harvey, *Mediaeval Gardens*, p. 3.
17. John H. Harvey, *Early Gardening Catalogues* (1972), p. 3, quoting *Capitulare de Villis IXX Imperiabilis.*
18. John H. Harvey, 'Vegetables in the Middle Ages', in *Journal of Garden History Society*, vol. 12, no. 1 (Spring 1985), quoting B.L. Egerton Roll 8347.
19. John H. Harvey, *Mediaeval Gardens*, p. 78.
20. Dorothy Hartley, *Food in England* (1954/1979 impr.), pp. 65- 6.
21. Gillian Painter and Elaine Power, *The Herb Garden Displayed* (1979), p. 194.
22. Frank Cullen, 'Cressing Temple, an Essex Manor', in *Seed Trade Review* (September 1949).
23. John H. Harvey, 'The First English Garden Book – Mayster Jon Gardener's treatise and its background', in *Journal of the Garden History Society*, vol. 12, no. 2 (Autumn 1985), p. 92.
24. H. T. Riley, *A Memorial of London* (1886).
25. Rev. Harold Smith, 'William Harrison and his "Description of England"', in *Essex Review*, vol. 28 (1919), pp. 100-101.
26. Philip Ziegler, *The Black Death* (1982), p. 242.
27. G. M. Trevelyan, *English Social History* (1944), pp. 8-9.
28. G. Oliver, *History of the City of Exeter* (1861), p. 74.
29. J. C. Drummond and Anne Wilbraham, *The Englishman's Food* (1959), p. 88.
30. *Ibid.*

Chapter 2

1. Hugh Johnson, 'The Origin of Plants No. 1 – The Seeds of Adventure', in *Telegraph Sunday Magazine*, 17 May 1981, p. 1.
2. Barbara Winchester, *Tudor Family Portrait* (1955).
3. Ronald Webber, *The Early Horticulturists* (1959), p. 20.
4. Rosetta Clarkson, *Herbs and Herbalists* (New York 1972), p. 236.
5. C. W. Johnson, *A History of English Gardening* (1829), p. 55.
6. Ronald Webber, *op. cit.*, p. 51.
7. *Ibid.*, p. 48, quoting Richard Bradley's *A general treatise of Husbandry and Gardening* (1726).
8. Eleanour Sinclair Rohde, *A Garden of Herbs* (New York 1969), p. 14, quoting Thomas Hyll, *The Profitable Art of Gardening* (1568, 1574).
9. Ronald Webber, *op. cit.*, p. 55.
10. *Ibid.*, p. 56.
11. G. M. Trevelyan, *English Social History* (1944), p. 293.
12. Ann Leighton, *Early English Gardens in New England* (1970), p. 61.
13. *Ibid.*, quoting from *Winthrop Papers*, vol. 3, Massachusetts Historical Society (1929).
14. Miles Hadfield, *A History of British Gardening* (1979), pp. 223-7.
15. Hilda Grieve, *A Transatlantic Gardening Friendship 1694- 1777*, Historical Association Essex Branch (1981), p. 34.
16. Joseph Kastner, *A World of Naturalists* (1978), p. 16.
17. *Ibid.*
18. Ray Desmond, 'The Problems of Transporting Plants', in *The Garden – a Celebration of One Thousand Years of British Gardening*, Victoria and Albert Museum Exhibition (1979), pp. 101-2.
19. *Ibid.*, p. 103.
20. Arthur F. J. Brown, *Essex at Work 1700-1815*, E.R.O. publication No. 49, (1969), p. 29.

Chapter 3

1. Arthur F. J. Brown, *Essex at Work 1700-1815* (1969), p. 29.
2. G. M. Trevelyan, *English Social History* (1944), p. 302.
3. John H. Harvey, *Early Nurserymen* (1974), p. 6.
4. John H. Harvey, 'Nurseries, Nurserymen and Seedsmen', in *The Garden – A Celebration of One Thousand Years of British Gardening*, Victoria and Albert Museum Exhibition (1979), p. 109.
5. *V.C.H.*, vol. 2 (1977 edn.), p. 481.
6. *The Rosarian's Year Book* (1886), p. 2, quoted as ref. in V.C.H., vol. 2 (1977 edn.), p. 481.
7. *V.C.H.*, vol. 2 (1977 edn.), p. 481.
8. Rev. Philip Morant, *The History of Antiquities of Essex*, 2nd. edn. (1768), p. 92.
9. In E.R.O., D/DU 144-20, 21, 23 & 28, D/DC 27/827/873 & 872.
10. Report of Board of Agriculture's Departmental Committee (1901), Commons Debate, 489, p. 1; Commons Debate, 493, pp. 17, 147. Question Nos. 5537, 5538, 5539 and 5541.
11. In E.R.O., (Great Coggeshall 17).
12. *V.C.H.*, vol. 2, p. 479.
13. *Ibid.*
14. *Ibid.*
15. Lawrence Wright, *Clean and Decent – the fascinating history of the bathroom and W.C.* (1960), p. 218.
16. From Mrs. Kitty Crayston, a one-time pupil of Kelvedon School.
17. In E.R.O., D/DDW T176/35.
18. *Ibid.* Extract from the *Essex Standard* newspaper, October 1839.
19. Leslie Gordon, *Poor Man's Nosegay* (1973), quoting Drury Phillips.
20. John Player, *Sketches of Saffron Walden 1843*, p. 48, quoted in correspondence from H. C. Stacey, Town Clerk (retd.), Saffron Walden.
21. *V.C.H.*
22. *Ibid.*, p. 480.

Chapter 4

1. Kenneth G. Farries, *Essex Windmills and Millwrights – An Historical Review*, vol. 1 (1985), p. 83.

2. Daniel Defoe, *A Tour Thro' the Whole Island of Great Britain 1724-1727.*
3. J. C. Drummond and Anne Wilbraham, *The Englishman's Food* (1939), p. 179, quoting William Ellis in *The Practical Farmer or Hertfordshire Husbandman* (1723).
4. J. C. Drummond and Anne Wilbraham, *op. cit.*, p. 180.
5. In *Journal of the Society of Arts*, vol. 2 (1787).
6. In the *Essex Chronicle*, Friday, 7 May 1920.
7. In *The Seedgrowers' Centenary - A History of One Hundred Years of Football at Coggeshall 1878-1978*, compiled by J. M. Ashton and N. W. Burton on behalf of Coggeshall Town Football Club.
8. John H. Harvey, *Mediaeval Gardens* (1981), p. 132.
9. Canon J. L. Fisher, 'Unpublished Introduction to his Mediaeval Farming Glossary', (E.R.O. T/Z35).
10. John H. Harvey, *Mediaeval Gardens*, pp. 79-80.
11. John H. Harvey, 'Nurseries, Nurserymen and Seedsmen' in *The Garden – A Celebration of One Thousand Years of British Gardening*, Victoria and Albert Museum Exhibition (1979), p. 105.
12. Petrus D. Crescentius (or Crescenzi), *Opus Ruralium Commodorum* (completed 1306, first printed 1401), R.H.S. edn. (1920).
13. Kay Sanecki, 'Tools of the Trade' in *The Garden – A Celebration*, Victoria and Albert Museum Exhibition (1979), p. 111.
14. A. J. Huxley, *Illustrated History of Gardening* (1978), p. 81.
15. J. Macky, *A Journey thro' England* (1772).
16. A. J. Huxley, *op. cit.*, p. 289, quoting the anonymous author of *The Gardener's New Kalendar* of 1758.
17. *Ibid.*
18. *Ibid.*
19. *Ibid.*, p. 284.

Chapter 5

1. In *Genealogical Quarterly*, vol. 23, No. 4 (Summer 1957).
2. The late Jack Taber of Crabbe's Farm, Kelvedon – in his scrap book of newspaper and other cuttings.
3. In *Nurseryman, Seedsman and Glasshouse Grower*, 23 October 1958, p. 655.
4. *Ibid.*
5. Charles McKean, *Architectural Guide to Cambridge and East Anglia since 1920* (1982), p. 137.
6. Phyllis Edwards, 'Illustrating new Introductions', in *The Garden – A Celebration*, Victoria and Albert Museum Exhibition (1979), p. 81.
7. Information from L. A. W. Prior (retd. Managing Director of Deal Cullen Seeds Ltd.). Story of one of the Somerset family of Bodger who subsequently settled in California.
8. Information from L. A. W. Prior.
9. Information from Kenneth Cutts (retd. crop-seed inspector of Cooper Taber Ltd.).
10. *Ibid.*
11. Information (1981) from John G. Keeling (late Director of Elsom's Seeds Ltd.).
12. Information (1981) from Ralph Gould (retd. plant breeder of Hurst's).
13. Information (1980) from B. Schooling Saunders (retd. employee of E. W. King).
14. Nathaniel Sherwood, Accounts book for 1939.
15. *Hurst Crop Research and Development Unit*, booklet produced by the Agricultural Holdings Company Ltd., July 1978, p. 3.
16. *Ibid.*, p. 1.
17. In the *Essex Chronicle*, 17 September 1982.
18. Information from Ralph Gould (retd. plant breeder and one- time apprentice of Hurst's).

Chapter 6

1. Frank Cullen, 'Youthful Memories' in *Seed Trade Review*, vol. 16, no. 2 (November 1964).
2. Information from Violet Cullen, wife of Tom Cullen junr.

Chapter 7

1. Mrs. Field, letter in Essex Record Office (T/Z 25/378).

2. Information from L. A. W. Prior.
3. Information from Roger Browning, farmer of Tey Brook Farm, Little Tey.
4. John H. Harvey, 'Nurseries, Nurserymen and Seedsmen', *loc. cit.*, p.110.
5. *Ibid.*
6. Carter's Tested Seeds Ltd., *1887 Catalogue*, preserved at Museum of English Rural Life, Reading, Berkshire.
7. Sally Festing, *The Story of Lavender* (London Borough of Sutton Libraries and Arts series, 1982).
8. John H. Harvey, *Mediaeval Gardens* (1981), p. 173.
9. Sally Festing, *op. cit.*
10. *Ibid.*
11. Rosetta Clarkson, *Herbs and Savory Seeds* (New York 1972), p. 250.
12. Information from L. A. W. Prior.
13. *Ibid.*
14. Charles W. J. Unwin, *Sweet Peas – their History, Development and Culture*, 3rd edn. (1952), p. 2.
15. *Ibid.*, p. 3.
16. David F. Archer in *The Sweet Pea Year Book, 1937* (The Sweet Pea Society).
17. *Ibid.*

Chapter 8

1. Freddie Boot and Aubrey Davenport, *The Creation of a Village – the story of Tiptree* (Marks Tey, n.d.), pp. 3-17.

Chapter 9

1. G. C. Hillman, 'Reconstructing crop husbandry practices from charred remains of crops' in R. Mercer (ed.), *Farming Practice in British Pre-History* (1981).
2. John Stow, *Survey of London* (1618 edn.).
3. Parliamentary Act, Edward VI, 1551, 2, 5 and 6, C14.
4. *Corn Factor's Exchange Minute Books*, *c.*1759, Guildhall Library, London.
5. Before the Second World War *Beerbohm's* was probably the most used daily circular of market prices. It gave very many corn, feeding-stuffs and similar commodity prices with an especially wide range of all the various seed species and varieties.
6. Oren L. Justice and Louis N. Bass, *Principles and Practice of Seed Storage*, U.S. Department of Agriculture (1978, republished 1979).
7. R. J. E. Harrington, 'Seed Storage and Longevity', in Kozlowskitt, *Seed Biology*, vol. 3 (1920), pp. 145-245.
8. O.G.H.A.I. (1923), *Botanical Magazine* (Tokyo), vol. 37, pp. 87-95.
9. J. H. Turner, *The nobility of seeds*, Kew Royal Botanic Gardens Bulletin – Miscellaneous Information No. 6, pp. 257-69.

Chapter 10

1. Maura Benham, *Goldhanger – an estuary village* (1977), p. 45.
2. R. J. Horlock, *Mistley Man's Log – Chronicles of a barging life told by A. H. (Chubb) Horlock* (1977), p. 33.
3. Gerald O. Rickwood, *The Annals of One Hundred Years of Flour Milling 1840-1940* (published by E. Marriage & Sons), p. 39.
4. A fuller account is given in the book by Chloe Cockerill and Daphne Woodward, *The Hythe, port, church and fishery* (E.Col. 1.387.1), to which I am indebted for much of the information on this port that is given in this chapter.
5. Sandall Knight, *A Hundred Years of Agricultural Trading 1863-1963* (Hasler's of Dunmow), p. 6.
6. *Ibid.*, p. 8.

Chapter 11

1. Frank Lewis, *Essex and Sugar* (1976), p. 14.
2. *Ibid.*, pp. 101, 102.

3. In *Friends Historical Society Journal*, No. 22 (1915).
4. In *M.A.F.F. Bulletin No. 153 - Sugar Beet Cultivation*, 1st edn. (1953).
5. *Ibid.*, 3rd. edn. (1970).

Chapter 12

1. John Booker, *Essex and the Industrial Revolution*, E.R.O. publication No. 66 (1974), p. 112.
2. Alma Oakes and Margot Hamilton Hill, *Rural Costume - Its Origin and Development in Western Europe and the British Isles* (1970), p. 214, quoting Worlidge's *Systema Agricultural* (1669).
3. *Ibid.*, quoting Peter Kalm's Account of his visit to England in 1748.
4. John Booker, *op. cit.*, Introduction, p. viii.
5. *Ibid.*, quoting J. J. Mechi, *Agricultural Improvement* (1845).
6. Tithe map, 1838 (E.R.O. D/DU 626/10 D/CT 101).
7. For a good description of these works together with some excellent pictures the reader is directed to an account in *The Implement and Machinery Review* of 10 June 1905. Much historic matter relating to this firm may also be seen at the Museum of Rural Life, Reading, Berkshire.
8. R. Hunt and Company Ltd., in Catalogue No. 800 (1900 edn.), p. 10, in Museum of Rural Life, Reading, Berkshire (TR-REE- P2/B1344).
9. John H. Harvey, *Mediaeval Gardens* (1981), p. 87.
10. Paul Lees, in *Horticultural Industry* (July 1980), p. 19.
11. Arthur F. J. Brown, *Essex at Work 1700-1815*, E.R.O. publication No. 49 (1969), p. 38.
12. *Ibid.*, pp. 7, 19.
13. Kenneth G. Farries, *Essex Windmills, Millers and Millwrights*, vol. 1, p. 83.
14. Paul Lees, *op. cit.*, p. 19.
15. J. C. Drummond and Anne Wilbraham, *The Englishman's Food*, p. 199.
16. Arthur F. J. Brown, *op, cit.*, p. 41.
17. *Ibid.*, p. 9.

Chapter 13

1. Miles Hadfield, *The History of British Gardening* (1960, new edn. 1979), p. 329.
2. *Ibid.*, pp. 271-3.
3. Richard Gorer, 'The Gardenesque Garden 1830-1890', in *The Garden – A Celebration*, Victoria and Albert Museum Exhibition (1979), p. 53.
4. G. Mastenbroek, *The Significance of Plant Breeding by the Private Sector*, U.P.O.V. Newsletter, Plant Variety Protection No. 31, pp. 20-8.
5. Information from Major C. X. S. Fenwick, M.V.O., son of David Fenwick.
6. The following information is condensed from an article in the *Essex County Standard* of 26 August 1966, and from a paper by David Fenwick, entitled 'The Production and Distribution of Flower Seeds', given in January 1966 to the 7th Askham Bryan Horticultural Technical Conference on 'New Perspectives in Horticulture'.
7. Information from Graham Scott (trials officer at Hurst's).
8. Barry Hutton, 'Exporting from By-Pass' in *Gardener's Chronicle Horticultural Trade Journal*, 26 June 1971, p. 14.

Chapter 14

1. Richard Gardiner, *Profitable Instructions for Manuring, Sowing and Planting of Kitchen Gardens* (1603).
2. Paul Neergaard, *Historical Development of Current Practices in Seed Testing*, Government Plant Protection Service, Copenhagen, Denmark (Proc. Int. S.T.A., No. 1, vol. 30, 919650).
3. G.P. Parliamentary Papers: C.D. 489, p. 1, lx and C.D. 493, p. 17, lx.
4. 'D. F.', 'Modern Seed Testing', in *Magazine of Commerce* (October 1903), copy in N.I.A.B. Library.
5. *Journal of Board of Agriculture*, vol. 25, No. 6 (September 1918), p. 477.
6. Information from Miss M. E. Pirrie who worked with Mr. Robson at the East Anglian Institute of Agriculture.
7. *Journal of Board of Agriculture*, vol. 26, No. 9, (December 1919).

8. Miles Hadfield, *A History of British Gardening* (1979), p. 283.
9. *Seed Science and Technology*, International Seed Testing Association (1976), 4:3:177.
10. Sir Harold Sanders, 'The N.I.A.B. 1945-1970', in Rosemary Sell, *From Seedtime to Harvest – the life of Frank Horne*, p. 102.
11. J. A. Donn and G. A. Wheatley, *N.V.R.S.: 25 Years of Progress* (repr. 1975), pp. 20-36.
12. Brian W. L. Walker (Director General of OXFAM), in *Bulletin of Ministry of Agriculture* (February 1981), p. 125.

Chronology of Events

1. John Boyes and Ronald Russel, *The Canals of the British Isles - the canals of Eastern England* (1977), Chapter 1.
2. Miles Hadfield, *A History of British Gardening* (1979), p. 253.
3. John Booker, *Essex and the Industrial Revolution*, p. 40.
4. *Ibid.*, quoting G. Woodcock in *Essex Countryside*, No. 86 (1964), p. 210.

Appendix G

1. Alan Percival. His diaries for 1945-50, in the possession of Alan Dann of Great Tey.

Index

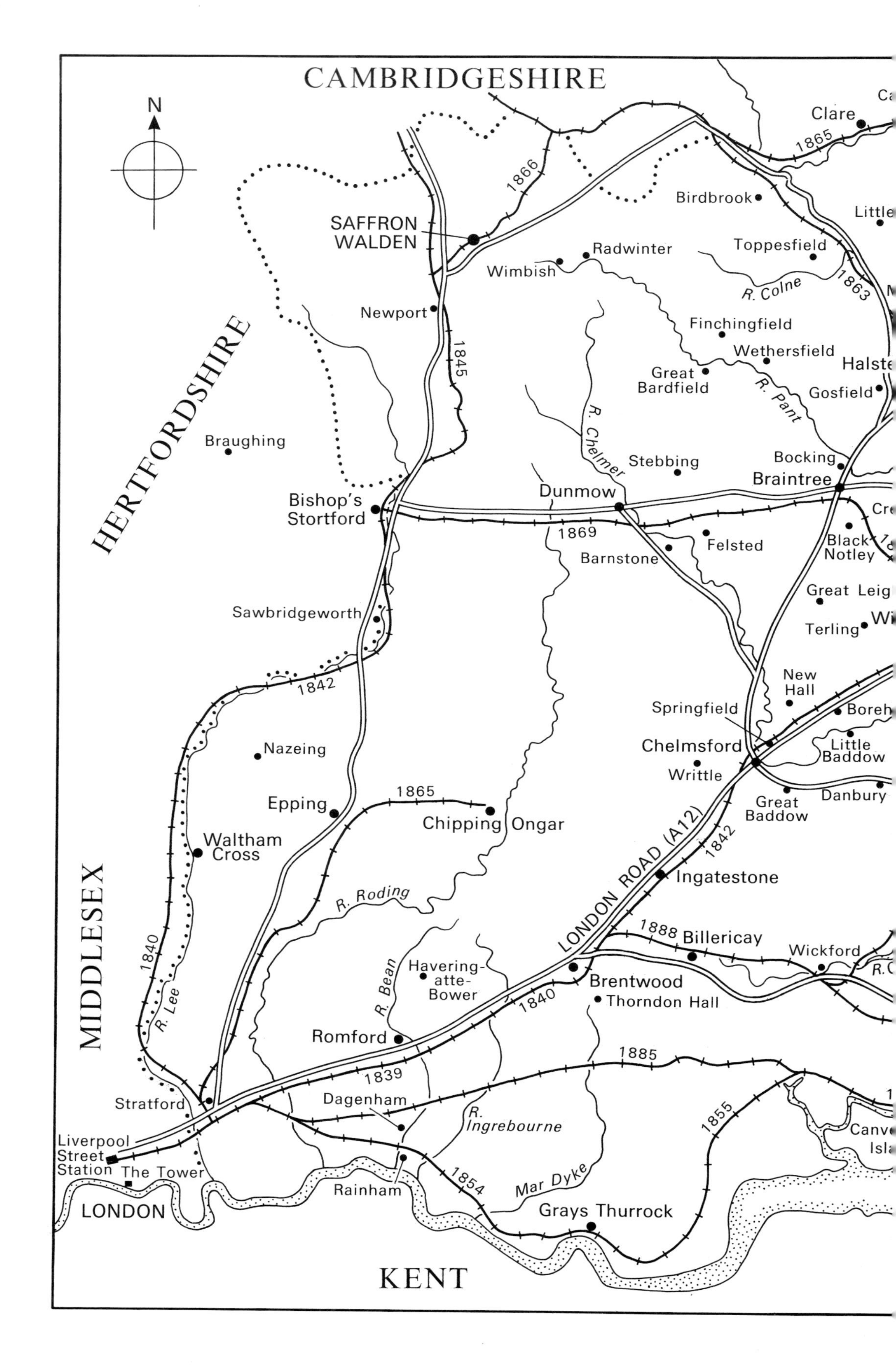

CAMBRIDGESHIRE
N
HERTFORDSHIRE
MIDDLESEX
KENT
Clare
1865
1866
SAFFRON
WALDEN
Birdbrook
Radwinter
Toppesfield
Wimbish
R. Colne
1863
Newport
Finchingfield
Wethersfield
1845
Great
Bardfield
R. Pant
Gosfield
Braughing
R. Chelmer
Stebbing
Bocking
Braintree
Dunmow
Bishop's
Stortford
1869
Felsted
Barnstone
Black
Notley
Terling
Sawbridgeworth
New
Hall
1842
Springfield
Little
Baddow
Nazeing
Chelmsford
Writtle
Epping
1865
Chipping Ongar
Great
Baddow
Danbury
Waltham
Cross
LONDON ROAD (A12)
1842
Ingatestone
R. Roding
1888 Billericay
Wickford
1840
R. Bean
Havering-
atte-
Bower
Brentwood
Thorndon Hall
R. Lee
1840
Romford
1885
1839
Stratford
Dagenham
R.
Ingrebourne
1855
Liverpool
Street
Station
The Tower
1854
Mar Dyke
Rainham
LONDON
Grays Thurrock